5/23/67

ALGEBRA
OF
MATRICES

MALCOLM F. SMILEY

University of California, Riverside

ALGEBRA
OF
MATRICES

Allyn and Bacon, Inc.

Boston, 1965

To Dorothy

PREFACE

The study of matric algebra is essential for applications, it serves as a good base on which to build the abstractions of contemporary algebra, and it is so rich in problems of an elementary character that it can well provide the student with his first experience of personal mathematical discovery.

My attempt in this text has been two-fold: I have tried to present the various topics in their proper mathematical setting and to present topics of special interest for applications. I have assumed that the reader has already had a good course in calculus, such, for example, as *Calculus with Analytic Geometry* by Johnson and Kiokemeister.

The first three chapters develop the basic algebra of matrices, the fundamental facts about determinants, and the theory of polynomials. Chapter Four is very useful in applications, since it constructs a theory of functions of a matrix and applies this theory to systems of differential equations. Chapter Five introduces the basic notion of vector space and the useful corollary idea of factor space. Chapter Six is an application of the idea of the dimension of a vector space to the computation of the rank of a matrix, and includes a complete discussion of the solution of systems of linear equations and Cramer's rule. Chapter Seven is a brief introduction to the use of matrices in the theory of finite two-person games. Chapter Eight introduces the notion of linear transformation and shows how the matrix of a linear transformation changes as the bases change; this leads us to the central problem of matric theory, similarity. A complete solution of this problem occupies Chapter Nine. Chapters Ten and Eleven consist of a derivation of some of the elementary properties of euclidean spaces and of unitary spaces. The final chapter, Chapter Twelve, consists of a glimpse at the difficult problems associated with quadratic forms. In an Appendix are presented some of the facts of elementary set theory. *The student is advised to consult this appendix whenever matters concerning sets, functions, maps, and the notations used for them puzzle him.* To facilitate identification of the particular notations we use, there is an Index of Symbols at the end of the book.

I have taught the material in this text as a one-semester course for a number of years at the State University of Iowa and at the University of California. In this text, no really serious difficulty will arise if Chapters Four and Seven are omitted, provided the instructor supplies (as he would) a brief discussion of the principal idempotents of a matrix.

The exercises in this text are numerous. Not all of them are easy. Many of the easier ones are intended merely as computational illustrations of the theory; more difficult exercises are not intended to be done overnight. I hope that the students will attach themselves to the more challenging exercises and stick long enough to gain a personal feeling of the joy that mathematical discovery can bring. A few exercises outline some famous theorems and proofs comprehensible to the serious student even at this early stage of his learning.

To list my indebtedness to my teachers, to my colleagues, and to my students for their contributions to this text is indeed impossible. However, I wish to thank my wife, Dr. Dorothy Manning Smiley, for her patient reading and criticism of the final form of the text. I thank Professor Frank W. Anderson for several suggestions for improvements. Some of these led to the inclusion of a proof of the Fundamental Theorem of Algebra and a discussion of the Principle of Inductive Definition. The editorial staff of Allyn and Bacon is also to be commended for its careful and painstaking work. Finally, I wish to thank Mrs. Jane N. Scully for her expert typing of the manuscript.

Riverside, California M. F. SMILEY

TABLE OF CONTENTS

CHAPTER 9   SIMILARITY OF MATRICES

CHAPTER 10   EUCLIDEAN SPACES

CHAPTER 11   UNITARY SPACES

CHAPTER 12   QUADRATIC FORMS AND
WITT'S THEOREM

APPENDIX   INTRODUCTORY SET THEORY

ALGEBRA
OF
MATRICES

1

RINGS AND
MATRIC RINGS

In this chapter we will introduce the fundamental concepts with which our subject must deal. It is no more
possible to discuss matric theory cogently without a
preliminary discussion of numbers than it is to talk about
cat-grins without talking about cats. Our first section
gives a rapid development of the fundamental properties
of numbers, which is based on the concept of a ring; there
is ample evidence that this concept is central both in
pure and in applied mathematics. The remainder of the
chapter is devoted to the discussion of matrices and the
fundamental operations of matric algebra.

/1/ RINGS AND THEIR ELEMENTARY PROPERTIES

One of the basic concepts of mathematics is that of a ring. In this section we shall define this concept, indicate a few examples which are familiar to the reader, and develop a few simple properties of rings.

Let R be a set† in which two binary compositions are defined: that is,

R1. To each ordered pair‡ (a, b) of elements of R there corresponds a unique sum $a + b$ which is an element of R.

R2. To each ordered pair (a, b) of elements of R there corresponds a unique product ab which is an element of R.

We call R a *ring* in case the following requirements hold:

R3. There is an element 0 in R such that $a + 0 = a$ for every a in R.

R4. Each element a in R has a negative $-a$ in R such that $a + (-a) = 0$.

R5. If a, b, and c are elements of R, then: (i), $(a + b) + c = a + (b + c)$; (ii), $(ab)c = a(bc)$; (iii), $a + b = b + a$; (iv), $a(b + c) = ab + ac$; and (v), $(a + b)c = ac + bc$.

---

† See the Appendix, Section 1.

‡ See the Appendix, Section 2.

The reader will note that these axioms are a (near) minimum set for a system of "numbers." The computational rules given in R5 have names: *associative law for addition, associative law for multiplication, commutative law for addition, right distributive law,* and *left distributive law,* respectively. No doubt the reader has already encountered these names. At any rate, he has already encountered the following rings: the ring of (ordinary) integers, Z; the ring of rational numbers, R_a; the ring of real numbers, R_e; the ring of complex numbers, K. Let us point out a few more examples of rings.

Example 1   This is the example of the ring $R[x]$ of polynomials in x with coefficients in a ring R. Let R be a ring. An expression
$$f(x) = c_0 + c_1 x + c_2 x^2 + \cdots + c_n x^n$$
is called a *polynomial in x with coefficients in R.* Such expressions are added and multiplied just as in elementary algebra with the aid of the rule $cx = xc$ for every c in R. It is easy to see that the set $R[x]$ of all such expressions is a ring relative to such addition and multiplication. The rings $Z[x]$, $R_a[x]$, $R_e[x]$, and $K[x]$ occur fairly frequently in elementary mathematics.

Example 2   Let k be a nonnegative integer. Then the set kZ of all integral multiples of k is a ring under the usual operations of addition and multiplication of (ordinary) integers. Since kZ is a subset of Z which is a ring relative to the operations in Z, we call kZ a *subring* of Z. Note that $0Z$ has just one element, 0.

Example 3   Let m be a positive integer. If $i = 0, \cdots, m - 1$, then let i_m denote the set $i + mZ$ of those integers which yield remainder i when divided by m. If also $j = 0, \cdots, m - 1$, then $i + j$ (or ij) belongs to a uniquely determined set $k_m = k + mZ$, and this set is called the sum (or the product) of i_m and j_m. It is usual to call the set (of sets) $\{i + mZ; \text{ where } i = 0, \cdots, m - 1\}$, the *integers modulo m* and to write Z/mZ for this set. Again, it is easy to verify that Z/mZ is a ring. The reader might find it instructive to write out the tables for addition and multiplication in $Z/2Z$, $Z/3Z$, $Z/4Z$, and $Z/5Z$. The tables for $Z/6Z$ are the following, where we have omitted the subscript 6 throughout.

	0	1	2	3	4	5
0	0	1	2	3	4	5
1	1	2	3	4	5	0
2	2	3	4	5	0	1
3	3	4	5	0	1	2
4	4	5	0	1	2	3
5	5	0	1	2	3	4

	0	1	2	3	4	5
0	0	0	0	0	0	0
1	0	1	2	3	4	5
2	0	2	4	0	2	4
3	0	3	0	3	0	3
4	0	4	2	0	4	2
5	0	5	4	3	2	1

Gauss used the notation $i \equiv j \pmod{m}$ to indicate that $i - j$ is divisible by m, that is, that i_m is equal to j_m. One reads "$i \equiv j$ $(\mathrm{mod}\ m)$" as "i is *congruent to j modulo m*." The source of the term *ring* may be seen if one considers the correspondence $i \to i_m$ of Z onto Z/mZ with $m > 1$. For example, if $m = 7$, one may regard 1_7 as all Sundays, 2_7 as all Mondays, etc. It is natural to regard the week as a circle of its days Sunday, $\cdots$, Saturday. The term *ring* for Z/mZ is a consequence of this. More generally, if $m > 1$, one may regard Z/mZ as the vertices of a regular m-sided polygon inscribed in a circle of circumference m. Visualize Z as the points on the real line L which have integral coordinates so arranged that C is tangent to L at 0. The correspondence $i \to i_m$ then wraps L around C infinitely many times.

Illustrative
Example

In $Z/15Z$, solve $11_{15}x = 1_{15}$. A method of trial will work: $11 \cdot 11 = 121 = (15)(8) + 1$, and we find that $x = 11_{15}$. But $3_{15}x = 1_{15}$ has no solution, for $3x = 1 + 15k$ is impossible for integers x and k.

Example 4   In calculus, one discusses functions $f(x)$ which are real-valued and continuous for every real number x (for example, e^x, x^3, and $\sin x$). Let $C(R_e)$ denote the set of all such functions. By fundamental properties of continuous functions, $C(R_e)$ is a ring, provided that we add and multiply functions according to the rules $(f + g)(x) = f(x) + g(x)$ and $(fg)(x) = f(x)g(x)$ for every real number x. The ring $C(R_e)$ has some important subrings. For example, the set $C'(R_e)$ of all real-valued functions which have a derivative for every real number x is of considerable importance.

Example 5   Let S be a set and let A and B be subsets† of S. Let AB denote the set of elements common to A and B (the intersection of A and B). Let $A + B$ denote the set of elements of S which belong either to A or to B *but not to both A and B* (the sum or symmetric difference of A and B). Relative to these compositions, the set 2^S of all subsets of S becomes a ring called the *Boolean ring of all subsets of S*. (If the reader has not already done so, he might find it instructive to verify the axioms for a ring in this case.)

The ring 2^S has some peculiar properties. Note especially that, in 2^S, $AA = A$ and $A + A = 0$.

Let this conclude our list of examples of rings for the present. We now turn to the task of deriving simple consequences of the axioms for a ring.

(1-1)   In a ring R, 0 is unique: if $a + x = a$ with a and x in R, then $x = 0$.

PROOF

Statement	Reason
1. $a + x = a$	By hypothesis
2. $(a + x) + (-a) = a + (-a)$	R1 and R4
3. $(x + a) + (-a) = 0$	R4 and R5 (part iii)
4. $x + [a + (-a)] = 0$	R5 (part i)
5. $x + 0 = 0$	R4
6. $x = 0$	R3

(1-2)   In a ring R, $-a$ is uniquely determined by a: if $a + x = 0$, then $x = -a$.

PROOF

Statement	Reason
1. $a + x = 0$	
2. $-a + (a + x) = -a + 0$	
3.	
4.	
5.	
6. $x = -a$	

The reader is expected to fill in the gaps in this proof!

† See the Appendix, Section 1.

(1-3)   In a ring R, $a0 = 0 = 0a$ for every a in R.

PROOF

Statement	Reason
1. $0 + 0 = 0$	R3
2. $a(0 + 0) = a0$	R2
3. $a0 + a0 = a0$	
4. $a0 = 0$	(1–1) with $a = x = a0$
5. $(0 + 0)a = 0a$	
6.	
7. $0a = 0$	

(1-4)   In a ring R, $(-a)b = a(-b) = -(ab)$, and $(-a)(-b) = ab$ for every a and b in R.

PROOF

Statement	Reason
1. $a + (-a) = 0$	R4
2. $[a + (-a)]b = 0b$	R2
3. $ab + (-a)b = 0$	R5 (part v) and (1–3)

The reader is expected to complete the proof.

One uses the very formal statement-reason form of proof only as an aid to the appreciation of the nature of a precise mathematical proof. It, like all other very formal methods of writing mathematics, is so cumbersome that it cannot be consistently adhered to. We abandon it forthwith.

To define *integral multiples ma of an element a of a ring R*, we pause to explain a somewhat unusual form of mathematical induction. Let $P(m)$ be a meaningful statement for each integer m and let (i) $P(0)$ be true and (ii) $P(m)$ be true if and only if $P(m + 1)$ is true, then $P(m)$ is true for every integer m. It is easy to prove this convenient induction principle from the usual one. To illustrate its use, let us define $0a = 0$ for an element a of a ring R (the first 0 is the integer 0, the second 0 is the zero of R) and let the equation $(m + 1)a = ma + a$ define $(m + 1)a$ if ma is defined and let it also define $ma = (m + 1)a + (-a)$ if

$(m + 1)a$ is defined.† By our induction principle, ma is defined for every integer m. We call ma an integral multiple of a. Concerning these integral multiples we have the following rules.

(1-5) If a is an element of a ring R and m and n are integers, then $(m + n)a = ma + na$, $(mn)a = m(na)$, $m(a + b) = ma + mb$, and $m(-a) = (-m)a = -(ma)$.

PROOF Let $P(n)$ be the statement that $(m + n)a = ma + na$ for every integer m. Then $P(0)$ becomes $(m + 0)a = ma + 0a$, which is the same as $ma = ma + 0$, which is true. Assume $P(n)$ and add a to each side to get $(m + n)a + a = (ma + na) + a = ma + (na + a)$ by R5. By using our definition of multiples we get $[(m + n) + 1]a = ma + (n + 1)a$ and $[m + (n + 1)]a = ma + (n + 1)a$ for every integer m, and this is $P(n + 1)$. Assume $P(n + 1)$; then $[m + (n + 1)]a = ma + (n + 1)a$. By using our definition of multiples we find that this becomes $(m + n)a + a = ma + (na + a)$. By R5 and the addition of $-a$ to each side we reach $P(n)$.

Now let $P(m)$ be the statement that $(mn)a = m(na)$ for every integer n. Then $P(0)$ reduces to $0 = 0$, which is true. Assume $P(m)$ and add na to each side to get $(mn)a + na = m(na) + na$. By using our definition of multiples, we find that $(mn + n)a = (m + 1)(na)$ for every integer n, that is, $P(m + 1)$ is true.

The remainder of the proof of (1-5) is left as an exercise.

If m is a *positive* integer, we define a^m for an element a of a ring R as follows. First a^1 is defined as a. Then we define a^{m+1} as $a(a^m)$ on the assumption that a^m has been defined.† By the ordinary principle of mathematical induction for the positive integers, a^m is defined for every positive integer m. Concerning these *powers* we have the following rules.

(1-6) If a is an element of a ring R and m and n are positive integers, then $a^{m+n} = (a^m)(a^n)$ and $a^{mn} = (a^m)^n$.

PROOF It is left as an exercise.

---

† The phrase "is defined" lacks precision. The meticulous reader who is bothered by it is advised to study the Principle of Inductive Definition, which is discussed in Section 5 of the Appendix.

The reader will note that negative powers do not exist in every ring. For example, 2^{-1} is not an integer, and even a^0 (which is sometimes defined as 1) may have no meaning in certain rings just because these rings fail to have an element that acts like 1 (the ring $2Z$ is an example of such a ring).

Definition

An element e of a ring R is an identity element of R in case $ea = a = ae$ for every element a in R.† When R has an identity element e, we define a^0 to be e for every $a \neq 0$ in R.

(1-7)   If a ring R has an identity element, this element is unique: if $ea = a = ae$ and $fa = a = af$ for every a in R, then $e = f$.

PROOF   Compute $ef = f = e$.

Because of (1-7), it is usual to denote the identity element of a ring R by 1, even though there is a bit of danger of confusing the identity elements of various rings.

(1-8)   Let R be a ring with identity element 1 and let a be in R. If there are elements x and y in R such that $ax = ya = 1$, then $x = y$.

PROOF   With $ax = 1$ we have $y(ax) = y1 = y$, $(ya)x = y$ by R5, $1x = y$, and $x = y$.

Definition

Let R be a ring with identity element 1 and let a be in R. We call a nonsingular in R (a unit of R) in case there are elements x and y in R such that $ax = ya = 1$.

Because of (1-8), it is usual to write $x = y = a^{-1}$ for a nonsingular element of a ring R and to call a^{-1} the *inverse* of a. For

† It may happen that $e = 0$. Then also $R = 0$, so that R has only one element.

a nonsingular element a of a ring R, we may define the negative powers of a by $a^n = (a^{-1})^{-n}$ and we may then prove the rules of (1-6) for all integers m and n. A somewhat more elegant method of handling the powers of a nonsingular element a of a ring R is to define $a^0 = 1$ and to let $a^{n+1} = a(a^n)$ define a^{n+1} when a^n is defined and let it define a^n when a^{n+1} is defined. The proof of (1-6) for all integers m and n (a being nonsingular) is then very like parts of the proof of (1-5).

It is by no means an easy task to determine the nonsingular elements of a given ring R with identity element 1. It is easy to see that ± 1 are the only nonsingular elements of Z. An element a_m of Z/mZ cannot be nonsingular if a and m have a common factor different from ± 1, for $a_m x = 1_m$ yields $ax = 1 + km$ for integers x and k. We shall prove later that, when a and m have no common factor different from ± 1, then a_m is nonsingular in Z/mZ. For example, with $m = 10$, $3_{10}7_{10} = 1_{10}$, and $9_{10}9_{10} = 1_{10}$, so that 1_{10}, 3_{10}, 7_{10}, and 9_{10} are the nonsingular elements of $Z/10Z$.

There are three classes of rings which should now be defined. A ring is called a *commutative ring* in case multiplication is commutative: $ab = ba$ for every a and b in R. A ring R is called a *division ring* in case R has an identity element $1 \neq 0$ and every nonzero element of R is nonsingular. A ring R is called a *field* in case it is a commutative division ring. The basic fields of mathematics are the field of rational numbers, R_a, the field of real numbers, R_e, and the field of complex numbers, K. The simplest division ring which is not commutative is the ring of real quaternions of Hamilton, whose precise definition we postpone until we have studied a bit of matrix theory.

(1-9)　　Let a and b be nonsingular elements of a ring R with identity element 1. Then ab is nonsingular and $(ab)^{-1} = b^{-1}a^{-1}$.

PROOF　　Compute $(ab)(b^{-1}a^{-1})$ and $(b^{-1}a^{-1})(ab)$, using R5.

A map† $a \to a^f$ of a ring R onto a ring R' establishes an *isomorphism* between R and R', in case the map is faithful† and preserves addition and multiplication. In detail: (i) to each a in R there corresponds a unique a^f in R', (ii) to each a' in R' there

_____
† See the Appendix, Section 2.

corresponds a unique a in R such that $a^f = a'$, and (iii) for every a and b in R we have $(a + b)^f = a^f + b^f$ and $(ab)^f = a^f b^f$.

When such a map f exists, we call the rings R and R' isomorphic and write $R \cong R'$. For certain purposes, isomorphic rings may be regarded as identical. The mapping $(a + bi) \to (a - bi)$ is an isomorphism of the field of complex numbers, K, onto K. The polynomial rings $R[x]$ and $R[y]$ are isomorphic via the map induced by replacing x by y. We shall encounter several further examples of isomorphic rings in our study of matric algebra.

We conclude this section with the statement (without proof) of some useful consequences of R5. Complete proofs of these results are a proper part of the foundations of mathematics. They may be found in, for example, *The Anatomy of Mathematics*, by Kerschner and Wilcox.

(1-10) Generalized associative law for multiplication: Let $a_1, \cdots, a_n$ be elements of a ring R; then the product $\prod_{i=1}^{n} a_i$ of these elements in order is uniquely defined, irrespective of the method of association used in computing it.

We content ourselves with a verification (by R5):

$$(a_1 a_2)(a_3 a_4) = a_1[a_2(a_3 a_4)] = a_1[(a_2 a_3)a_4]$$
$$= [a_1(a_2 a_3)]a_4 = [(a_1 a_2)a_3]a_4.$$

(1-11) Generalized associative and commutative laws for addition: Let $a_1, \cdots, a_n$ be elements of a ring R; then the sum $\sum_{i=1}^{n} a_i$ of these elements is uniquely defined, irrespective of the order of the elements and the method of association used in computing it.

Again we give only a verification of a special case (by R5):

$$(a_1 + a_2) + a_3 = a_1 + (a_2 + a_3) = a_1 + (a_3 + a_2)$$
$$= (a_1 + a_3) + a_2 = (a_3 + a_1) + a_2$$
$$= a_3 + (a_1 + a_2) = a_3 + (a_2 + a_1)$$
$$= (a_3 + a_2) + a_1 = (a_2 + a_3) + a_1$$
$$= a_2 + (a_3 + a_1) = a_2 + (a_1 + a_3)$$
$$= (a_2 + a_1) + a_3.$$

(1-12)   Generalized distributive laws: Let c and $a_1, \cdots, a_n$ be elements of a ring R; then

$$c\left(\sum_{i=1}^{n} a_i\right) = \sum_{i=1}^{n} ca_i \quad \text{and} \quad \left(\sum_{i=1}^{n} a_i\right)c = \sum_{i=1}^{n} a_ic.$$

The following is a particularly useful consequence of (1-11).

(1-13)   Let a_{ij} (where $i = 1, \cdots, m$, and $j = 1, \cdots, n$) be elements of a ring R. Then

$$\sum_{i=1}^{m} \sum_{j=1}^{n} a_{ij} = \sum_{j=1}^{n} \sum_{i=1}^{m} a_{ij}.$$

The rule (1-13) permits us to interchange the order of summation at will when the limits of the summations are independent of i and j. On the other hand,

$$\sum_{i=1}^{10} \sum_{j=i}^{10} a_{ij} = \sum_{j=1}^{10} \sum_{i=1}^{j} a_{ij}.$$

The reader will appreciate that this case requires very careful handling. In a later chapter we deliberately avoid it by introducing many zero summands.

(1-14)   Let $a_1, \cdots, a_n$ be elements of a commutative ring R. Then the product $\prod_{i=1}^{n} a_i$ of these elements is uniquely defined, irrespective of the order of the elements and the method of association used in computing it.

/ 2 / MATRICES AND THE BASIC OPERATIONS OF MATRIX ALGEBRA

In this section we define matrices, show how to add and multiply them, and derive some of the elementary consequences of the definitions.

Let R be a ring. A rectangular array

(1)
$$A = \begin{bmatrix} a_{11} & a_{12} & \cdots & a_{1n} \\ a_{21} & a_{22} & \cdots & a_{2n} \\ \vdots & \vdots & & \vdots \\ a_{m1} & a_{m2} & \cdots & a_{mn} \end{bmatrix}$$

of elements of R is called a *matrix of elements of R*. Thus, a matrix is a function whose domain is a set

$$\{(i,j); \quad i = 1, \cdots, m, \quad j = 1, \cdots, n\}$$

and whose range is contained in R. The pictorial representation (1) is quite helpful (in a sense it represents the graph of A), and we make a great deal of use of it. For example, we say that a_{ij} is the element of A which is in the ith row and jth column of A, and we call A an m-by-n matrix because (1) has m rows and n columns. If

$$B = \begin{bmatrix} b_{11} & b_{12} & \cdots & b_{1n} \\ b_{21} & b_{22} & \cdots & b_{2n} \\ \vdots & \vdots & & \vdots \\ b_{m1} & b_{m2} & \cdots & b_{mn} \end{bmatrix}$$

is also an m-by-n matrix of elements of R, we may form the sum $A + B$ by adding corresponding elements of A and B:

$$A + B = \begin{bmatrix} a_{11} + b_{11} & a_{12} + b_{12} & \cdots & a_{1n} + b_{1n} \\ a_{21} + b_{21} & a_{22} + b_{22} & \cdots & a_{2n} + b_{2n} \\ \vdots & \vdots & & \vdots \\ a_{m1} + b_{m1} & a_{m2} + b_{m2} & \cdots & a_{mn} + b_{mn} \end{bmatrix}.$$

We may immediately observe the following consequences, whose proofs are left to the reader to develop.

M1. To each ordered pair (A, B) of m-by-n matrices of elements of R there corresponds a unique sum $A + B$ which is an m-by-n matrix of elements of R.

M2. (This will be given later.)

M3. There is an m-by-n matrix 0 of elements of R such that $A + 0 = A$ for every m-by-n matrix A of elements of R.

M4. Each m-by-n matrix A of elements of R has a negative $-A$ which is an m-by-n matrix of elements of R such that $A + (-A) = 0$.

The problem of defining multiplication of matrices arises next. A simple method suggests itself: multiply corresponding elements. This method is, unfortunately, of very limited use. The applications demand a more complicated method. For example, consider

(2)
$$\begin{aligned} ax + by &= c, \\ dx + ey &= f. \end{aligned}$$

One "sees" some matrices:

$$A = \begin{bmatrix} a & b \\ d & e \end{bmatrix}, \qquad C = \begin{bmatrix} c \\ f \end{bmatrix}, \qquad Y = [x \; y], \qquad X = \begin{bmatrix} x \\ y \end{bmatrix}.$$

It is *customary* to write (2) as

$$\begin{bmatrix} a & b \\ d & e \end{bmatrix}\begin{bmatrix} x \\ y \end{bmatrix} = \begin{bmatrix} c \\ f \end{bmatrix} \quad \text{or as} \quad AX = C.$$

If we adopt this convention our definition of the product of two matrices is fixed. We define the *product* $P = AB$ *of matrices* A and B of elements of R only if A is m-by-n and B is n-by-q. When this requirement is satisfied, we define the element p_{ik} in the ith row and kth column of P as the sum of the products of the elements in the ith row of A and the corresponding elements in the kth column of B, or, mathematically,

$$p_{ik} = \sum_{j=1}^{n} a_{ij}b_{jk} \qquad (i = 1, \cdots, m; \quad k = 1, \cdots, q).$$

It will not be until somewhat later in our study that the true justification for this method of multiplication of matrices will come to light.

Illustrative
Example

$$\begin{bmatrix} 1 & 2 & -1 \\ 0 & 5 & 7 \end{bmatrix}\begin{bmatrix} 4 & 3 & 2 & 8 \\ 5 & 1 & -1 & 7 \\ 2 & 0 & 5 & 6 \end{bmatrix} = \begin{bmatrix} 12 & 5 & -5 & 16 \\ 39 & 5 & 30 & 77 \end{bmatrix}.$$

Many facts about matrices may be illustrated by the 2-by-2 case. Let

$$A = \begin{bmatrix} a & b \\ c & d \end{bmatrix}$$

have elements in R, where R is a *commutative* ring. We define

$$\det A = ad - bc \quad \text{and} \quad \operatorname{adj} A = \begin{bmatrix} d & -b \\ -c & a \end{bmatrix}.$$

Note that det A is an element of R, while adj A is a *matrix* of elements of R. We easily verify that

$$A(\text{adj } A) = (\text{adj } A)A = \begin{bmatrix} \det A & 0 \\ 0 & \det A \end{bmatrix}.$$

If B also is a 2-by-2 matrix of elements of R, then one may verify by computation that

$$\det (AB) = (\det A)(\det B).$$

In a later chapter we shall derive these results for any n.

If $A = [a_{ij}]$ where $i = 1, \cdots, m$, and $j = 1, \cdots, n$ is a matrix of elements of a ring R and $c \in R$, it is convenient to define cA as the matrix

$$cA = [ca_{ij}] \qquad \text{where } i = 1, \cdots, m, \quad \text{and} \quad j = 1, \cdots, n.$$

We may also define Ac in a similar manner.

We are now ready to complete our basic list of properties of these matric operations.

M2. If A is an m-by-n matrix of elements of R and B is an n-by-q matrix of elements of R, then there is a unique product AB which is an m-by-q matrix of elements of R.

M5. Let A, B, and C be matrices of elements of R; then: (i), $(A + B) + C = A + (B + C)$; (ii), $(AB)C = A(BC)$; (iii), $A + B = B + A$; (iv), $A(B + C) = AB + AC$; (v), $(A + B)C = AC + BC$; all in the sense that, if either member of one of these equations is defined, then so is the other member and the two members are equal.

PARTIAL PROOF   Let A, B, C be m-by-n, r-by-q, and s-by-t matrices, respectively. If $(AB)C$ is defined, then AB is defined and $n = r$ and AB is m-by-q. Since $(AB)C$ is defined, $q = s$, and it follows that BC is defined and is r-by-t and hence that $A(BC)$ is defined because $n = r$. Assume that $n = r$ and $q = s$, so that the members of (ii) are defined. The element in the ith row and the lth column of the left member $(AB)C$ of (ii) is given by

$$\sum_{k=1}^{s} \left(\sum_{j=1}^{n} a_{ij}b_{jk} \right) c_{kl}.$$

Apply (1-12), R5, (1-13), and (1-12) to obtain

$$\sum_{k=1}^{s}\left(\sum_{j=1}^{n}a_{ij}b_{jk}\right)c_{kl} = \sum_{k=1}^{s}\sum_{j=1}^{n}(a_{ij}b_{jk})c_{kl}$$
$$= \sum_{k=1}^{s}\sum_{j=1}^{n}a_{ij}(b_{jk}c_{kl})$$
$$= \sum_{j=1}^{n}\sum_{k=1}^{s}a_{ij}(b_{jk}c_{kl})$$
$$= \sum_{j=1}^{n}a_{ij}\left(\sum_{k=1}^{s}b_{jk}c_{kl}\right)$$

which is the element in the ith row and lth column of $A(BC)$. This proves (ii). The remaining equations are established similarly and their proofs are left to the reader.

/ 3 /   MATRIC RINGS

In this section we discuss the totality of n-by-n matrices with elements in a ring R, and we observe a few properties of this set.

Let R be a ring and let R_n be the set of all n-by-n matrices with elements in R. Since the product AB and the sum $A + B$ of two elements A and B of R_n are always defined, a glance at the results of Section 2 shows that R_n is a ring. This ring is the central object of study in matric algebra. That some study is needed is illustrated by the following facts about $(R_e)_2$:

$$\begin{bmatrix}1 & 0\\0 & 0\end{bmatrix}\begin{bmatrix}0 & 0\\1 & 1\end{bmatrix} = \begin{bmatrix}0 & 0\\0 & 0\end{bmatrix},$$

$$\begin{bmatrix}0 & 0\\1 & 1\end{bmatrix}\begin{bmatrix}1 & 0\\0 & 0\end{bmatrix} = \begin{bmatrix}0 & 0\\1 & 0\end{bmatrix}.$$

It is possible, then, that $AB = 0$, $BA \neq 0$, $A \neq 0$, and $B \neq 0$ in $(R_e)_2$ but such things cannot happen in our familiar ring of all real numbers. The imaginative reader may note the almost frightening ring $((((Z_2)_3)_5)_7)_{11}$. However, in a later section of this chapter we shall see that $(R_n)_m$ is isomorphic to R_{nm}, and this essentially reduces our monster to Z_{2310}.

When R has an identity element 1, then so does R_n: the n-by-n matrix

$$I = \begin{bmatrix} 1 & 0 & \cdots & 0 & 0 \\ 0 & 1 & \cdots & 0 & 0 \\ \vdots & \vdots & & \vdots & \vdots \\ 0 & 0 & \cdots & 1 & 0 \\ 0 & 0 & \cdots & 0 & 1 \end{bmatrix}$$

satisfies $AI = A = IA$ for all A in R_n. We call I an *identity matrix*. Being a ring with identity I (when R has an identity 1), R_n has nonsingular elements A, that is, matrices A in R_n, which have inverses A^{-1} in R_n such that $AA^{-1} = A^{-1}A = I$. In a later chapter we shall give methods for finding the nonsingular matrices in R_n for certain rings R. The rule $(AB)^{-1} = B^{-1}A^{-1}$ is still valid in R_n for nonsingular matrices A and B by (1-9).

We can derive a useful criterion for the nonsingularity of a matrix A in R_2, provided that R is commutative and has an identity element 1. For, if A is nonsingular in R_2, then $AA^{-1} = I$ yields $(\det A)(\det A^{-1}) = \det I = 1$, so that $\det A$ is nonsingular in R. Conversely, if we assume that $\det A$ is nonsingular in R, then we may verify that $(\det A)^{-1} \operatorname{adj} A$ is effective as A^{-1}, since

$$(\det A)^{-1}(\operatorname{adj} A)A = (\det A)^{-1} \begin{bmatrix} \det A & 0 \\ 0 & \det A \end{bmatrix} = I$$

and $A(\det A)^{-1} \operatorname{adj} A = (\det A)^{-1}A(\operatorname{adj} A) = I$.

With these facts about R_2 at hand, we are ready to define the simplest division ring which is not commutative. We consider the set $\mathscr{Q}$ of matrices of K_2 (K = the complex field) of the special form

$$\begin{bmatrix} z & w \\ -\overline{w} & \overline{z} \end{bmatrix}.$$

Here $z = a + bi$, $w = c + di$, $\overline{z} = a - bi$, and $\overline{w} = c - di$, where a, b, c, and d are real numbers. To show that $\mathscr{Q}$ is a division ring we must show that $\mathscr{Q}$ is closed relative to addition and matric multiplication and that every nonzero q in $\mathscr{Q}$ has an inverse in $\mathscr{Q}$. Direct computation will show that $\mathscr{Q}$ is, indeed, closed relative to addition and matrix multiplication. We omit this computation.

If $q \neq 0$ and q is in $\mathcal{Q}$, then $\det q = z\bar{z} + w\bar{w}$ is a nonzero real number. Thus q^{-1} exists in K_2. But

$$q^{-1} = (\det q)^{-1} \begin{bmatrix} \bar{z} & -w \\ \bar{w} & z \end{bmatrix}$$

is in $\mathcal{Q}$ because of the reality of $(\det q)^{-1}$. Thus $\mathcal{Q}$ is a division ring. We shall see in a moment that it is not commutative. W. R. Hamilton discovered $\mathcal{Q}$ about a century ago and he called $\mathcal{Q}$ the *(ring of real) quaternions*. Let us see the reason for this name. For q in $\mathcal{Q}$, we may write

$$q = a \begin{bmatrix} 1 & 0 \\ 0 & 1 \end{bmatrix} + b \begin{bmatrix} i & 0 \\ 0 & -i \end{bmatrix} + c \begin{bmatrix} 0 & 1 \\ -1 & 0 \end{bmatrix} + d \begin{bmatrix} 0 & i \\ i & 0 \end{bmatrix}.$$

With the notation

$$\mathbf{I} = \begin{bmatrix} 1 & 0 \\ 0 & 1 \end{bmatrix}, \quad \mathbf{i} = \begin{bmatrix} i & 0 \\ 0 & -i \end{bmatrix}, \quad \mathbf{j} = \begin{bmatrix} 0 & 1 \\ -1 & 0 \end{bmatrix}, \quad \mathbf{k} = \begin{bmatrix} 0 & i \\ i & 0 \end{bmatrix}$$

we have $q = a\mathbf{I} + b\mathbf{i} + c\mathbf{j} + d\mathbf{k}$ and

$$\mathbf{i}^2 = \mathbf{j}^2 = \mathbf{k}^2 = -\mathbf{I}, \quad \mathbf{ij} = \mathbf{k} = -\mathbf{ji},$$
$$\mathbf{jk} = \mathbf{i} = -\mathbf{kj}, \quad \mathbf{ki} = \mathbf{j} = -\mathbf{ik}$$

as is easily checked. Note also that

$$\det q = a^2 + b^2 + c^2 + d^2,$$

and

$$\operatorname{adj} q = a\mathbf{I} - b\mathbf{i} - c\mathbf{j} - d\mathbf{k}$$

while, for $q \neq 0$,

$$q^{-1} = (a^2 + b^2 + c^2 + d^2)^{-1}(a\mathbf{I} - b\mathbf{i} - c\mathbf{j} - d\mathbf{k})$$

which extends the usual formula

$$(a + bi)^{-1} = (a^2 + b^2)^{-1}(a - bi)$$

for a nonzero complex number $a + bi$.

/4/ THROUGH THE LOOKING GLASS

In Section 3 we saw that there are many rings which are not commutative. When R is a ring that is not commutative, we may construct a ring denoted by R°; this is the same as R, except that multiplication in R° is defined "backwards," that is, in R°, $a \cdot b = ba$. It is easy to see that R° is a ring. For example, consider $(a \cdot b) \cdot c = c(ba) = (cb)a = a \cdot (b \cdot c)$, whence it is seen that a part of R5 holds in R°. One has $R^\circ = R$, if, and only if, R is commutative. Since R° is, in a sense, the mirror-image of R, we may call it the *"ring opposed to R."* Other names for R° are *"the anti-isomorph of R"* and the *"right-left dual of R."*

Let R be a ring; then we have the rings $(R_n)^\circ$ and $(R^\circ)_n$. To discover the relation between these rings, we introduce, for A in R_n, the matrix A^T in $(R^\circ)_n$ obtained by interchanging the rows and columns of A and then regarding the result as a matrix in $(R^\circ)_n$. We may then prove that

(1) $(A + B)^T = A^T + B^T$, $(AB)^T = B^T A^T$, and $(A^T)^T = A$

for all A and B in R_n. We give the proof only for the second equation of (1). The element in the kth row and ith column of $(AB)^T$ is

$$\sum_{j=1}^n a_{ij} b_{jk},$$

which is regarded as an element of R°. On the other hand, the element of R° in the kth row and the ith column of $B^T A^T$ is

$$\sum_{j=1}^n b_{jk} \cdot a_{ij} = \sum_{j=1}^n a_{ij} b_{jk}.$$

This proves the second equation of (1). By (1) we see that the rings $(R_n)^\circ$ and $(R^\circ)_n$ are isomorphic since T is a faithful map of R_n onto $((R^\circ)_n)^\circ$, which preserves both addition and multiplication.

Illustrative
Example

Let

$$A = [\mathbf{i} \quad \mathbf{j}] \qquad \text{and} \qquad B = \begin{bmatrix} \mathbf{k} & \mathbf{j} \\ \mathbf{i} & \mathbf{j} \end{bmatrix}$$

have elements in $\mathscr{Q}$, the ring of real quaternions. Then $AB =$ $[-\mathbf{j} - \mathbf{k}, \mathbf{k} - \mathbf{I}]$. The matrices

$$B^{\mathrm{T}} = \begin{bmatrix} \mathbf{k} & \mathbf{i} \\ \mathbf{j} & \mathbf{j} \end{bmatrix}, \qquad A^{\mathrm{T}} = \begin{bmatrix} \mathbf{i} \\ \mathbf{j} \end{bmatrix}$$

have their elements in $\mathscr{Q}^{\circ}$. Then

$$B^{\mathrm{T}}A^{\mathrm{T}} = \begin{bmatrix} \mathbf{k}\cdot\mathbf{i} + \mathbf{i}\cdot\mathbf{j} \\ \mathbf{j}\cdot\mathbf{i} + \mathbf{j}\cdot\mathbf{j} \end{bmatrix} = \begin{bmatrix} \mathbf{ik} + \mathbf{ji} \\ \mathbf{ij} + \mathbf{j}^2 \end{bmatrix} = (AB)^{\mathrm{T}}.$$

The matrix A^{T} is called the *transpose* of A. One sees that the equations (1) are valid whenever their terms are defined. These equations are particularly useful when R is commutative, since then the trip into R° is unnecessary.

/ 5 / BLOCK MULTIPLICATION

In this section we discuss a method of performing matrix multiplication which is of both theoretical and practical value.

An m-by-n matrix of elements of a ring R may be considered to be made up of smaller matrices in many different ways. For example,

$$A = \begin{bmatrix} 0 & 1 & 2 & 3 \\ -1 & 0 & 1 & 2 \end{bmatrix} = [A_{11} \quad A_{12}],$$

provided that

$$A_{11} = \begin{bmatrix} 0 & 1 \\ -1 & 0 \end{bmatrix} \qquad \text{and} \qquad A_{12} = \begin{bmatrix} 2 & 3 \\ 1 & 2 \end{bmatrix}.$$

We call such a representation of A a decomposition of A into *blocks* A_{tq}, where $t = 1, \cdots, r$, and $q = 1, \cdots, s$. Let B be an n-by-h matrix such that $P = AB$ is defined, and let B_{uv}, where $u = 1, \cdots, w$, and $v = 1, \cdots, z$, be the blocks of a decomposition of B. If $w = s$ and if all the matric products appearing are defined, then

$$P_{tv} = \sum_{q=1}^{s} A_{tq}B_{qv}, \qquad \text{where } t = 1, \cdots, r, \quad \text{and} \quad v = 1, \cdots, z$$

are the blocks of a decomposition of $P = AB$. At first sight this seems like a formidable result to prove. However, let us first observe that it is a direct consequence of the definition of matric multiplication that A may be split into blocks of rows and that B may be split into blocks of columns. This reduces our problem to showing that

$$AB = [A_1 \quad A_2 \quad \cdots \quad A_s]\begin{bmatrix} B_1 \\ B_2 \\ \vdots \\ B_s \end{bmatrix} = [A_1B_1 + \cdots + A_sB_s].$$

(1)

The ith row of A may be regarded as composed of the ith rows of each of $A_1, \cdots, A_s$ placed one after the other from left to right. The jth column of B may be regarded as composed of the jth columns of each of $B_1, \cdots, B_s$ placed one under the other from top to bottom. The element in the ith row and jth column of AB is then seen to be the sum for $q = 1, \cdots, s$ of the elements in the ith row and jth column of A_qB_q. Thus $AB = A_1B_1 + \cdots + A_sB_s$ and (1) is proved. This completes our proof of the block multiplication rule.

Illustrative
Example

Let

$$A = \begin{bmatrix} A_{11} & A_{12} \\ A_{21} & A_{22} \end{bmatrix}, \qquad B = \begin{bmatrix} B_{11} \\ B_{21} \end{bmatrix},$$

where

$$A_{11} = [1 \quad 2], \qquad A_{12} = [5], \qquad B_{11} = \begin{bmatrix} 4 & 2 & -1 \\ 1 & 3 & 4 \end{bmatrix},$$

$$A_{21} = \begin{bmatrix} 4 & 0 \\ -2 & 3 \end{bmatrix}, \qquad A_{22} = \begin{bmatrix} 7 \\ -2 \end{bmatrix}, \qquad B_{21} = [5 \quad 0 \quad 2],$$

$$AB = \begin{bmatrix} A_{11}B_{11} + A_{12}B_{21} \\ A_{21}B_{11} + A_{22}B_{21} \end{bmatrix}$$

$$= \begin{bmatrix} \begin{bmatrix} 6 & 8 & 7 \end{bmatrix} + \begin{bmatrix} 25 & 0 & 10 \end{bmatrix} \\ \begin{bmatrix} 16 & 8 & -4 \\ -5 & 5 & 14 \end{bmatrix} + \begin{bmatrix} 35 & 0 & 14 \\ -10 & 0 & -4 \end{bmatrix} \end{bmatrix}$$

$$= \begin{bmatrix} 31 & 8 & 17 \\ 51 & 8 & 10 \\ -15 & 5 & 10 \end{bmatrix},$$

which may be compared with the usual method of computing AB.

One also notes that we get A^T by interchanging the rows and columns of blocks of A and transposing each block. Thus, for the previous illustrative example we have

$$A^\mathrm{T} = \begin{bmatrix} A_{11}{}^\mathrm{T} & A_{21}{}^\mathrm{T} \\ A_{12}{}^\mathrm{T} & A_{22}{}^\mathrm{T} \end{bmatrix}.$$

As an application of the block multiplication rule, let us indicate the proof that R_{mn} and $(R_m)_n$ are isomorphic. Each matrix in R_{mn} (where R is a ring) may be decomposed into n^2 blocks, each of which is in R_m. It is evident that this decomposition into blocks is preserved under addition, and the block multiplication rule assures us it is also preserved under multiplication. Since this correspondence between R_{mn} and $(R_m)_n$ is clearly a faithful map of R_{mn} onto $(R_m)_n$, we conclude that R_{mn} and $(R_m)_n$ are isomorphic.

EXERCISES FOR CHAPTER 1

1. Cite the theorems from calculus which justify the statement that $C'(R_e)$ is a ring.
2. In $Z/17Z$, solve the following equations for x: (a) $5_{17}x = 1_{17}$. (b) $4_{17}x = 5_{17}$.
3. The numbers $2^2 + 1 = 5$, $2^4 + 1 = 17$, $2^8 + 1 = 257$, and $2^{16} + 1 = 65{,}537$ are all primes. Show that $2^{32} + 1$ is not a prime by noting that, in $Z/641Z$, $5_{641} \cdot (2_{641})^7 = (-1)_{641}$ and using this result to prove that $2^{32} + 1$ is divisible by 641.
4. Is it possible to solve $5_{16}x = 1_{16}$ in $Z/16Z$? Can one solve $4_{16}x = 10_{16}$?
5. Using diagrams, verify that 2^S is a ring.
6. Fill in the gaps in the proofs of (1-2) to (1-4).
7. Complete the proof of (1-5).
8. What are the identity elements of the following rings: $R = K$, $K[x]$, $C(R_e)$, $C(R_e)[x]$, $Z/5Z$, $Z/10000Z$, 2^S?
9. What are the nonsingular elements of the rings Z, $Z/16Z$, $R_e[x]$, $C(R_e)$?
10. Verify the associative law for matric multiplication for

$$A = [1 \quad 0 \quad -1], \qquad B = \begin{bmatrix} 2 & -1 & 5 \\ 3 & 0 & 0 \\ 4 & 2 & 1 \end{bmatrix}, \qquad C = \begin{bmatrix} 2 \\ -1 \\ 3 \end{bmatrix}.$$

11. If AB and BA are both defined, must A and B be square?
12. Let R be a commutative ring with identity element 1. Show that, if A and X in R_2 satisfy $AX = I$, then $XA = I$.

13. Let A be in Z_2. When is A nonsingular?
14. Let A be in $(R_a[x])_2$. When is A nonsingular?
15. Let A be in $(Z[x])_2$. When is A nonsingular?
16. Let A be in $(C(R_e)[x])_2$. When is A nonsingular?
17. Consider the equations

$$\sum_{j=1}^{n} a_{ij}x_j = c_i \qquad (i = 1, \cdots, n),$$

where a_{ij} and c_i are in R, a ring with identity element 1. Write these equations in matric form as $AX = C$, with $A = [a_{ij}; i, j = 1, \cdots, n]$ and with $X^T = [x_1, \cdots, x_n]$ and $C^T = [c_1, \cdots, c_n]$. If A is nonsingular in R_n, solve for X.

18. Show that in Exercise 17 the existence of a solution X for every C implies that $AB = I$ for some B in R_n.

19. Use the method of Exercise 17 to solve the equations

$$2_{15}x_1 + 3_{15}x_2 = 4_{15},$$
$$-2_{15}x_1 + 5_{15}x_2 = 3_{15}$$

in $Z/15Z$.

20. Let D be a division ring and let A and X in D_2 satisfy $AX = I$. Show that $XA = I$.

21. Consider the following matrices and verify that $(AB)^T = B^T A^T$:

$$A = [\mathbf{i} \quad \mathbf{j} \quad \mathbf{k}], \qquad B = \begin{bmatrix} \mathbf{j} \\ \mathbf{k} \\ \mathbf{i} \end{bmatrix}.$$

22. Let K be the field of all complex numbers $z = a + bi$ with a and b real numbers. Prove that the map $z \to \bar{z} = a - bi$ of K onto K has the properties $\overline{z_1 + z_2} = \bar{z}_1 + \bar{z}_2$, $\overline{z_1 z_2} = (\bar{z}_1)(\bar{z}_2)$, and $\overline{\overline{z}_1} = z_1$ for all z_1 and z_2 in K; that is, prove that $z \to \bar{z}$ is an isomorphism of K onto K.

23. Let

$$P = \begin{bmatrix} A & 0 \\ B & C \end{bmatrix}$$

with A nonsingular. Show that P is nonsingular if and only if C is nonsingular, and find the inverse of P.

24. Assume that the matrices A, B, and C are nonsingular. Show that the matrix

$$\begin{bmatrix} A & 0 & 0 \\ X & B & 0 \\ Y & W & C \end{bmatrix}$$

is nonsingular and find a formula for its inverse.

25. Find

$$\begin{bmatrix} 1 & 0 & 0 & 0 & 0 \\ a & 1 & 0 & 0 & 0 \\ 0 & b & 1 & 0 & 0 \\ 0 & 0 & c & 1 & 0 \\ 0 & 0 & 0 & d & 1 \end{bmatrix}^{-1}.$$

26. Consider the set K_0 of all matrices of $(R_e)_2$ of the form

$$z = \begin{bmatrix} a & b \\ -b & a \end{bmatrix}.$$

Show that K_0 is isomorphic to the complex field K.

27. Let P be as in Exercise 23. Develop a formula for P^n, where $n = 1, 2, \cdots$.

28. Let R be a commutative ring with identity element 1, and let

$$A = \begin{bmatrix} a & b \\ c & d \end{bmatrix}$$

be in R_2. Show that

$$\det (xI - A) = \det \begin{bmatrix} x - a & -b \\ -c & x - d \end{bmatrix}$$
$$= x^2 - (a + d)x + ad - bc$$

and that $A^2 - (a + d)A + (ad - bc)I = 0$.

29. With A as in Exercise 28, assume that det A is nonsingular in R and show that $A^{-1} = (\det A)^{-1}[(a + d)I - A]$.

30. With A as in Exercise 28, show that adj $A = (a + d)I - A$.

31. Apply Exercises 28 to 30 to $\mathscr{2}$, the ring of real quaternions.

32. Let R be a commutative ring and let A be in R_n. Define

$$\text{Trace } A = \sum_{i=1}^{n} a_{ii}.$$

Prove that Trace $(aA) = a$ Trace A, that Trace $(A + B) =$ Trace $A +$ Trace B, and that Trace $(AB) =$ Trace (BA) for all A and B in R_n.

33. Find a formula for A^n, where $n = 1, 2, \cdots$, if

$$A = \begin{bmatrix} 1 & 0 & 0 & 0 \\ 0 & 1 & 0 & 0 \\ 2 & 4 & -1 & 0 \\ -1 & 5 & 0 & -1 \end{bmatrix}$$

by writing

$$A = \begin{bmatrix} I & 0 \\ C & -I \end{bmatrix}$$

and using block multiplication.

34. In the ring 2^S, what is a necessary condition on A and B in 2^S for $AX = B$ to have a solution X in 2^S? Is the solution X ever unique?

35. If R is a ring, a mapping $a \to a'$ of R into R is called a derivation in R in case

$$(a + b)' = a' + b'$$
$$(ab)' = ab' + a'b$$

for all a and b in R.

(a) Show that the derivative (in the calculus sense) is a derivation in the ring $C^\infty(R_e)$, where $C^\infty(R_e)$ consists of the set of all elements of $C(R_e)$ which have derivatives of all orders at every real value.

(b) Show that, in the ring $R[x]$, where R is any ring with identity 1, the *formal derivative*

$$(a_0 + a_1 x + \cdots + a_n x^n)' = a_1 + 2a_2 x + \cdots + na_n x^{n-1}$$

is a derivation.

(c) Show that, if R is a ring and a is a fixed element of R, then, $b' = ba - ab$ for every b in R, defines a derivation in R.

(d) If R is a ring, then, for a and b in R, $[a, b] = ab - ba$ is called the commutator of a and b. Prove Jacobi's Identity: $[a, [b, c]] + [b, [c, a]] + [c, [a, b]] = 0$ for all a, b, and c in R.

36. If $a \to a'$ is a derivation in a ring R, we may define (as in calculus) higher derivatives inductively, by setting $a^{(0)} = a$, $a^{(n+1)} = (a^{(n)})'$. Prove Leibniz's rule:

$$(ab)^{(n)} = \sum_{i=0}^{n} \binom{n}{i} a^{(i)} b^{(n-i)},$$

where $\binom{n}{i}$ denote the binomial coefficients.

37. Let R be a *finite* ring with identity element $1 \neq 0$, in which $a, b \neq 0$ in R implies $ab \neq 0$. Show that R is a division ring. [*Hint:* If $a \neq 0$, then $\{ax; x \in R\} = R$.]

38. Use Exercise 37 to prove that Z/mZ is a field if m is a prime positive integer.

39. Let R be a ring with identity 1 so that R_n has identity I. Prove that $AX = XA$ for every X in R_n if and only if $A = cI$ where $cx = xc$ for every $x \in R$.

2

DETERMINANTS

In this chapter we introduce the determinant of a matrix in R_n provided that R is commutative. A theory of determinants for certain noncommutative rings exists, but this theory is too advanced to be treated here. We start, in Section 1, with a very limited discussion of permutations of finite sets. Determinants are defined and their basic properties derived in Section 2. In the final section the Gaussian method of computing determinants is explained.

/1/ SOME FACTS
ABOUT PERMUTATIONS

A faithful map of a set S onto S is called a *permutation* of S. We are particularly interested in the case in which $S = \{1, \cdots, n\}$. For this case we may specify a permutation of S by means of a table of values:

$$\begin{matrix} 1 & 2 & 3 & \cdots & n \\ i_1 & i_2 & i_3 & \cdots & i_n \end{matrix}$$

where the second row is just a rearrangement of the numbers $1, 2, 3, \cdots, n$. Since the arrangement $i_1\, i_2 \cdots i_n$ uniquely determines the permutation, it is customary to call such arrangements permutations also. Consider a specific arrangement $i_1\, i_2 \cdots i_n$. The *number of inversions due to* i_k *in* $i_1\, i_2 \cdots i_n$ is the number of i_r with $r < k$ and $i_r > i_k$. Thus, in 456321, the number of inversions due to 4, 5, 6 is zero, the number due to 3 is three, the number due to 2 is four, and the number due to 1 is five. The sum of the number of inversions in $i_1\, i_2 \cdots i_n$ due to $i_1, i_2, \cdots, i_n$ is called the (total) *number of inversions in* $i_1\, i_2 \cdots i_n$. For 456321 this number is twelve.

P1. Interchanging two numbers in a permutation changes the number of inversions by an odd number.

PROOF   This is clear when the two numbers are adjacent, for then the number of inversions increases or decreases by 1. If r numbers separate the two numbers to be interchanged, we may effect the interchange of the two numbers by $2r + 1$ interchanges of adjacent numbers. Since the sum of an odd number of odd numbers is odd, we see that the number of inversions changes by an odd number.

P2.   If one permutation is changed into a second permutation by s interchanges of two numbers and also by t interchanges of two numbers, then $(-1)^s = (-1)^t$, that is, s and t are both even or s and t are both odd.

PROOF   Let q and q' be the number of inversions of the first and second permutations, respectively. Then, by P1,

$$q' = q + c_1 + \cdots + c_s = q + d_1 + \cdots + d_t,$$

where c_j and d_k $(j = 1, \cdots, s; k = 1, \cdots, t)$ are odd integers. If s is even, then $c_1 + \cdots + c_s = d_1 + \cdots + d_t$ is even, and hence t is even. If s is odd, then $c_1 + \cdots + c_s$ is odd and so is t.

We shall call a permutation *even* or *odd* according as its number of inversions is even or odd. Then a permutation is even or odd according as it can be obtained from 1 2 3 $\cdots$ n by an even or by an odd number of interchanges. For if q is the number of inversions of the permutation, we can replace the permutation by 1 2 3 $\cdots$ n by q interchanges of adjacent numbers. Starting with 1 2 3 $\cdots$ n and performing these same interchanges in reverse order, we obtain the original permutation. For example, 4321 has six inversions. Letting "- - -" indicate an interchange of adjacent numbers, we have 4321 - - - 4312 - - - 4132 - - - 1432 - - - 1423 - - - 1243 - - - 1234,   and   1234 - - - 1243 - - - 1423 - - - 1432 - - - 4132 - - - 4312 - - - 4321.

Finally, we need to discuss the inverse of a permutation. Let us consider the permutation

$$
\begin{array}{cccc}
1 & 2 & 3 & 4 \\
4 & 3 & 1 & 2
\end{array}
$$

We interchange columns in this array so as to arrange the second row in natural order:

$$
\begin{array}{cccc}
3 & 4 & 2 & 1 \\
1 & 2 & 3 & 4
\end{array}
$$

The permutation 3421 is the *inverse* of 4312. In general, if $i_1 \; i_2 \; \cdots \; i_n$ is a permutation, we obtain its inverse by forming the array

$$
\begin{array}{ccccc}
1 & 2 & 3 & \cdots & n \\
i_1 & i_2 & i_3 & \cdots & i_n
\end{array}
$$

and interchanging columns so as to arrange the second row in natural order:

$$
\begin{array}{ccccc}
j_1 & j_2 & j_3 & \cdots & j_n \\
1 & 2 & 3 & \cdots & n
\end{array}
$$

Then $j_1 \; j_2 \; \cdots \; j_n$ is the *inverse* of $i_1 \; i_2 \; \cdots \; i_n$. Note that the inverse of a permutation is even or odd according as the permutation itself is even or odd, for the interchanges which yield $j_1 \; j_2 \; \cdots \; j_n$ from $12 \; \cdots \; n$ *and* replace $i_1 \; i_2 \; \cdots \; i_n$ by $12 \; \cdots \; n$ will replace $12 \; \cdots \; n$ by $i_1 \; i_2 \; \cdots \; i_n$ if they are performed in reverse order.

Illustrative
Example

The permutation 643512 has $0 + 1 + 2 + 1 + 4 + 4$ inversions and is even. We have

643512 - - - 143562 - - - 123564 - - - 123465 - - - 123456,

and four interchanges arrange 643512 in natural order. Arranging the table

$$
\begin{array}{cccccc}
1 & 2 & 3 & 4 & 5 & 6 \\
6 & 4 & 3 & 5 & 1 & 2
\end{array}
$$

so that the second row is in natural order, we obtain

$$
\begin{array}{cccccc}
5 & 6 & 3 & 2 & 4 & 1 \\
1 & 2 & 3 & 4 & 5 & 6
\end{array}
$$

Thus the inverse of 643512 is 563241, which has $0 + 0 + 2 + 3 + 2 + 5$ inversions and is therefore even.

/ 2 / DEFINITION AND BASIC PROPERTIES OF DETERMINANTS

We are now ready to introduce determinants of matrices in R_n assuming that R is commutative. The definition which we adopt is an ancient one, but it leads very easily to the fundamental properties of determinants, as the arguments of this section will show.

In order to secure an economical definition of determinants, we define $\epsilon_{i_1 \ldots i_n}$ as the integer 1 if $i_1\, i_2\, \cdots\, i_n$ is an even permutation, as the integer -1 if $i_1\, i_2\, \cdots\, i_n$ is an odd permutation, and as the integer 0 if two of the indices $i_1\, i_2\, \cdots\, i_n$ are equal.

Now let R be a commutative ring and let $A = [a_{ij}]$, where i and j equal $1, \cdots, n$, be a matrix of R_n. We define the *determinant* of A as the sum

$$(1) \qquad \det A = \sum_{i_1,i_2,\ldots,i_n=1}^{n} \epsilon_{i_1 i_2 \ldots i_n} a_{1i_1} a_{2i_2} \cdots a_{ni_n}.$$

We now discuss the cases $n = 2$ and $n = 3$. For $n = 2$, only $\epsilon_{12} = 1$ and $\epsilon_{21} = -1$ are nonzero, so that

$$\det \begin{bmatrix} a_{11} & a_{12} \\ a_{21} & a_{22} \end{bmatrix} = \epsilon_{12} a_{11} a_{22} + \epsilon_{21} a_{12} a_{21} = a_{11} a_{22} - a_{12} a_{21}$$

in agreement with the usual elementary definition. For $n = 3$ we have $\epsilon_{123} = \epsilon_{231} = \epsilon_{312} = 1$ and $\epsilon_{213} = \epsilon_{321} = \epsilon_{132} = -1$ and all other $\epsilon_{i_1 i_2 i_3} = 0$. Thus, as usual,

$$\det \begin{bmatrix} a_{11} & a_{12} & a_{13} \\ a_{21} & a_{22} & a_{23} \\ a_{31} & a_{32} & a_{33} \end{bmatrix} = \epsilon_{123} a_{11} a_{22} a_{33} + \epsilon_{231} a_{12} a_{23} a_{31}$$
$$+ \epsilon_{312} a_{13} a_{21} a_{32} + \epsilon_{213} a_{12} a_{21} a_{33}$$
$$+ \epsilon_{321} a_{13} a_{22} a_{31} + \epsilon_{132} a_{11} a_{23} a_{32}$$
$$= a_{11} a_{22} a_{33} + a_{12} a_{23} a_{31} + a_{13} a_{21} a_{32}$$
$$- a_{12} a_{21} a_{33} - a_{13} a_{22} a_{31} - a_{11} a_{23} a_{32}.$$

For a permutation $i_1\, i_2\, \cdots\, i_n$, let $j_1\, j_2\, \cdots\, j_n$ be its inverse. Then, by (1-14),

$$\epsilon_{i_1 i_2 \cdots i_n} a_{1i_1} a_{2i_2} \cdots a_{ni_n} = \epsilon_{j_1 j_2 \cdots j_n} a_{j_1 1} a_{j_2 2} \cdots a_{j_n n}.$$

By using (1-3) and R3 and the fact that $\epsilon_{i_1 i_2 \cdots i_n} = 0$ when two of the indices are equal, we see that

(2) $$\det A = \sum_{j_1, j_2, \cdots, j_n = 1}^{n} \epsilon_{j_1 j_2 \cdots j_n} a_{j_1 1} a_{j_2 2} \cdots a_{j_n n}.$$

From (1) and (2) it follows immediately that

(3) $$\det A = \det A^{T}.$$

If A has identical kth and lth rows, the two terms of (1) which correspond to the permutations $i_1\ i_2\ \cdots\ i_k\ \cdots\ i_l\ \cdots\ i_n$ and $i_1\ i_2\ \cdots\ i_l\ \cdots\ i_k\ \cdots\ i_n$ add to zero, since

$$\epsilon_{i_1 i_2 \cdots i_k \cdots i_l \cdots i_n} = -\epsilon_{i_1 i_2 \cdots i_l \cdots i_k \cdots i_n}.$$

It follows that $\det A = 0$ if A has two identical rows (or two identical columns).

By (1) and (2), an interchanging of two rows or of two columns changes the sign of the determinant. More generally, let A_1 be the matrix obtained by applying the permutation $k_1\ k_2\ \cdots\ k_n$ to the rows of A. Then

$$\det A_1 = \epsilon_{k_1 k_2 \cdots k_n} \det A = \sum_{i_1, i_2, \cdots, i_n = 1}^{n} \epsilon_{i_1 i_2 \cdots i_n} a_{k_1 i_1} a_{k_2 i_2} \cdots a_{k_n i_n}.$$

In fact, this formula remains true if $k_1\ k_2\ \cdots\ k_n$ is not a permutation of $12\ \cdots\ n$ for, if $k_i = k_j$ with $i \neq j$, then A_1 has equal ith and jth rows and all members of our formula are zero.

Now let $B = [b_{jk}]$, where j and k equal $1, \cdots, n$, also be a matrix of R_n. Then free use of the computation rules of Section 1, Chapter 1, gives

(4)
$$\begin{aligned}
(\det A)(\det B) &= \sum_{i's} a_{1i_1} a_{2i_2} \cdots a_{ni_n}\, \epsilon_{i_1 i_2 \cdots i_n} \det B \\
&= \sum_{i's} a_{1i_1} a_{2i_2} \cdots a_{ni_n} \sum_{j's} \epsilon_{j_1 j_2 \cdots j_n} b_{i_1 j_1} b_{i_2 j_2} \cdots b_{i_n j_n} \\
&= \sum_{j's} \epsilon_{j_1 j_2 \cdots j_n} \left(\sum_{i_1 = 1}^{n} a_{1i_1} b_{i_1 j_1} \right) \left(\sum_{i_2 = 1}^{n} a_{2i_2} b_{i_2 j_2} \right) \cdots \\
&\qquad\qquad\qquad\qquad\qquad \left(\sum_{i_n = 1}^{n} a_{ni_n} b_{i_n j_n} \right) \\
&= \det (AB).
\end{aligned}$$

One may compute the value of a determinant by expansion

on a row or on a column. To obtain the expansion of det A on the kth row of A, we use the definition (1) to write

$$\det A = \sum_{i_k=1}^{n} a_{ki_k} A_{i_k k}$$

where

$$A_{i_k k} = \sum_{i_1,\cdots,i_k,\cdots,i_n=1}^{n} \epsilon_{i_1 i_2 \cdots i_n} a_{1i_1} \cdots \hat{a}_{ki_k} \cdots a_{ni_n}.$$

Here the circumflex placed over a symbol means that the symbol is to be deleted. Now, $\epsilon_{i_1 i_2 \cdots i_n}$ is zero if some $i_j = i_k$ for $j \neq k$, while it is $(-1)^{k+i_k} \epsilon_{i_1 \cdots i_k \cdots i_n}$ otherwise. For, if we let

$$i_1 \cdots \hat{i}_k \cdots i_n \overset{s}{-\!-} 1 \cdots \hat{i}_k \cdots n$$

where $-\overset{s}{-}-$ denotes the performance of s interchanges, then

$$i_1 i_2 \cdots i_n \overset{k-1}{-\!-\!-\!-} i_k i_1 i_2 \cdots \hat{i}_k \cdots i_n \overset{s}{-\!-} i_k 1\, 2 \cdots \hat{i}_k \cdots$$
$$n \overset{i_k-1}{-\!-\!-\!-} 1\, 2 \cdots n$$

shows that $s + (k-1) + (i_k - 1)$ interchanges put $i_1 i_2 \cdots i_n$ in natural order, and

$$\epsilon_{i_1 \cdots i_n} = (-1)^{k+i_k} \epsilon_{i_1 \cdots i_k \cdots i_n}$$

is thereby proved. It follows that

$$A_{i_k k} = (-1)^{k+i_k} \det M_{i_k k},$$

where $M_{i_k k}$ is the matrix obtained by deleting the kth *row* and the i_kth *column* of A. We call $A_{i_k k}$ the *cofactor* of a_{ki_k} in A. An analogous discussion with the use of (2) yields expansions of det A on the columns of A:

$$\det A = \det A^{\mathrm{T}} = \sum_{i_k=1}^{n} A_{ki_k} a_{i_k k}.$$

When $k \neq l$, we obtain

$$0 = \sum_{j=1}^{n} a_{kj} A_{jl} = \sum_{j=1}^{n} A_{lj} a_{jk}$$

because these sums yield determinants of matrices with two identical rows or two identical columns, respectively.

For the sake of economy, let us define the matrix, for A in R_n:

$$\text{adj } A = [A_{ij}] \qquad (i, j = 1, \cdots, n).$$

We call adj A the *adjoint* of A. Observe the interchange of rows and columns in the computation of adj A.

Thus

$$A_{ij} = (-1)^{i+j} \det M_{ij}$$

where M_{ij} is obtained by deleting the ith *column* and the jth *row* of A.

Let us also introduce the matrix diag $(a_1, a_2, \cdots, a_n) = D = [d_{ij}]$ of R_n, which has $d_{ii} = a_i$ and $d_{ij} = 0$ if $i \neq j$. We may then state all of the facts about expansions on rows and columns in the equations:

(5) $A(\text{adj } A) = (\text{adj } A)A = \text{diag } (\det A, \det A, \cdots, \det A).$

Illustrative
Example

Let

$$A = \begin{bmatrix} x & -1 & 0 \\ 0 & x & -1 \\ 2 & 4 & x \end{bmatrix}$$

in $(R_a[x])_3$; then

$$\text{adj } A = \begin{bmatrix} x^2 + 4 & x & 1 \\ -2 & x^2 & x \\ -2x & -4x - 2 & x^2 \end{bmatrix}.$$

We then see that $A(\text{adj } A) = (x^3 + 4x + 2)I = (\text{adj } A)A$. Now, det $A = x^3 + 4x + 2$ can also be found directly by adding x times the second column to the first column and then x^2 times the third column to the first column, and finally expanding on the first column.

When R has an identity element, we may use (4) and (5) to prove that A is nonsingular in R_n if and only if det A is nonsingular in R. When det A is nonsingular in R, then the matrix $[A_{ij}(\det A)^{-1}]$ is the inverse of A in R_n. This yields a test of nonsingularity in R_n but provides a very inefficient method of computing the inverse of a matrix unless n is very small. To prove our test of nonsingularity, let A be nonsingular in R_n so that $AX = I$ for some X in R_n. By (4), $(\det A)(\det X) = \det I = 1$ (by the definition), and $\det A$ is nonsingular in R since R is commutative. Conversely, let $(\det A)^{-1}$ exist in R and set $X = [A_{ij}(\det A)^{-1}]$. By using (5), we easily see that $AX = XA = $ diag $(1, 1, \cdots, 1) = I$.

/ 3 / COMPUTATION OF DETERMINANTS WHEN R IS A FIELD

This final section is devoted to Gauss's method for the computation of determinants of matrices with elements in a field.

Let us first observe a few simple consequences of the definition (1). Let R be a commutative ring and let A be in R_n.

D1. As a function of one of its rows (or columns), $\det A$ is linear; that is, multiplication of each element of a row (column) of A by an element c in R has the effect of multiplying the determinant by c. If the ith row of A has the form $a_{ij} = b_{ij} + c_{ij}$ $(j = 1, \cdots, n)$, then $\det A = \det B + \det C$, where B and C are obtained from A by replacing the ith row of A with b_{ij} $(j = 1, \cdots, n)$ and with c_{ij} $(j = 1, \cdots, n)$, respectively.

D2. Interchanging two rows (columns) of A changes the sign of the determinant.

From these simple properties and the fact that the determinant of a matrix with two identical rows (columns) is zero we derive the following useful property.

D3. If a multiple of one row (column) of a matrix is added to a different row (column), then the determinant is unchanged; that is, if B is obtained from A by replacing a_{ij} with $a_{ij} + ca_{kj}$, where $j = 1, \cdots, n$, and $i \neq k$, then $\det B = \det A$.

The use of these three properties leads to a systematic method of computing $\det A$ for A in F_n, F being a field. If every element in the first column of A is zero, $\det A$ is zero by the definition.

Otherwise, at most an interchange of rows puts a nonzero element a in the $(1, 1)$ position. The use of D3 causes a replacement of all the other elements in the first column with zeros, for if b is in the $(k, 1)$ position and $k \neq 1$, the addition of $-a^{-1}b$ times the first row to the kth row replaces b with 0. (Note that we are using the fact that F is a field: every nonzero element of F is nonsingular in F.) When this process is complete, by D2 and D3 we see that

$$\det A = \pm \det \begin{bmatrix} a & X \\ 0 & B \end{bmatrix}.$$

We then have $\det A = \pm a \det B$. Repetition of the process ultimately yields $\det A$.

Illustrative
Example

Let

$$A = \begin{bmatrix} 0 & 4 & 5 & 0 \\ 1 & 3 & 6 & 2 \\ 2 & -1 & -1 & -1 \\ -1 & 2 & 0 & 4 \end{bmatrix}$$

in $(R_a)_4$. The Gauss process proceeds as follows:

$$\det A = -\det \begin{bmatrix} 1 & 3 & 6 & 2 \\ 0 & 4 & 5 & 0 \\ 2 & -1 & -1 & -1 \\ -1 & 2 & 0 & 4 \end{bmatrix}$$

$$= -\det \begin{bmatrix} 1 & 3 & 6 & 2 \\ 0 & 4 & 5 & 0 \\ 0 & -7 & -13 & -5 \\ 0 & 5 & 6 & 6 \end{bmatrix}$$

$$= -\det \begin{bmatrix} 4 & 5 & 0 \\ 0 & -17/4 & -5 \\ 0 & -1/4 & 6 \end{bmatrix} = -4 \det \begin{bmatrix} -17/4 & -5 \\ -1/4 & 6 \end{bmatrix}$$

$$= -4 \det \begin{bmatrix} -17/4 & -5 \\ 0 & 107/17 \end{bmatrix} = 107.$$

Observe that such an algorithm as that of Gauss can easily be programmed for a computer.

It is natural to call a square matrix T *lower triangular* if $t_{ij} = 0$ for $i < j$. From the definition we see at once that $\det T = t_{11}t_{22}\cdots t_{nn}$ for T a lower triangular matrix. We leave it to the reader to verify (from the definition) that this result may easily be generalized to

$$\det \begin{bmatrix} A_1 & 0 & \cdots & 0 \\ X_{21} & A_2 & \cdots & 0 \\ \vdots & \vdots & & \vdots \\ X_{q1} & X_{q2} & \cdots & A_q \end{bmatrix} = (\det A_1)\cdots(\det A_q),$$

provided that the matrices $A_1, \cdots, A_q$ are square.

EXERCISES FOR CHAPTER 2

1. Classify the twenty-four permutations of 1, 2, 3, 4 as even or odd.

2. Show that the function

$$A(x_1, \cdots, x_n) = \prod(x_j - x_i) \quad \text{where } i < j, \text{ and } i, j = 1, \cdots, n$$

changes sign when two of its arguments are interchanged. Deduce from this, that if $i_1 \, i_2 \, \cdots \, i_n$ can be replaced with $1 \, 2 \, \cdots \, n$ by s interchanges and also by t interchanges, then $(-1)^s = (-1)^t$. This result permits the classification of permutations as even and odd without recourse to inversions.

3. Find the inverse of the permutation 7346512 and verify that this inverse has the same *parity* (evenness or oddness) as 7346512.

4. Find the inverse of the permutation $n(n - 1) \, \cdots \, 21$.

5. Solve for x:

$$\det \begin{bmatrix} x & 1 & x \\ 0 & x & 1 \\ 2 & x & 1 \end{bmatrix} = 10.$$

6. Find $\epsilon_{n(n-1)\cdots 21}$.

7. For what values of n is the permutation $n(n - 1) \, \cdots \, 21$ even?

8. Use the definition of det A to find

$$\det \begin{bmatrix} 2 & 0 & 1 \\ 3 & 1 & 0 \\ 0 & 2 & 3 \end{bmatrix}.$$

9. The usual definition of determinants restricts $i_1 \cdots i_n$ in $\epsilon_{i_1 \cdots i_n}$ to permutations. What is the advantage of the introduction of the zero terms in the definition (1) given in the text?

10. Show that:

$$\det \begin{bmatrix} 3 & 5 & 2 & 12 \\ 2 & 4 & 1 & 6 \\ 2 & -3 & 0 & 2 \\ 2 & 4 & 2 & 7 \end{bmatrix} = 41.$$

11. Evaluate:

$$\det \begin{bmatrix} x-1 & -1 & -1 \\ -1 & x-1 & -1 \\ -1 & -1 & x-1 \end{bmatrix}.$$

12. Evaluate:

$$\det \begin{bmatrix} x & -1 & 0 \\ 0 & x & -1 \\ 4 & 3 & x-2 \end{bmatrix}.$$

13. Evaluate the following, of size n by n:

$$\det \begin{bmatrix} 0 & 0 & \cdots & 0 & 1 \\ 0 & 0 & \cdots & 1 & 0 \\ \vdots & \vdots & & \vdots & \vdots \\ 0 & 1 & \cdots & 0 & 0 \\ 1 & 0 & \cdots & 0 & 0 \end{bmatrix}.$$

14. Show that

$$\det \begin{bmatrix} x & -1 & 0 \\ 0 & x & -1 \\ c & b & x+a \end{bmatrix} = x^3 + ax^2 + bx + c.$$

15. Show that

$$\det \begin{bmatrix} x & -1 & 0 & \cdots & 0 & 0 \\ 0 & x & -1 & \cdots & 0 & 0 \\ \cdot & \cdot & \cdot & \cdots & \cdot & \cdot \\ 0 & 0 & 0 & \cdots & x & -1 \\ c_0 & c_1 & c_2 & \cdots & c_{n-2} & x + c_{n-1} \end{bmatrix}$$

is equal to $x^n + c_{n-1}x^{n-1} + \cdots + c_2x^2 + c_1x + c_0$. (Hint: Use induction on n and expand on the first row.)

16. Given A, B in R_n with R a commutative ring with identity element 1. Form

$$C = \begin{bmatrix} A & 0 \\ -I & B \end{bmatrix}.$$

Then $\det C = (\det A)(\det B)$. By adding multiples of certain rows of C to other rows of C, show that

$$\det C = \det \begin{bmatrix} 0 & AB \\ -I & B \end{bmatrix} = (-1)^n \det \begin{bmatrix} AB & 0 \\ B & -I \end{bmatrix} = \det (AB).$$

This provides another proof of the rule $\det (AB) = (\det A)(\det B)$.

17. Factor:

$$\det \begin{bmatrix} 1 & a & bc \\ 1 & b & ca \\ 1 & c & ab \end{bmatrix}.$$

18. Factor:

$$\det \begin{bmatrix} 1 & 1 & 1 \\ x^2 & y^2 & z^2 \\ x^3 & y^3 & z^3 \end{bmatrix}.$$

19. Show that

$$\det \begin{bmatrix} 1 & 1 & 1 \\ x_1 & x_2 & x_3 \\ x_1^2 & x_2^2 & x_3^2 \end{bmatrix} = (x_2 - x_1)(x_3 - x_1)(x_3 - x_2).$$

With the notation of Exercise 2, the result is $A(x_1, x_2, x_3)$.

20. Generalize Exercise 19.

21. Let the elements of $A = [a_{ij}]$ $(i, j = 1, \cdots, n)$ be real differentiable functions of x for $a \le x \le b$. Find a rule for computing the derivative of det A.

22. Apply Rolle's Theorem to

$$F(x) = \det \begin{bmatrix} 1 & 1 & 1 \\ f(x) & f(a) & f(b) \\ g(x) & g(a) & g(b) \end{bmatrix}$$

and obtain an extended mean value theorem.

23. Let $f(x)$, $g(x)$, and $h(x)$ be real differentiable functions of x for $a \le x \le b$. Apply Rolle's Theorem to

$$F(x) = \det \begin{bmatrix} f(x) & f(a) & f(b) \\ g(x) & g(a) & g(b) \\ h(x) & h(a) & h(b) \end{bmatrix}.$$

24. Show that

$$\det \begin{bmatrix} a & b & c & d \\ -b & a & -d & c \\ -c & d & a & -b \\ -d & -c & b & a \end{bmatrix} = (a^2 + b^2 + c^2 + d^2)^2.$$

25. Solve for x:

$$\det \begin{bmatrix} a + x & x & x \\ x & b + x & x \\ x & x & c + x \end{bmatrix} = 0.$$

26. If A is nonsingular in R_n (R commutative), what is det (adj A)?

27. Let A in $(R_e)_n$ satisfy $a_{ji} = -a_{ij}$ $(i, j = 1, \cdots, n)$. Show that, if n is odd, det A is zero.

28. Let A in $(R_e)_n$ satisfy

$$a_{ii} > 0 \quad \text{and} \quad a_{ii} > \sum_{j \ne i} |a_{ij}| \quad (i = 1, \cdots, n).$$

Prove that det $A > 0$.

29. Permutations of S, being faithful maps of S onto S, can be composed† via $(f \circ g)(s) = f(g(s))$. Show that $f \circ g$ is a permutation of S if f and g are, that the associative law holds, that there is a permutation e of S such that $e \circ f = f = f \circ e$

† See the Appendix, Section 3.

for all permutations f of S, and that every permutation of S has an inverse f^{-1} which is a permutation of S such that $f \circ f^{-1} = e = f^{-1} \circ f$. These facts prove that the set of all permutations of S forms a group (see Exercise 15 of the Appendix for a definition of *group*).

3

POLYNOMIALS

In this chapter we develop a few elementary properties of polynomials. In the first section we discuss the division process for polynomials. The remainder and factor theorems are then derived from a useful rule for substitution. In the second section we discuss polynomials with coefficients in a field, the greatest common divisor of two polynomials, and the factorization of polynomials.

/ 1 / SOME ELEMENTARY PROPERTIES
OF POLYNOMIALS

In this section, R is a ring with identity element 1. We do not assume that R is commutative. Our main purpose is to observe the modifications of the usual division and substitution processes for polynomials, modifications made necessary by the (possible) noncommutativity of R. The important application we have in mind is, of course, to the case in which R is a matric ring. Recall that $R[x]$ was defined in Chapter 1 as the ring of all polynomials in x with coefficients in R.

If

(1) $f(x) = a_0 + a_1 x + \cdots + a_n x^n$ where $a_n \neq 0$

is a polynomial in $R[x]$, we define the *degree* of f, $\deg f$, as n. The degree of the zero polynomial is defined as $-\infty$. We call a_n the leading coefficient of f. When a_n is 1, we call f *monic*. Concerning degrees we have the rules:

(2)
$$\deg \ (f + g) \leq \max \ (\deg f, \deg g),$$
$$\deg \ (fg) \leq \deg f + \deg g.$$

If the leading coefficient of either f or g is nonsingular in R, then

(3) $$\deg \ (fg) = \deg f + \deg g.$$

Thus, if R is a division ring, then $f \in R[x]$ is nonsingular in $R[x]$ if and only if f is constant and nonsingular in R.

Illustrative
Example

If
$$f(x) = \begin{bmatrix} 1 & 2 \\ 0 & 1 \end{bmatrix} + \begin{bmatrix} 0 & 0 \\ 1 & 0 \end{bmatrix} x^2$$

and
$$g(x) = \begin{bmatrix} 1 & 0 \\ -2 & 3 \end{bmatrix} + \begin{bmatrix} 0 & 0 \\ 0 & 1 \end{bmatrix} x,$$

then
$$f(x)g(x) = \begin{bmatrix} -3 & 6 \\ -2 & 3 \end{bmatrix} + \begin{bmatrix} 0 & 2 \\ 0 & 1 \end{bmatrix} x + \begin{bmatrix} 0 & 0 \\ 1 & 0 \end{bmatrix} x^2$$

so that $\deg (fg) = 2 < \deg f + \deg g = 3$.

Our first observation about $R[x]$ concerns division.

(3-1) Let f and g be in $R[x]$ and let the leading coefficient of g be nonsingular. Then, first, there are unique polynomials q_ρ and r_ρ in $R[x]$ such that

$$f = q_\rho g + r_\rho \qquad \text{and} \qquad \deg r_\rho < \deg g,$$

and, second, there are unique polynomials q_λ and r_λ in $R[x]$ such that

$$f = g q_\lambda + r_\lambda \qquad \text{and} \qquad \deg r_\lambda < \deg g.$$

PROOF Select a polynomial of the form $r = f - hg$ of least degree. Suppose that $k = \deg r \geq \deg g = m$. Let c_k and b_m be the leading coefficients of r and g, respectively. With $d = c_k b_m^{-1}$ and $l = k - m$, $r - dx^l g$ is of the form $f - hg$ and of degree less than k, contrary to our choice of r. Hence $\deg r < \deg g$, and we put $r_\rho = r$ and $q_\rho = h$. We use the basic rules about degrees, (2) and (3), to prove that the right-quotient and right-remainder are unique. Assume that

$$q_\rho g + r_\rho = q'g + r' \qquad \text{and} \qquad \deg r' < \deg g.$$

Then, by (2),

(4) $$\deg (q' - q_\rho)g = \deg (r_\rho - r') < \deg g.$$

But (3) tells us that

$$\deg (q' - q_\rho)g = \deg (q' - q_\rho) + \deg g.$$

This equation, together with (4), shows that $q' - q_\rho \neq 0$ is impossible. Thus $q' - q_\rho = 0$, $q' = q_\rho$, and $r' = r_\rho$. This proves our first statement in (3-1); we omit the analogous proof of the second.

Our proof of (3-1) yields the usual method of computation of q_ρ and r_ρ. For, let a_n and b_m be the leading coefficients of f and g, respectively. When $\deg f = n < m = \deg g$, we have $q_\rho = 0$ and $r_\rho = f$. When $n \geq m$, we compute

$$f_1 = f - dx^l g$$

where $d = a_n b_m^{-1}$ and $l = n - m$. Then f_1 is of degree at most $n - 1$. The process is repeated, f_1 replacing f, etc., until r_ρ (of degree less than m) is obtained.

Illustrative
Example

Divide $x^3 + \mathbf{i}x^2 + \mathbf{j}x + \mathbf{k}$ by $x - \mathbf{i}$ both right and left.

$$
\begin{array}{l}
\phantom{x^3 + {}} x^2 + 2\mathbf{i}x \ + (\mathbf{j} - 2) \\
\hline
x^3 + \ \ \mathbf{i}x^2 + \mathbf{j}x + \mathbf{k} \ \big|\, x - \mathbf{i} \\
x^3 - \ \ \mathbf{i}x^2 \\
\hline
 2\mathbf{i}x^2 \\
 2\mathbf{i}x^2 + 2x \\
\hline
\phantom{x^3 + 2\mathbf{i}x^2} (\mathbf{j} - 2)x \\
\phantom{x^3 + 2\mathbf{i}x^2} (\mathbf{j} - 2)x + \mathbf{k} + 2\mathbf{i} \\
\hline
\phantom{x^3 + 2\mathbf{i}x^2 + \mathbf{k}} - 2\mathbf{i}
\end{array}
$$

This shows that $q_\rho(x) = x^2 + 2\mathbf{i}x + (\mathbf{j} - 2)$ and that $r_\rho = -2\mathbf{i}$. Shifting $x - \mathbf{i}$ to the left of the dividend, the process is repeated to give $q_\lambda(x) = q_\rho(x)$ and $r_\lambda = 2\mathbf{k} - 2\mathbf{i}$. Here we have replaced the I of $\mathcal{2}$ by 1 and have omitted writing the coefficient 1 as is usual for polynomials.

We must consider the process of substituting an element c of R for x in a polynomial $f(x)$ in $R[x]$. We have assumed that $xa = ax$ for every a in R; and this is surely an essential property of x. But when R is not commutative we will have $ac \neq ca$ for some

a and c *in* R. We define, therefore, two values of $f(x)$ at $x = c$:

$$f_\rho(c) = a_0 + a_1c + \cdots + a_nc^n,$$
$$f_\lambda(c) = a_0 + ca_1 + \cdots + c^na_n.$$

These elements of R, $f_\rho(c)$ and $f_\lambda(c)$, are called the *right-hand value of* $f(x)$ *at* $x = c$ and the *left-hand value of* $f(x)$ *at* $x = c$, respectively. One may use the usual method of synthetic substitution to compute these values:

a_2	a_1	a_0	$\underline{ c}$
	a_2c	$a_1c + a_2c^2$	
a_2	$a_1 + a_2c$	$a_0 + a_1c + a_2c^2 = f_\rho(c)$	

Here the coefficients of $f(x) = a_0 + a_1x + a_2x^2$ occupy the first line (in reverse order). Starting with a_2 (rewritten in the third line), we multiply it by c on the right and record the result under a_1 in the second line. We then add to obtain $a_1 + a_2c$, multiply this by c on the right, and record the result under a_0 in the second line. Adding, we obtain $f_\rho(c)$.

$\underline{c}$	a_2	a_1	a_0
		ca_2	$ca_1 + c^2a_2$
	a_2	$a_1 + ca_2$	$a_0 + ca_1 + c^2a_2 = f_\lambda(c)$

Great care must be exercised in computing the values of a product fg of two polynomials at $x = c$. The following rule (the Substitution Theorem) is quite helpful.

(3-2)　　　Let $f(x) = a_0 + a_1x + \cdots + a_nx^n$ be a polynomial in $R[x]$ and c be in R; then we have

$$(fg)_\rho(c) = a_0g_\rho(c) + a_1g_\rho(c)c + \cdots + a_ng_\rho(c)c^n,$$
$$(gf)_\lambda(c) = g_\lambda(c)a_0 + cg_\lambda(c)a_1 + \cdots + c^ng_\lambda(c)a_n.$$

PROOF　　　The proof is clear from the definitions, since

$$f(x)g(x) = a_0g(x) + a_1g(x)x + \cdots + a_ng(x)x^n,$$
$$g(x)f(x) = g(x)a_0 + xg(x)a_1 + \cdots + x^ng(x)a_n.$$

Three important corollaries flow from (3-2).

Corollary 1

If $g_\rho(c) = 0$, then $(fg)_\rho(c) = 0$. If $g_\lambda(c) = 0$, then $(gf)_\lambda(c) = 0$.

Corollary 2 (Remainder Theorem)

(i) Let $f(x) = q_\rho(x)(x - c) + r_\rho$ with r_ρ in R; then $f_\rho(c) = r_\rho$.
(ii) Let $f(x) = (x - c)q_\lambda(x) + r_\lambda$ with r_λ in R; then $f_\lambda(c) = r_\lambda$.

Corollary 3 (Factor Theorem)

Let $f(x)$ be in $R[x]$ and let c be in R. Then $x - c$ is a right (left) factor of $f(x)$ if and only if $f_\rho(c) = 0$ $(f_\lambda(c) = 0)$.

Illustrative
Example

Verify the remainder theorem for the division of the previous illustrative example. We have $f_\rho(\mathbf{i}) = \mathbf{i}^3 + \mathbf{ii}^2 + \mathbf{ji} + \mathbf{k} = -2\mathbf{i}$ and $f_\lambda(\mathbf{i}) = \mathbf{i}^3 + \mathbf{i}^2\mathbf{i} + \mathbf{ij} + \mathbf{k} = -2\mathbf{i} + 2\mathbf{k}$.

Illustrative
Example

Produce a polynomial $f(x)$ and a c in R such that $f_\rho(c) = 0$ while $f_\lambda(c) \neq 0$. We know that $f(x) = q(x)(x - c)$. A very simple example is $f(x) = (x - \mathbf{j})(x - \mathbf{i}) = x^2 - (\mathbf{i} + \mathbf{j})x - \mathbf{k}$, where $f_\lambda(\mathbf{i}) = \mathbf{i}^2 - \mathbf{i}(\mathbf{i} + \mathbf{j}) - \mathbf{k} = -\mathbf{ij} - \mathbf{k} = -2\mathbf{k}$.

/ 2 / POLYNOMIALS WITH COEFFICIENTS IN A FIELD

Many of the concepts and processes described in Section 1 are simpler when R is commutative. For later work we need some information about $F[x]$, where F is a field. In this section we first discuss the greatest common divisor of two polynomials in $F[x]$ and then derive the fundamental theorem on factorization into irreducible factors.

Throughout this section, F is a field. Of course $F[x]$ is not a field, but it is important to observe that the product fg of two polynomials in $F[x]$ can be zero only when at least one of the polynomials, f or g, is zero; this follows at once from (3). This property permits cancellation of nonzero polynomials: if $fg = fh$ and $f \neq 0$, then $g = h$.

We say that a polynomial g in $F[x]$ *divides* a polynomial f in $F[x]$ in case we have $f = gh$ for some polynomial h in $F[x]$. With this terminology we are in a position to describe the greatest common divisor of two polynomials of $F[x]$.

(3-3)   Let $f(x)$ and $g(x)$ be polynomials in $F[x]$, not both zero. Then there is a unique monic polynomial $d(x)$ of least degree of the form $a(x)f(x) + b(x)g(x)$ for polynomials $a(x)$ and $b(x)$ in $F[x]$. The polynomial $d(x)$ is the greatest common divisor of $f(x)$ and $g(x)$ in the sense that (i) d is monic, (ii) d divides both f and g, (iii) if p is in $F[x]$ and divides both f and g, then p divides d.

PROOF   Since one of f and g is not zero, there are monic polynomials of the form $af + bg$ for certain a and b in $F[x]$. This proves the existence of $d(x)$. Suppose that d does not divide f. Using (3-1) we can write $f = qd + r$, with q and r in $F[x]$, and with $\deg r < \deg d$ and $r \neq 0$. Since $r \neq 0$, αr is monic for some α in F. But, since $\alpha r = \alpha f - \alpha q d = (\alpha - \alpha q a)f - \alpha q b g = a_1 f + b_1 g$ and αr has degree less than that of d, this is impossible. Hence d divides f and, likewise, divides g. If p in $F[x]$ divides both f and g, then, since $d = af + bg$, p divides d. We have proved that d has the three properties given in (3-3). Now assume that d_1 also has these properties. By the second property of (3-3) for d_1, d_1 divides both f and g, and the third property of (3-3) for d then yields that d_1 divides d. By symmetry, d divides d_1. Thus $d = hd_1 = hh'd$, $hh' = 1$, and h is in F, and $d = hd_1$ gives $h = 1$ since both d and d_1 are monic.

Our proof suggests the usual computational procedure (known as Euclid's algorithm) for finding d. One performs a sequence of divisions, if $g \neq 0$:

$$
\begin{array}{ll}
f = q_1 g + r_1 & \deg r_1 < \deg g \\
g = q_2 r_1 + r_2 & \deg r_2 < \deg r_1 \\
r_1 = q_3 r_2 + r_3 & \deg r_3 < \deg r_2 \\
\quad \cdot \quad \cdot \quad \cdot \quad \cdot \quad \cdot \quad \cdot & \quad \cdot \quad \cdot \quad \cdot \quad \cdot \\
r_{n-1} = q_{n+1} r_n + r_{n+1} & \deg r_{n+1} < \deg r_n \\
r_n = q_{n+2} r_{n+1} &
\end{array}
$$

which must terminate in, at most, $(\deg g) + 2$ steps. Then $d = \beta r_{n+1}$ where β is so chosen in F as to make d monic. It is easy to see that the three properties hold for this choice of d which is, therefore, the desired greatest common divisor of f and g.

Euclid's algorithm shows that the greatest common divisor d of f and g in $F[x]$ has coefficients in the least field which contains the coefficients of f and g. If we consider a field $F_1 \supset F$, then the greatest common divisor of f and g in $F_1[x]$ is still d. For example, the greatest common divisor of $x^3 + 1$ and $x^2 - x - 2$ in $R_a[x]$ is $x + 1$; it is still $x + 1$ in $K[x]$.

When the greatest common divisor of f, $g \in F[x]$ is 1, we call f and g *relatively prime*. For example, $x^2 - 1$ and $x^3 - 2$ are relatively prime in $R_a[x]$.

The Euclid algorithm is really not suitable for computing the greatest common divisor of f and g in the form $d = af + bg$. A neat method of doing this is as follows. Construct the matrix

(1)
$$\begin{bmatrix} f & 1 & 0 \\ g & 0 & 1 \end{bmatrix}.$$

If there is a nonsingular matrix

$$\begin{bmatrix} a & b \\ r & s \end{bmatrix}$$

in $(F[x])_2$ such that

(2)
$$\begin{bmatrix} a & b \\ r & s \end{bmatrix} \begin{bmatrix} f & 1 & 0 \\ g & 0 & 1 \end{bmatrix} = \begin{bmatrix} d & a & b \\ 0 & r & s \end{bmatrix},$$

with d a monic polynomial of $F[x]$, then $d = af + bg$ is the greatest common divisor of f and g. Surely every common divisor of f and g divides d. In $(F[x])_2$, let

$$\begin{bmatrix} A & B \\ R & S \end{bmatrix} = \begin{bmatrix} a & b \\ r & s \end{bmatrix}^{-1}.$$

Thus
$$\begin{bmatrix} f & 1 & 0 \\ g & 0 & 1 \end{bmatrix} = \begin{bmatrix} A & B \\ R & S \end{bmatrix} \begin{bmatrix} d & a & b \\ 0 & r & s \end{bmatrix}.$$

From this we see that $f = Ad$ and $g = Rd$. This means that d divides both f and g and is, therefore, the desired greatest common divisor of f and g. Let us consider the following nonsingular matrices of $(F[x])_2$:

$$\begin{bmatrix} 1 & 0 \\ c(x) & 1 \end{bmatrix}, \quad \begin{bmatrix} 1 & c(x) \\ 0 & 1 \end{bmatrix}, \quad \begin{bmatrix} a_0 & 0 \\ 0 & 1 \end{bmatrix},$$

$$\begin{bmatrix} 1 & 0 \\ 0 & a_0 \end{bmatrix}, \quad \begin{bmatrix} 0 & 1 \\ 1 & 0 \end{bmatrix},$$

where $c(x)$ is a polynomial in $F[x]$ and a_0 is a nonzero element of F. The effect of left multiplication by these matrices is seen to be the addition of a polynomial multiple of one row to a different row (first and second matrices), the multiplication of a row by a nonzero element of F (third and fourth matrices), and the interchange of two rows (fifth matrix). Since the product of nonsingular matrices is nonsingular, we may perform a sequence of these operations to obtain the desired equation (2). This matric process is a convenient method for computing the greatest common divisor d of f and g in the form $d = af + bg$.

Illustrative
Example

Find the greatest common divisor of $x^3 - 1$ and $x^4 - 1$ in $R_a[x]$. Letting $\rightarrow$ denote a permissible operation, we have

$$\begin{bmatrix} x^3 - 1 & 1 & 0 \\ x^4 - 1 & 0 & 1 \end{bmatrix} \rightarrow \begin{bmatrix} x^3 - 1 & 1 & 0 \\ x - 1 & -x & 1 \end{bmatrix}$$

$$\rightarrow \begin{bmatrix} 0 & x^3 + x^2 + x + 1 & -(x^2 + x + 1) \\ x - 1 & -x & 1 \end{bmatrix}$$

$$\rightarrow \begin{bmatrix} x - 1 & -x & 1 \\ 0 & x^3 + x^2 + x + 1 & -(x^2 + x + 1) \end{bmatrix}.$$

We see that $x - 1 = -x(x^3 - 1) + (x^4 - 1)$ is the desired greatest common divisor.

Illustrative
Example

Use the same method, replacing a_0 with ± 1 and $c(x)$ with any integer, to find the greatest common divisor of 714 and 2177 in Z.

$$\begin{bmatrix} 714 & 1 & 0 \\ 2177 & 0 & 1 \end{bmatrix} \rightarrow \begin{bmatrix} 714 & 1 & 0 \\ 35 & -3 & 1 \end{bmatrix} \rightarrow \begin{bmatrix} 14 & 61 & -20 \\ 35 & -3 & 1 \end{bmatrix}$$

$$\rightarrow \begin{bmatrix} 14 & 61 & -20 \\ 7 & -125 & 41 \end{bmatrix} \rightarrow \begin{bmatrix} 0 & 311 & -102 \\ 7 & -125 & 41 \end{bmatrix}$$

$$\rightarrow \begin{bmatrix} 7 & -125 & 41 \\ 0 & 311 & -102 \end{bmatrix}.$$

This gives $7 = (-125)(714) + 41(2177)$ as the desired greatest common divisor.

We turn now to the problem of factoring polynomials in $F[x]$. We call a monic nonconstant polynomial p in $F[x]$ an *irreducible polynomial* in case the only monic nonconstant factor of p is p itself. For any field F, $x - \alpha$ is irreducible for α in F. If $F = K$ (the complex field), every irreducible polynomial has the form $x - \alpha$ with α in K. One calls a field F *algebraically closed* in case the only irreducible polynomials in $F[x]$ are of the form $x - \alpha$ with α in F. The real field, R_e, is not algebraically closed, since certain quadratic polynomials $x^2 + \beta x + \gamma$ are irreducible in $R_e[x]$, namely those for which $\beta^2 - 4\gamma < 0$. If $F = R_a$, the rational field, further possibilities arise: $x^2 - 2$ and $x^3 - 2$ are irreducible polynomials of $R_a[x]$.

The fact that K is algebraically closed is often called the Fundamental Theorem of Algebra. The many known proofs depend on ideas of Gauss. Here is a sketch of one of them. Let $f(z) \in K[z]$ and suppose that $f(z) \neq 0$ for all $z \in K$. The heart of the proof is to show that, given any $z \in K$, there is a $w \in K$ such that $|f(w)| < |f(z)|$. Set $h = w - z$ and use Taylor's expansion to obtain

$$(f(w))/(f(z)) = 1 + d_k h^k + \cdots + d_n h^n$$

with $d_k \neq 0$. Write $h = r(\cos \theta + i \sin \theta)$, $d_k = s(\cos \alpha + i \sin \alpha)$ in polar form and choose θ so that $\alpha + k\theta = 180°$ and $d_k h^k = -sr^k$. Then choose r positive and so small that $sr^k < 1$ and

$$|d_{k+1} h + \cdots + d_n h^{n-k}| < s$$

for all h with $|h| < r$. Then for every such r we obtain

$$|(f(w))/(f(z))| < 1 - sr^k + sr^k = 1.$$

Writing $z = x + iy$ and $|f(z)| = F(x, y)$, we see that $F(x, y)$ is continuous on the square $S(R)$: $|x| + |y| \leq R$ and hence attains its minimum $M_R \neq 0$ at a point z_R in this set†. Since $|f(z)| \to \infty$ as $|z| \to \infty$, there is an R_0 such that $|f(z)| > |f(0)|$ for z outside $S(R_0)$. There is a $w \in K$ with $|f(w)| < |f(z_{R_0})| \leq |f(0)|$. Then w is in $S(R_0)$, contrary to the choice of z_{R_0}.

By using (3-3) we may now derive the key lemma on factorization.

(3-4)   If p is an irreducible polynomial of $F[x]$ and if p divides a product fg of two polynomials in $F[x]$, then p divides f or p divides g.

PROOF   Suppose that p does not divide f; then the greatest common divisor of p and f is 1, $ap + bf = 1$ for certain polynomials a and b in $F[x]$, and $apg + bfg = g$, from which it is evident that p divides g.

It follows at once by induction that, if p is an irreducible polynomial of $F[x]$ and p divides $f_1 \cdots f_n$ for polynomials $f_i \in F[x]$ (where $i = 1, \cdots, n$), then p divides some f_k (where $k = 1, \cdots, n$).

We are now ready to state the Fundamental Theorem of Arithmetic for polynomials of $F[x]$.

(3-5)   First, every nonconstant monic polynomial of $F[x]$ is a product of irreducible factors. Second, if

(3) $$p_1 p_2 \cdots p_r = q_1 q_2 \cdots q_s$$

with p_i and q_j irreducible polynomials of $F[x]$ ($i = 1, \cdots, r$; $j = 1, \cdots, s$), then $r = s$ and there is a permutation $j_1 \, j_2 \, \cdots \, j_r$ such that $p_i = q_{j_i}$ ($i = 1, \cdots, r$).

PROOF   Suppose some monic nonconstant polynomial f of $F[x]$ cannot be factored into irreducible factors. Choose such a polynomial f of least degree. Clearly, f is not itself irreducible and, hence, $f = gh$ where g is monic, nonconstant, and different from f. It follows that h is monic and hence nonconstant. Since $\deg f = \deg g + \deg h$, both g and h have degree less than that of f and each is, therefore, a product of irreducible factors; and our supposition must be false.

† See *Calculus with Analytic Geometry* by Johnson and Kiokemeister, Boston, 1957, p. 535.

Now suppose we have (3) with $r \neq s$. Choose the least r for which this happens. Clearly, $r < s$. By (3-4), p_1 divides some q_{j_1} with $j_1 = 1, \cdots, s$, and it follows that $p_1 = q_{j_1}$ because q_{j_1} is irreducible. Cancelling these equal factors in (3) violates our choice of r. This proves that $r = s$ when (3) holds. Suppose that (3) holds with $r = s$ and that the q's are not just a permutation of the p's. Choose the least r for which this happens. Again by (3-4), we obtain $p_1 = q_{j_1}$. Cancelling these equal factors in (3) again violates the choice of r. This completes the proof of (3-5).

Using (3-5), we may write every f in $F[x]$ in the form

(4) $$f = \alpha p_1^{e_1} p_2^{e_2} \cdots p_k^{e_k}$$

where α is in F, p_i is irreducible ($i = 1, \cdots, k$), p_i is not equal to p_j if i is not equal to j, and each e_i ($i = 1, \cdots, k$) is a positive integer. The factorization (4) is essentially unique by (3-5). We call each $p_i^{e_i}$ an *elementary divisor* of f. We shall have occasion to use these elementary divisors in a later chapter.

Illustrative
Example

List the elementary divisors of $(x^4 + 1)(x^3 - 1)(x - 1)^2$ in $R_a[x]$, $R_e[x]$, and $K[x]$. One should observe that $x^4 + 1$ is reducible in $R_e[x]$ since

$$(x^4 + 2x^2 + 1) - 2x^2 = [(x^2 + 1) + \sqrt{2}x][(x^2 + 1) - \sqrt{2}x],$$

these factors being irreducible in $R_e[x]$ but, of course, reducible in $K[x]$. Let the factors of $x^2 + 1 + \sqrt{2}x$ and $x^2 + 1 - \sqrt{2}x$ in $K[x]$ (obtained from the quadratic formula) be $(x - z)$, $(x - \bar{z})$, $(x - w)$, $(x - \bar{w})$, respectively. The required elementary divisors in $R_a[x]$ are $x^4 + 1$, $(x - 1)^3$, and $x^2 + x + 1$. In $R_e[x]$ they are $(x^2 - \sqrt{2}x + 1)$, $(x^2 + \sqrt{2}x + 1)$, $(x - 1)^3$, and $x^2 + x + 1$. In $K[x]$ they are $(x - z)$, $(x - \bar{z})$, $(x - w)$, $(x - \bar{w})$, $(x - t)$, $(x - \bar{t})$, and $(x - 1)^3$, where t is a root of $x^2 + x + 1 = 0$ in K.

EXERCISES FOR CHAPTER 3

1. Divide $x^3 + ax^2 + bx + c$ by $x^2 + dx + e$ both right and left. Here a, b, c, d, e are in any ring R with identity element 1.

In the following three exercises, verify the Remainder Theorem (both right and left).

2. $f(x) = x^7 - 5x + 4$, $c = 1$, R the ring of integers.

3. $f(x) = x^3 + x + 1$, $c = 1$, $R = Z/3Z$.

4. $f(x) = \begin{bmatrix} 1 & 0 \\ 0 & 1 \end{bmatrix} x^3 - \begin{bmatrix} 0 & 0 \\ 0 & 3 \end{bmatrix} x + \begin{bmatrix} 5 & -7 \\ 0 & 1 \end{bmatrix}$,

$$c = \begin{bmatrix} 1 & 0 \\ 1 & 1 \end{bmatrix}.$$

5. Let

$$C = \begin{bmatrix} \lambda & 0 & 0 & 0 \\ 1 & \lambda & 0 & 0 \\ 0 & 1 & \lambda & 0 \\ 0 & 0 & 1 & \lambda \end{bmatrix}.$$

Show that $(C - \lambda I)^4 = 0$.

6. Show that right synthetic substitution of $x = c$ in $f(x)$ in $R[x]$ yields the right quotient, as well as the right remainder, on division of $f(x)$ by $x - c$. Because of this the process is often called synthetic *division*.

7. Show by example that we may have $f_\rho(c) \neq 0$ and $f_\lambda(c) \neq 0$ for $f(x) = g(x)(x - c)h(x)$, where g and h are in $R[x]$ and c is in R.

8. Let

$$A = \begin{bmatrix} a & b \\ c & d \end{bmatrix}$$

be in $(R_a)_2$. Define $f(x) = Ix^2 - (a + d)Ix + (ad - bc)I$ in $(R_a)_2[x]$. Show that $f_\rho(A) = f_\lambda(A) = 0$.

9. The remainders, on division of $f(x)$ in $R_a[x]$ by $x - 1$ and by $x - 2$, are 4 and -2, respectively. What is the remainder when $f(x)$ is divided by $(x - 1)(x - 2)$?

10. Multiply the matrices:

$$\begin{bmatrix} x & x^2 + 1 \\ x & 1 \end{bmatrix}, \quad \begin{bmatrix} 0 & x \\ x^2 & 1 \end{bmatrix}.$$

Multiply the matric polynomials:

$$\begin{bmatrix} 0 & 1 \\ 0 & 0 \end{bmatrix} x^2 + \begin{bmatrix} 1 & 0 \\ 1 & 0 \end{bmatrix} x + \begin{bmatrix} 0 & 1 \\ 0 & 1 \end{bmatrix},$$

$$\begin{bmatrix} 0 & 0 \\ 1 & 0 \end{bmatrix} x^2 + \begin{bmatrix} 0 & 1 \\ 0 & 0 \end{bmatrix} x + \begin{bmatrix} 0 & 0 \\ 0 & 1 \end{bmatrix}.$$

In what sense are the two results the same?

11. Let f and g in $F[x]$ (where F is a field) have the greatest common divisor $1 = af + bg$, with a and b in $F[x]$. Show that there are uniquely determined polynomials a_1 and b_1 in $F[x]$ such that $\deg a_1 < \deg g$, $\deg b_1 < \deg f$ and $1 = a_1 f + b_1 g$, assuming f or g is nonconstant. [*Hint:* Divide a by g.]

12. Express the greatest common divisor of 450 and 1375 in the form $d = a(450) + b(1375)$, a and b being integers.

13. Express the greatest common divisor d of f and g in $R_e[x]$ in the form $d = af + bg$, given $f = x^3 - 1$, $g = x^4 - 2x^3 + 1$.

14. Find the elementary divisors of

$$f(x) = (x^3 - 1)^3(x^2 - 1)^2(x^2 - 3x + 2)^5$$

in $R_a[x]$, $R_e[x]$, and $K[x]$.

15. What are the elementary divisors of 1964 in Z?

16. Express the greatest common divisor, in $R_e[x]$, of $f = x^3 + 1$ and $g = x^4 - 2x^3 - 3$ in the form $d = af + bg$ with a and b in $R_e[x]$.

17. Given f and g relatively prime polynomials of $K[x]$, show that $1/(fg) = (a/f) + (b/g)$ for uniquely determined polynomials a and b in $K[x]$ with deg $a <$ deg f and deg $b <$ deg g, assuming f or g is nonconstant.

18. Show that the greatest common divisor of $f_1, \cdots, f_n$ in $F[x]$ (where F is a field) may be expressed as $a_1 f_1 + \cdots + a_n f_n$ with a_i in $F[x]$ $(i = 1, \cdots, n)$. Indicate a method of finding the polynomials $a_1, \cdots, a_n$.

19. Express the greatest common divisor of $f_1 = x^2 - 1$, $f_2 = x^3 - 1$, and $f_3 = x^4 + 1$ in the form $d = a_1 f_1 + a_2 f_2 + a_3 f_3$ with a_1, a_2, and a_3 in $R_a[x]$.

20. Prove that every pair of nonzero positive integers has a greatest common divisor.

21. Find the elementary divisors of $(x^2 - 1)^2$, $(x^4 + 4)^2$, and $(x^3 - 1)^3$, in $R_a[x]$, $R_e[x]$, and $K[x]$.

22. Show that, if d is the greatest common divisor of f and g in $R_e[x]$, then d is still the greatest common divisor of f and g in $K[x]$.

23. Let the nonconstant polynomials $f_1, \cdots, f_k$ in $F[x]$, where F is a field, be relatively prime in pairs. Show that there are uniquely determined polynomials $a_1, \cdots, a_k$ in $F[x]$ such that

$$\deg a_i < \deg f_i \qquad (i = 1, \cdots, k)$$

and

$$\frac{1}{f_1 f_2 \cdots f_k} = \frac{a_1}{f_1} + \cdots + \frac{a_k}{f_k}.$$

(See Exercises 26 and 27.)

24. A commutative ring R is called an *integral domain* if R has an identity element and if $ab = ac$ for a, b, and c in R and $a \neq 0$ implies that $b = c$. Show that if R is an integral domain, so is $R[x]$.

25. Let R be an integral domain. Call $u \in R$ a *unit* in case u is nonsingular in R. Call a nonunit $p \in R$ *prime* in case $p = ab$ for a and $b \in R$ only if a or b is a unit of R. Call R a unique factorization domain *(ufd)* if every nonunit of $R \neq 0$ has a factorization into primes of R which is unique up to the order of the prime factors and unit factors. (For example, Z is a *ufd* and $F[x]$ is also a *ufd*.) *If R is a ufd, so is $R[x]$.* For, considering degrees, we see that every nonunit of $R[x]$ has a

factorization into prime factors. Suppose uniqueness of factorization fails. Then we may choose $f \in R[x]$ of minimal degree such that $f = p_1 \cdots p_r = q_1 \cdots q_s$ where p_i and q_j are primes of $R[x]$ and p_i is not equal to uq_j for all i and j and all units u of R. Furthermore, we may assume $0 < m = \deg p_1 \leq \deg q_1 = n$ and $m \geq \deg p_i$ $(i = 1, \cdots, r)$ and $n \geq \deg q_j$ $(j = 1, \cdots, s)$. Let a and b be the leading coefficients of p_1 and q_1, respectively. Construct $g = af - bp_1 x^{n-m} q_2 \cdots q_s = (aq_1 - bp_1 x^{n-m})q_2 \cdots q_s$. If $g = 0$, by Exercise 24 we have $aq_1 = bp_1 x^{n-m}$. If $g \neq 0$, then $\deg g < \deg f$, so that g has a unique factorization into primes of $R[x]$. But p_1 divides g and p_1 is not equal to uq_j $(j = 2, \cdots, s)$, so that p_1 must divide aq_1. This proves that $aq_1 = p_1 h$ for $h \in R[x]$. Now this implies that $a \in R$ divides $(p_1 - ax^m)h$ of degree less than f. If $p_1 = ax^m$, then a is a unit and q_1 is equal to $p_1 h_1$, so that h_1 is a unit, a contradiction. If $p_1 - ax^m \neq 0$, then $(p_1 - ax^m)h = a(q_1 - x^m h)$ has a unique factorization into primes of $R[x]$. Now, no prime factor of a can divide $p_1 - ax^m$, since p_1 has only unit factors of degree zero. Hence, every prime factor of a divides h. It follows that a divides h and q_1 is equal to $p_1 h_1$ for $h_1 \in R[x]$, a contradiction. This proof of a famous theorem of Gauss is due to C. H. Giffen, a young contemporary American mathematician.

26. Let R be a commutative ring such that $ab \neq 0$ if $a \neq 0$ and $b \neq 0$ in R. Consider the set

$$\mathscr{R} = \{(a, b); a \in R, b \in R, b \neq 0\}.$$

If (a, b) and $(a', b') \in \mathscr{R}$, write $(a, b) \sim (a', b')$ in case $ab' = a'b$, and define

$$a/b = \{(a', b'); (a, b) \sim (a', b')\}$$

and $F = \{a/b; (a, b) \in \mathscr{R}\}$. Motivated by the rules for dealing with fractions, show that F is a field which contains an isomorphic copy of R. We call F the *field of fractions* of R.

27. Show that, if $R = F[x]$, where F is a field, then the field of fractions of R consists of the rational functions of x with coefficients in F; that is, it consists of the functions $f(x)/g(x)$ with $f(x)$ in $F[x]$ and $g(x)$ nonzero in $F[x]$.

4

MATRIC POLYNOMIALS AND FUNCTIONS OF MATRICES

In this chapter we first show that a square matrix, with elements in a commutative ring which has an identity element, is a root of a polynomial equation with co-efficients in the given ring; this is the famous Hamilton–Cayley Theorem. We then develop the spectral theory for square matrices of complex numbers. This exceedingly interesting and useful theory has many applications. We present only one: the solution of systems of linear homogeneous differential equations with constant coefficients.

/ 1 / THE HAMILTON–CAYLEY THEOREM

In this section we apply some of the results of Chapter 3 to matrices. The connection between the idea of a square matrix whose elements are polynomials and the idea of a polynomial whose coefficients are square matrices is first explained. We then proceed to find, for a square matrix A, a polynomial with numerical coefficients that has A as a zero. This very useful result will be applied in the remaining sections of the chapter to obtain an interesting decomposition of square matrices with complex elements.

Let R be a ring with identity element 1, and let A be a square matrix whose elements are in $R[x]$ (that is, polynomials in x with coefficients in R). For example,

$$A = \begin{bmatrix} x^3 + 3x + 1 & x^2 - 1 \\ x + 2 & 4 \end{bmatrix}.$$

If we wish, we may associate with A a polynomial in x,

$$A^\varphi = \begin{bmatrix} 1 & -1 \\ 2 & 4 \end{bmatrix} + \begin{bmatrix} 3 & 0 \\ 1 & 0 \end{bmatrix} x + \begin{bmatrix} 0 & 1 \\ 0 & 0 \end{bmatrix} x^2 + \begin{bmatrix} 1 & 0 \\ 0 & 0 \end{bmatrix} x^3$$

whose coefficients are matrices. The correspondence $A \to A^\varphi$ establishes an isomorphism between the rings $(R[x])_n$ and $R_n[x]$.

It is immaterial which point of view we adopt, but it is convenient to have these two ways of viewing matric polynomials.

As an example, let R be a commutative ring with identity 1. Then $R[x]$ is also a commutative ring and 1 is its identity element. Consider an n-by-n matrix A with elements in R, and form

$$f_A(x) = \det (xI - A).$$

Then $f_A(x)$ is a monic polynomial of degree n with coefficients in R. We call $f_A(x)$ the *characteristic polynomial of* A. By a fundamental property of determinants,

$$(xI - A) \operatorname{adj} (xI - A) = f_A(x)I.$$

This equation, when interpreted in $R_n[x]$, asserts that $xI - A$ is a left factor of $f_A(x)I$. The factor theorem then yields that the left-hand value of $f_A(x)I$ at $x = A$ is zero. But the coefficients of $f_A(x)I$ are matrices of the form bI, with b in R, and hence commute with A, so that there is no need to distinguish right- and left-hand values. This argument proves the Hamilton–Cayley Theorem.

Hamilton–Cayley Theorem

If A is an n-by-n matrix with elements in a commutative ring R with identity 1, and if

$$f_A(x) = \det (xI - A) = a_0 + a_1 x + \cdots + a_{n-1}x^{n-1} + x^n,$$

then

$$f_A(A) = a_0 I + a_1 A + \cdots + a_{n-1}A^{n-1} + A^n = 0.$$

It is easily seen that $a_0 = (-1)^n \det A$, and we may derive the formula

$$-A^{-1} = (-1)^n (\det A)^{-1}(a_1 I + a_2 A + \cdots + a_{n-1}A^{n-2} + A^{n-1})$$

when A is nonsingular. But this formula is only one of a host of practical consequences of the Hamilton–Cayley theorem, some of which we shall explain in the following sections of this chapter.

Illustrative
Example

Let

$$A = \begin{bmatrix} 0 & 1 & 0 \\ 0 & 0 & 1 \\ 2 & -3 & 4 \end{bmatrix},$$

so that $\det(xI - A) = x^3 - 4x^2 + 3x - 2$. One computes

$$A^2 = \begin{bmatrix} 0 & 0 & 1 \\ 2 & -3 & 4 \\ 0 & -10 & 13 \end{bmatrix},$$

$$A^3 = \begin{bmatrix} 2 & -3 & 4 \\ 8 & -10 & 13 \\ 26 & -31 & 42 \end{bmatrix} = 4A^2 - 3A + 2I,$$

which verifies the Hamilton–Cayley Theorem.

/ 2 / SPECTRAL THEORY FOR FINITE COMPLEX MATRICES: THE CASE OF SIMPLE ROOTS

Let us limit ourselves now to the case of a square matrix A whose elements are complex numbers. Let us assume that

$$f(x) = \det(xI - A) = (x - r_1)(x - r_2)\cdots(x - r_n)$$

in which $r_1, \cdots, r_n$ are distinct complex numbers. We then know that

$$(A - r_1 I)(A - r_2 I)\cdots(A - r_n I) = 0.$$

Let us expand $1/f(x)$ into the partial fractions:

(1) $$\frac{1}{(x - r_1)\cdots(x - r_n)} = \frac{a_1}{x - r_1} + \cdots + \frac{a_n}{x - r_n}.$$

(One may easily show that $a_i = 1/f'(r_i)$ $(i = 1, \cdots, n)$, for, if we clear of fractions and then substitute $x = r_i$, we obtain

$$1 = a_i(r_i - r_1) \cdots \overbrace{(r_i - r_i)} \cdots (r_i - r_n)$$

while

$$f'(r_i) = (r_i - r_1) \cdots \overbrace{(r_i - r_i)} \cdots (r_i - r_n)$$

is clear from the rule for differentiating a product of factors. (As on page 33, the circumflex indicates deletion.) Of course, the reader knows the usual method of finding a_i by clearing of fractions and substituting $x = r_i$ in the result.)

We write (1) as

$$(2) \quad 1 = a_1 \prod_{j \neq 1} (x - r_j) + a_2 \prod_{j \neq 2} (x - r_j) + \cdots + a_n \prod_{j \neq n} (x - r_j).$$

Remark. Since the validity of the equation (2) will be of importance for our discussion of matric theory, let us prove (2) without recourse to the calculus. We choose

$$a_i = 1 / \prod_{j \neq i} (r_i - r_j) \qquad (i = 1, \cdots, n),$$

and we let $p(x)$ be the polynomial in $K[x]$ obtained by subtracting 1 from the right-hand member of (2). Then it is clear that $p(r_i) = 0$ $(i = 1, \cdots, n)$ and that the degree of $p(x)$ is at most $n - 1$. By the factor theorem, $x - r_i$ divides $p(x)$ $(i = 1, \cdots, n)$. Observe that $x - r_1, \cdots, x - r_n$ are distinct monic irreducibles of $K[x]$. Suppose $p(x) \neq 0$; then the factorization of $p(x)$ into monic irreducibles of $K[x]$ includes the product $(x - r_1) \cdots (x - r_n)$ of degree n. But then the degree of $p(x)$ would be at least n, a contradiction.

We now substitute $x = A$ in (2) and find that

$$I = E_1 + E_2 + \cdots + E_n$$

where

$$E_i = a_i \prod_{j \neq i} (A - r_j I).$$

Note that

$$E_i A = A E_i \qquad (i = 1, \cdots, n),$$

$$E_i(A - r_i I) = 0 \quad \text{or} \quad E_i A = r_i E_i,$$

$$E_i E_j = 0 \qquad (i \neq j).$$

Since

$$E_i = E_i I = E_i^2 \qquad (i = 1, \cdots, n),$$

we call the matrices E_i (which are polynomials in A) *idempotent*. We call the equation $I = E_1 + E_2 + \cdots + E_n$ the *resolution of the identity determined by* A. The idempotents $E_1, \cdots, E_n$ are called *the idempotents associated with* A.

Illustrative
Example

Find the idempotents for

$$A = \begin{bmatrix} 0 & 1 & 0 \\ 0 & 0 & 1 \\ 4 & 4 & -1 \end{bmatrix}.$$

Here $\det(xI - A) = x^3 + x^2 - 4x - 4 = (x^2 - 4)(x + 1)$, so that $r_1 = -2$, $r_2 = -1$, $r_3 = 2$, and $a_1 = 1/4$, $a_2 = -1/3$, $a_3 = 1/12$, where $a_i = 1/f'(r_i)$. Then:

$$E_1 = (1/4)(A + I)(A - 2I) = (1/4) \begin{bmatrix} -2 & -1 & 1 \\ 4 & 2 & -2 \\ -8 & -4 & 4 \end{bmatrix},$$

$$E_2 = (-1/3)(A + 2I)(A - 2I) = (-1/3) \begin{bmatrix} -4 & 0 & 1 \\ 4 & 0 & -1 \\ -4 & 0 & 1 \end{bmatrix},$$

$$E_3 = (1/12)(A + 2I)(A + I) = (1/12) \begin{bmatrix} 2 & 3 & 1 \\ 4 & 6 & 2 \\ 8 & 12 & 4 \end{bmatrix}.$$

One may easily verify that $I = E_1 + E_2 + E_3$ and that $E_i E_k = 0$ for $i \neq k$.

The idempotents associated with A will be exceedingly useful in working with the matrix A. As a first step, consider any polynomial in $K[x]$

$$p(x) = c_0 + c_1 x + \cdots + c_m x^m.$$

By the remainder theorem,

$$p(x) = p(r_i) + (x - r_i)p_i(x).$$

Hence,

$$p(A)E_i = p(r_i)E_i + (A - r_iI)p_i(A)E_i = p(r_i)E_i.$$

By addition we get

$$p(A) = p(r_1)E_1 + \cdots + p(r_n)E_n.$$

With the matrix A of the previous illustrative example, we have $A^{200} = 2^{200}E_1 + E_2 + 2^{200}E_3$, a result which would take a bit of time to arrive at by direct computation.

Remark. It sometimes happens that the characteristic polynomial of A may be replaced by a polynomial $m(x)$ *of lower degree*, such that $m(A) = 0$. For example, if

$$A = \begin{bmatrix} -1 & 0 & 0 \\ 0 & 1 & 0 \\ 0 & 0 & 1 \end{bmatrix},$$

then the characteristic polynomial is $(x + 1)(x - 1)^2$, but it is clear that $(A + I)(A - I) = 0$. It is of advantage in the spectral theory to use the polynomial $m(x)$ *of least degree*, such that $m(A) = 0$. It will not be until Chapter 9 that we shall have a general method of finding $m(x)$.

/ 3 / SPECTRAL THEORY FOR FINITE COMPLEX MATRICES: POWER SERIES IN A MATRIX AND TRANSCENDENTAL FUNCTIONS OF A MATRIX

Having found an exceedingly simple method of computing polynomials in a square complex matrix, it is natural that we proceed to power series in such a matrix. We do so in this section for the case of simple roots. We then use these power series to solve certain systems of differential equations.

If A is an n-by-n matrix of complex numbers, then we define

$$p(A) = c_0 I + c_1 A + c_2 A^2 + \cdots + c_n A^n + \cdots$$

provided that all of the n^2 series involved converge. If $p(z)$ is such that each of the Taylor's series,

$$p(z) = p(r_i) + p'(r_i)(z - r_i) + \frac{p''(r_i)}{2}(z - r_i)^2 + \cdots$$

converges for $|z - r_i| < \epsilon_i$ with $\epsilon_i > 0$ $(i = 1, \cdots, n)$, then

$$p(A)E_i = p(r_i)E_i$$

and, as in the case of polynomials,

$$p(A) = p(r_1)E_1 + \cdots + p(r_n)E_n.$$

A particularly useful function is the exponential

$$p(z) = e^z = 1 + z + \frac{z^2}{2!} + \frac{z^3}{3!} + \cdots.$$

As an illustration, let us find e^A for the matrix

$$A = \begin{bmatrix} -4 & 9 \\ -2 & 5 \end{bmatrix}.$$

Here

$$f(x) = \det(xI - A) = \det \begin{bmatrix} x + 4 & -9 \\ 2 & x - 5 \end{bmatrix} = x^2 - x - 2$$

$$= (x - 2)(x + 1).$$

We have

$$r_1 = 2, \qquad r_2 = -1, \qquad a_1 = 1/3, \qquad a_2 = -(1/3),$$

$$E_1 = (1/3)(A - r_2 I), \qquad E_2 = -(1/3)(A - r_1 I),$$

$$E_1 = (1/3)\begin{bmatrix} -3 & 9 \\ -2 & 6 \end{bmatrix}, \qquad E_2 = -(1/3)\begin{bmatrix} -6 & 9 \\ -2 & 3 \end{bmatrix},$$

$$e^A = e^2 E_1 + e^{-1} E_2$$

$$= \begin{bmatrix} -e^2 + 2e^{-1} & 3e^2 - 3e^{-1} \\ (-2/3)e^2 + (2/3)e^{-1} & 2e^2 - e^{-1} \end{bmatrix}.$$

If we choose $p(z) = e^{zt}$, where t is any real number, then

$$p(A) = e^{At} = e^{r_1 t}E_1 + \cdots + e^{r_n t}E_n.$$

If we agree to define

$$\frac{d}{dt}(B) = \frac{d}{dt}[b_{ij}(t)] = \left[\frac{d}{dt}b_{ij}(t)\right],$$

then we may obtain

(1) $$\frac{d}{dt}(e^{At}) = r_1 e^{r_1 t}E_1 + \cdots + r_n e^{r_n t}E_n = Ae^{At}$$

since

$$A = r_1 E_1 + \cdots + r_n E_n.$$

(Observe that we differentiate a matrix of functions by differentiating each of its elements.) The relation (1) permits us to solve certain differential equations rather economically. For example, to solve the system

$$\frac{dx_1}{dt} = -4x_1 + 9x_2,$$

$$\frac{dx_2}{dt} = -2x_1 + 5x_2,$$

we write it in matrix form,

$$\frac{d}{dt}\begin{bmatrix} x_1 \\ x_2 \end{bmatrix} = \begin{bmatrix} -4 & 9 \\ -2 & 5 \end{bmatrix}\begin{bmatrix} x_1 \\ x_2 \end{bmatrix}$$

or as $(d/dt)X = AX$, where

$$X = \begin{bmatrix} x_1 \\ x_2 \end{bmatrix}, \qquad A = \begin{bmatrix} -4 & 9 \\ -2 & 5 \end{bmatrix}.$$

If we set $X = e^{At}X_0$, in which $X_0 = [x_{10}, x_{20}]^{\mathrm{T}}$ is independent of t, then

$$\frac{dX}{dt} = Ae^{At}X_0 = AX$$

and we have the general solution of this system. When we note that

$$(e^{At})_{t=0} = E_1 + \cdots + E_n = I,$$

we see that X_0 is the matrix of values of $X = e^{At}X_0$ at $t = 0$. Since

$$e^{At} = \frac{e^{2t}}{3}\begin{bmatrix} -3 & 9 \\ -2 & 6 \end{bmatrix} - \frac{e^{-t}}{3}\begin{bmatrix} -6 & 9 \\ -2 & 3 \end{bmatrix}$$

$$= \begin{bmatrix} -e^{2t} + 2e^{-t} & 3e^{2t} - 3e^{-t} \\ -(2/3)e^{2t} + (2/3)e^{-t} & 2e^{2t} - e^{-t} \end{bmatrix},$$

we find that

$$X = \begin{bmatrix} (-x_{10} + 3x_{20})e^{2t} + (2x_{10} - 3x_{20})e^{-t} \\ [(-2/3)x_{10} + 2x_{20}]e^{2t} + [(2/3)x_{10} - x_{20}]e^{-t} \end{bmatrix}.$$

/4/ SPECTRAL THEORY FOR FINITE COMPLEX MATRICES: THE CASE OF MULTIPLE ROOTS

The reader is aware that the method of partial fractions becomes a bit more complicated when the denominator has multiple roots; nonetheless, it still works. In this section we briefly outline the effect that multiple roots have on our computation of polynomials and power series in a square complex matrix. We conclude with a numerical illustrative example.

Let us assume, then, that A is an n-by-n matrix of complex numbers for which

$$f(x) = f_A(x) = \det (xI - A) = (x - r_1)^{m_1} \cdots (x - r_k)^{m_k}$$

where $r_1, \cdots, r_k$ are distinct complex numbers. Then we have

(1) $$\frac{1}{f(x)} = \frac{a_1(x)}{(x - r_1)^{m_1}} + \cdots + \frac{a_k(x)}{(x - r_k)^{m_k}}$$

where $a_i(x)$ is a polynomial with complex coefficients of degree at most $m_i - 1$ $(i = 1, \cdots, k)$. The determination of the polynomials $a_i(x)$ is explained in calculus. Their existence is assured by the fact that the polynomials $(x - r_1)^{m_1}, \cdots, (x - r_k)^{m_k}$ are relatively prime in pairs (see Chapter 3). From (1) we obtain

(2) $$1 = a_1(x) \prod_{j \neq 1} (x - r_j)^{m_j} + \cdots + a_k(x) \prod_{j \neq k} (x - r_j)^{m_j}.$$

Remark. Again the reader may wish to see a proof of this identity which is independent of the discussion in calculus. Let us first prove a lemma.

Lemma

If g and h are nonconstant and relatively prime polynomials in $F[x]$, where F is a field, then there are unique polynomials $a, b \in F[x]$ such that

$$ag + bh = 1, \qquad \deg a < \deg h, \qquad \text{and} \qquad \deg b < \deg g.$$

PROOF   There are polynomials a_1 and b_1 in $F[x]$ such that $a_1 g + b_1 h = 1$. Divide a_1 by h to get $a_1 = hq + a$ with $\deg a < \deg h$; then $1 = ag + bh$ with $b = b_1 + qg$. Since $\deg (bh) = \deg (1 - ag) < \deg h + \deg g$, we see that $\deg b < \deg g$. This proves the *existence* of a and b. To prove the *uniqueness* of a and b, assume that $a_2 g + b_2 h = 1$, $\deg a_2 < \deg h$, and $\deg b_2 < \deg g$. Then $(a - a_2)g = -(b - b_2)h$. Because g and h are relatively prime, g must divide $b - b_2$. But the degree of $b - b_2$ is less than the degree of g. Hence $b - b_2 = 0$, $b = b_2$, and $a - a_2 = 0$, and $a = a_2$.

Let us apply the lemma to

$$g(x) = \prod_{j \neq i} (x - r_j)^{m_j} \qquad \text{and} \qquad h(x) = (x - r_i)^{m_i}$$

to obtain unique polynomials $a_i(x)$ and $b_i(x)$ in $K[x]$ such that

$$a_i(x) \prod_{j \neq i} (x - r_j)^{m_j} + b_i(x)(x - r_i)^{m_i} = 1$$

and

$$\deg a_i < m_i \qquad \text{and} \qquad \deg b_i < (\deg f) - m_i.$$

Define $p(x)$ as the right-hand member of (2) minus 1. Then the degree of $p(x)$ is less than the degree of $f(x)$. But $(x - r_i)^{m_i}$ divides $p(x)$ because $(x - r_i)^{m_i}$ divides

$$a_i(x) \prod_{j \neq i} (x - r_j)^{m_j} - 1.$$

It follows that $f(x)$ divides $p(x)$ by the unique factorization theorem in $F[x]$. This is possible only if $p(x) = 0$, since $\deg p < \deg f$. This completes the proof of (2).

In the present case, we define

$$E_i = a_i(A) \prod_{j \neq i} (A - r_j I)^{m_j},$$

and obtain

$$I = E_1 + \cdots + E_k,$$

$$E_j^2 = E_j, \qquad E_j E_l = 0, \qquad \text{where } j \neq l.$$

However, the best we can say for the product $(A - r_i I)^s E_i$ is that it is zero for $s = m_i$:

$$(A - r_i I)^{m_i} E_i = 0.$$

For this reason, the computation of a power series $p(x)$ for $x = A$ must include more terms than in the case of simple roots.

Let the Taylor expansions

$$p(x) = p(r_i) + p'(r_i)(x - r_i) + \cdots$$
$$+ \frac{p^{(m_i - 1)}(r_i)}{(m_i - 1)!} (x - r_i)^{m_i - 1} + \cdots$$

converge near $x = r_i$ (where $i = 1, \cdots, k$); then the following equations

$$p(A)E_i = p(r_i)E_i + p'(r_i)(A - r_i I)E_i + \cdots$$
$$+ \frac{p^{(m_i - 1)}(r_i)}{(m_i - 1)!} (A - r_i I)^{m_i - 1} E_i$$

yield

$$p(A) = \sum_{i=1}^{k} \sum_{j=0}^{m_i - 1} \frac{p^{(j)}(r_i)}{j!} (A - r_i I)^j E_i.$$

As an illustration of this formula, let us compute e^A for the matrix

$$A = \begin{bmatrix} 2 & 0 & 0 \\ 1 & 2 & 0 \\ 0 & 1 & 4 \end{bmatrix}.$$

Here

$$f(x) = f_A(x) = \det (xI - A) = (x - 2)^2(x - 4),$$

and

$$\frac{1}{f(x)} = \frac{cx + d}{(x - 2)^2} + \frac{a}{x - 4} = \frac{(-1/4)x}{(x - 2)^2} + \frac{1/4}{x - 4}$$

gives

$$a_1(x) = -x/4 \qquad \text{and} \qquad a_2(x) = 1/4.$$

This leads to the expressions

$$E_1 = (-1/4)A(A - 4I) = (-1/4)\begin{bmatrix} -4 & 0 & 0 \\ 0 & -4 & 0 \\ 1 & 2 & 0 \end{bmatrix},$$

$$E_2 = (1/4)(A - 2I)^2 = (1/4)\begin{bmatrix} 0 & 0 & 0 \\ 0 & 0 & 0 \\ 1 & 2 & 4 \end{bmatrix}.$$

For our computation of e^A we have

$$e^A = [e^2I + e^2(A - 2I)]E_1 + e^4E_2$$
$$= e^2(A - I)E_1 + e^4E_2$$
$$= e^2\begin{bmatrix} 1 & 0 & 0 \\ 1 & 1 & 0 \\ -3/4 & -1/2 & 0 \end{bmatrix} + e^4\begin{bmatrix} 0 & 0 & 0 \\ 0 & 0 & 0 \\ 1/4 & 1/2 & 1 \end{bmatrix}$$
$$= \begin{bmatrix} e^2 & 0 & 0 \\ e^2 & e^2 & 0 \\ (-3/4)e^2 + (1/4)e^4 & (-1/2)e^2 + (1/2)e^4 & e^4 \end{bmatrix}.$$

EXERCISES FOR CHAPTER 4

1. Here is another proof of the Hamilton–Cayley Theorem. Let A be in R_n, R a commutative ring with identity element 1. Write $f_A(x) = \det(xI - A) = a_0 + a_1x + \cdots + a_{n-1}x^{n-1} + x^n$ and write $C = \operatorname{adj}(xI - A) = C_0 + C_1x + \cdots + C_{n-1}x^{n-1}$, with C_i in R_n $(i = 0, \cdots, n-1)$. Then $(xI - A)C = f_A(x)I$ becomes

$$C_0x + C_1x^2 + \cdots + C_{n-1}x^n - AC_0 - AC_1x - \cdots - AC_{n-1}x^{n-1}$$
$$= a_0I + a_1Ix + a_2Ix^2 + \cdots + a_{n-1}Ix^{n-1} + x^nI.$$

    Equate coefficients of like powers of x and use the resulting equations to obtain $f_A(A) = 0$.

2. Verify the Hamilton–Cayley Theorem directly for $n = 2, 3$.

3. Let

$$A = \begin{bmatrix} -1 & -1 \\ 2 & 2 \end{bmatrix}.$$

    Find the idempotents for A and find e^{At}. Does A have a square root?

4. Find the idempotents for

$$A = \begin{bmatrix} 0 & 1 \\ -6 & -7 \end{bmatrix}.$$

5. Find the idempotents for

$$A = \begin{bmatrix} 0 & 1 & 0 \\ 0 & 0 & 1 \\ 10 & 13 & 2 \end{bmatrix}.$$

6. Find e^{At} for

$$A = \begin{bmatrix} 0 & 1 \\ 9 & 8 \end{bmatrix}.$$

7. Find e^{At} for

$$A = \begin{bmatrix} 0 & 1 & 0 \\ 0 & 0 & 1 \\ 0 & 1 & 0 \end{bmatrix}.$$

8. Find e^{At} for

$$A = \begin{bmatrix} 0 & 1 & 0 \\ 0 & 0 & 1 \\ 2 & 1 & -2 \end{bmatrix}.$$

9. Find e^{At} in real form for

$$A = \begin{bmatrix} 0 & 1 \\ -4 & 0 \end{bmatrix}.$$

You may use Euler's relation: $e^{iu} = \cos u + i \sin u$, for u real.

10. Consider the differential equation $d^2y/dt^2 - 5dy/dt + 6y = 0$, with initial values $y = a$ and $dy/dt = b$ when $t = 0$. Setting $y_1 = y$ and $y_2 = dy/dt$, write the equation as the following and solve

$$d/dt \begin{bmatrix} y_1 \\ y_2 \end{bmatrix} = \begin{bmatrix} 0 & 1 \\ -6 & 5 \end{bmatrix} \begin{bmatrix} y_1 \\ y_2 \end{bmatrix}.$$

11. Repeat Exercise 10 for the system $d^3y/dt^3 - 4d^2y/dt^2 + dy/dt + 6y = 0$, with initial values $y = a$, $dy/dt = b$, and $d^2y/dt^2 = c$ when $t = 0$.

12. Solve $d^2y/dt^2 + 4y = 0$, with initial values $y = a$ and $dy/dt = b$ when $t = 0$.

13. Solve $d^2y/dt^2 - 8dy/dt - 9y = 0$, with initial values $y = a$ and $dy/dt = b$ when $t = 0$.

14. Solve $d^3y/dt^3 - dy/dt = 0$, with the initial values of Exercise 11.

15. Solve $d^4y/dt^4 + 2d^2y/dt^2 + y = 0$, with initial values $y = a$, $dy/dt = b$, $d^2y/dt^2 = c$, and $d^3y/dt^3 = d$ when $t = 0$.
16. For the matrix of Exercise 3, find $\sin A$ and $\cos A$. Is it true that $\sin^2 A + \cos^2 A = I$?
17. Let

$$A = \begin{bmatrix} 3 & 2 & 0 \\ 1 & 2 & -1 \\ 1 & 2 & 2 \end{bmatrix}.$$

Verify that the characteristic polynomial of A is $(x-2)^2(x-3)$. Find e^{At}.
18. Repeat Exercise 16 for the matrix of Exercise 17.
19. Discuss the system $d^2x/dt^2 + K^2x = 0$, where $x^T = [x_1, \cdots, x_n]$ and K is a complex n-by-n matrix.
20. Let R be a ring with identity element 1, in which $2a = 0$ for a in R implies that $a = 0$. Let $a_1, \cdots, a_n$ be elements of R which satisfy

$$a_1 + a_2 + \cdots + a_n = 1,$$
$$a_i(a_1 + \cdots + \hat{a}_i + \cdots + a_n) = 0,$$
$$(a_i + a_j)(a_1 + \cdots + \hat{a}_i + \cdots + \hat{a}_j + \cdots + a_n) = 0$$

for $i \neq j$ and $i, j = 1, \cdots, n$. Prove that $a_i a_k = 0$ for $i \neq k$ and $i, k = 1, \cdots, n$ and hence that, $a_i^2 = a_i$ for $i = 1, \cdots, n$.
21. Let A in K_n be such that its characteristic roots are real, distinct, and positive. The spectral form of A^m is

$$A^m = r_1^m E_1 + \cdots + r_n^m E_n$$

where $f_A(x) = (x - r_1)\cdots(x - r_n)$. If we choose notation so that r_1 is the largest positive root, then A^mX is about the same as $r_1^m E_1 X$ for large m and all n-by-1 matrices X. The ratios of corresponding entries of $A^{m+1}X$ and A^mX should then approximate r_1 for m large. With

$$A = \begin{bmatrix} 1 & 1 \\ 1 & 3 \end{bmatrix} \quad \text{and} \quad X = \begin{bmatrix} 1 \\ 0 \end{bmatrix},$$

test this approximation for $m = 6$. Can you imagine how this method might *not* give r_1?

22. Find the idempotents for

$$A = \begin{bmatrix} 0 & 1 & 0 & 0 \\ 0 & 0 & 0 & 0 \\ 0 & 0 & 1 & 1 \\ 0 & 0 & 1 & 1 \end{bmatrix}.$$

23. Find e^{At} for the matrix A of Exercise 22.
24. Does the spectral theory provide a square root for the matrix A of Exercise 22? Does this matrix have a square root?

5

VECTOR SPACES

After the algebraic preliminaries of the preceding chapters, we are well equipped to begin the study of the geometrical background of matric theory. The geometry involved is more general than that studied in plane or solid analytic geometry. In this chapter we introduce the basic concepts of this geometry and develop a few of its elementary theorems.

/ 1 / VECTOR SPACES OVER
A DIVISION RING

It is the purpose of this section to define vector spaces and to state a few of the rules for computing with vectors. Like the concept of ring, the concept of vector space has many diverse particular instances. We point out the few of these which should, even now, be comprehensible to the student. The material we present parallels so closely that of Section 1 of Chapter 1 that we have felt no need to essentially repeat the earlier proofs.

Throughout this section, D will be a division ring and we will refer to the elements α, β, γ, etc., of D as *scalars*. A D *vector space* is a set X in which two compositions (vector addition and scalar multiplication) are defined in accordance with:

V1.   To each ordered pair (x, y) of elements of X there corresponds a unique sum $x + y$ which is an element of X,

V2.   If α is in D and x is in X, there is a unique element αx in X called the scalar product of α and x,

and these compositions satisfy the following further requirements:

V3.   There is an element 0 in X such that $x + 0 = x$ for every x in X.

V4.   Each element x in X has a negative, $-x$, such that $x + (-x) = 0$.

V5.   If x, y, and z are elements of X and if α and β are elements of D, then $(x + y) + z = x + (y + z)$, $(\alpha\beta)x = \alpha(\beta x)$,

$x + y = y + x$, $\alpha(x + y) = \alpha x + \alpha y$, $(\alpha + \beta)x = \alpha x + \beta x$, and $1x = x$.

When X is a D vector space, the elements of X are called *vectors*. One must rely on the context for the proper interpretation of the symbol 0, which is used to denote both the zero scalar of D and the zero vector of X.

Let us point out a few elementary examples of vector spaces.

Example 1   Let D be a division ring (for example, $D = R_a$, R_e, K, or $\mathcal{2}$). Let $X = V_m(D)$ be the set of all 1-by-m matrices

(1) $x = [x_1, \cdots, x_m]$

with x_i in D, $(i = 1, \cdots, m)$. For α in D, define

$$\alpha x = [\alpha]x = [\alpha x_1, \cdots, \alpha x_m].$$

Using the results of Chapter 1, we can easily verify that the rules V1 to V5 hold. It is customary to call the matrix (1) a *row vector* and to refer to x_i as the ith component of x. The reader will note that $V_m(D)$ essentially consists of the set of all ordered m-tuples of elements of D. Addition of these vectors and multiplication by a scalar in D is performed by the rules for matrices. In the symbol $V_m(D)$, which we adopt from now on, D is the given division ring, m indicates the number of components for each vector, and V reminds us that the whole set $V_m(D)$ is a D vector space. The reader has already encountered $V_2(R_e)$ and $V_3(R_e)$ in his study of analytic geometry and calculus.

Example 2   Since a multiple $cf(x)$ of a function $f(x)$ in $C(R_e)$ by a real number c is again in $C(R_e)$, we may regard $C(R_e)$ as an R_e vector space. The rules V1 to V5 are merely a part of the assertion that $C(R_e)$ is a ring with identity element.

Example 3   Let $D = R_a$, $X = R_e$. Again the rules evidently hold and we may regard R_e as an R_a vector space.

Example 4   Let A be an m-by-n matrix of elements of D. The set X_0 of vectors x in $V_m(D)$ for which $xA = 0$ is a D vector space. To verify this we have only to show that, if x and y are in X_0 and α is in D, then $x + y$ and αx are in X_0:

$$(x + y)A = xA + yA = 0 + 0 = 0,$$
$$(\alpha x)A = \alpha(xA) = \alpha 0 = 0.$$

One sees from this example that vector spaces naturally arise when one considers the problem of solving a system of homogeneous linear equations.

Example 5   Let A be an m-by-n matrix of elements of D. The set Y of vectors y in $V_n(D)$ for which $y = xA$ for some x in $V_m(D)$ is a D vector space. For, if y and z are in Y so that $y = xA$ and $z = uA$ with x and u in $V_m(D)$, while α is in D, we have

$$y + z = xA + uA = (x + u)A, \qquad \alpha y = \alpha(xA) = (\alpha x)A$$

and these equations show that $y + z$ and αy are in Y.

Example 6   Let Y be the set of real solutions of the real homogeneous linear differential equation

$$x\frac{d^2y}{dx^2} + x^2\frac{dy}{dx} + y = 0.$$

Then Y is an R_e vector space.

These elementary examples give us only a dim idea of the scope of the vector space concept. One of the major aims of this text is to prepare the reader for the multitudinous occurrences of this concept in modern mathematics, both pure and applied.

As we noted in the introduction to this section, the elementary properties of vector spaces parallel those of rings so closely that we are content to state them without proof.

TV1.   In a D vector space X, 0 is unique: if $x + z = x$ with x and z in X, then $z = 0$.

TV2.   In a D vector space X, $-x$ is uniquely determined by x: if $x + y = 0$ with x and y in X, then $y = -x$.

TV3.   In a D vector space X, $\alpha 0 = 0 = 0x$ for every α in D and every x in X.

TV4.   In a D vector space X, $(-\alpha)x = \alpha(-x) = -(\alpha x)$ and $(-\alpha)(-x) = \alpha x$ for every α in D and every x in X.

Integral multiples of vectors may be defined as in rings.

However, because $1x = x$ for every x in a D vector space X, there is no particular need for these integral multiples. Since multiplication of two vectors is not postulated for a D vector space, there is no possibility of considering powers of vectors unless further assumptions are made. Therefore we state no rules analogous to R5–R10.

There remain, then, only the analogs of the generalized computational rules.

  TV11. Let $x_1, \cdots, x_n$ be vectors of a D vector space X. Then the sum $\sum_{i=1}^{n} x_i$ of these vectors is uniquely defined, irrespective of the order of the vectors and the method of association used in computing the sum.

  TV12. Let $x_1, \cdots, x_n$ be vectors of a D vector space X and let $\alpha, \alpha_1, \cdots, \alpha_n$ be in D. Then

$$\alpha \sum_{i=1}^{n} x_i = \sum_{i=1}^{n} \alpha x_i \quad \text{and} \quad \left(\sum_{i=1}^{n} \alpha_i\right) x_1 = \sum_{i=1}^{n} \alpha_i x_1.$$

  TV13. Let x_{ij} be a vector of a D vector space X $(i = 1, \cdots, m; j = 1, \cdots, n)$, then

$$\sum_{i=1}^{m} \sum_{j=1}^{n} x_{ij} = \sum_{j=1}^{n} \sum_{i=1}^{m} x_{ij}.$$

/ 2 / SUBSPACES, LINEAR INDEPENDENCE, AND BASES

  The main purpose of this section is to introduce the idea which corresponds to that of a "coordinate system" in analytic geometry. Since perpendicularity of vectors has no meaning for general D vector spaces, we must develop some substitute for this concept. When we have accomplished this, we find it easy to introduce coordinates and to discuss the dimension of a D vector space.

  Let X be a D vector space (D a division ring) throughout this section.

  A subset Y of X which is a D vector space relative to the compositions of X is called a D *subspace of* X. Fortunately, there is a simple test for this: a nonempty subset Y of X is a D subspace of X if and only if whenever y and z are in Y and α is in D, then

$y + z$ and αy are also in Y. The obvious D subspaces of X are X itself and the set 0 consisting of the zero vector of X alone. These two subspaces are called "trivial" or "improper." As it is easy to see, the intersection of a family of subspaces is again a subspace. Hence every nonempty subset S of X is contained in a least D subspace $\langle S \rangle$ of X which contains S. We call $\langle S \rangle$ the D *span* of the subset S of X. It is not difficult to find a formula for $\langle S \rangle$:

$$\langle S \rangle = \left\{ \sum_{i=1}^{n} \alpha_i x_i; \ n \in Z_+, \ \alpha_i \in D, \ x_i \in S \right\}.$$

Here Z_+ denotes the set of *positive* integers. We define the span of the empty subset of X to be the empty subset of X.

Illustrative
Example

Let $X = V_3(R_e)$. What are the subspaces of X? We have noted that 0 and X are always subspaces of X. If Y is a nonzero subspace of X, then Y contains a nonzero vector y_1. Being a subspace, Y must then contain every scalar multiple αy_1 of y_1. Geometrically, this means that Y contains all vectors that terminate on the line joining y_1 to the origin. We may say that Y contains this line through the origin. Thus all lines through the origin correspond to subspaces of X. If Y has a vector y_2 not on the line $\langle y_1 \rangle$, then Y contains every vector of the form $\alpha_1 y_1 + \alpha_2 y_2$. These vectors fill out a plane through the origin. Thus all planes through the origin correspond to subspaces of X. If Y contains a vector y_3 not in the plane $\langle y_1, y_2 \rangle$, then Y contains every vector of the form $\alpha_1 y_1 + \alpha_2 y_2 + \alpha_3 y_3$ and must be the whole three-space X. We now see that the subspaces of $V_3(R_e)$ consist of 0, lines through the origin, planes through the origin, and $V_3(R_e)$ itself.

Illustrative
Example

Determine the span of the vectors $x_1 = (1, 0, 1, 0, 0, 1)$, $x_2 = (0, 1, 0, 0, 0, 2)$, and $x_3 = (-1, 1, -1, 0, 0, 1)$ in $V_6(R_e)$.

It is clear that, since $x_3 = -x_1 + x_2$, then $\langle x_1, x_2, x_3 \rangle = \langle x_1, x_2 \rangle$. From the definition,

$$\langle x_1, x_2 \rangle = \{(\alpha, \beta, \alpha, 0, 0, \alpha + 2\beta); \alpha, \beta \in R_e\}.$$

If S is a nonempty subset of X and $y \in X$, it is natural to say that y is D *linearly dependent on* S if $y \in \langle S \rangle$. Those subsets $S \neq \{0\}$ for which no x in S is D linearly dependent on the set T obtained by deleting x from S are called D *linearly independent.*† Thus a subset $S \neq \{0\}$ is D linearly independent (D-li) when no proper subset T of S spans $\langle S \rangle$. Another way of saying that S is D-li is as follows: if $x_i \in S$ and $\alpha_i \in D$ ($i = 1, \cdots, n$) and if

(1) $\alpha_1 x_1 + \alpha_2 x_2 + \cdots + \alpha_n x_n = 0$ with $x_i \neq x_j$ when $i \neq j$,

then $\alpha_i = 0$ ($i = 1, \cdots, n$). For, when this requirement holds and $T \subset S$, we may take $x \in S$ and $x \notin T$ and see that $x \notin \langle T \rangle$, since otherwise

$$x = \sum_{i=1}^{n} \alpha_i x_i \quad \text{with} \quad x_i \in T \quad \text{and} \quad \alpha_i \in D \quad (i = 1, \cdots, n)$$

which is in violation of our requirement (recall that $0 \neq 1$ in D). Conversely, let S be D-li and let (1) hold. If $n > 1$ and $\alpha_i \neq 0$, we could obtain $x_i \in \langle x_1, \cdots, \hat{x}_i, \cdots, x_n \rangle$ and $\langle S \rangle = \langle T \rangle$, with T the set obtained by deleting x_i from S, which is a contradiction. If $n = 1$ and $\alpha_1 \neq 0$, then $x_1 = 0$, $0 \in S$, violating S is D-li. Practical tests for D linear independence will be developed in a later chapter.

Illustrative
Example

In $V_6(R_e)$, is the following set of vectors R_e-li?

$$x_1 = (1, 2, -1, 0, 2, 1),$$
$$x_2 = (2, 4, -2, 0, 2, 2),$$
$$x_3 = (0, 1, -1, 1, 1, 0).$$

† Observe that if $0 \in S \neq \{0\}$, then S is not D linearly independent because $0 \in \langle T \rangle$ for all nonempty subsets T. A set S consisting of a single vector x is D linearly independent if and only if $x \neq 0$.

Assume that $\alpha_1 x_1 + \alpha_2 x_2 + \alpha_3 x_3 = 0$. This means that

$$\alpha_1 + 2\alpha_2 = 0,$$
$$2\alpha_1 + 4\alpha_2 + \alpha_3 = 0,$$
$$-\alpha_1 - 2\alpha_2 - \alpha_3 = 0,$$
$$\alpha_3 = 0,$$
$$2\alpha_1 + 2\alpha_2 + \alpha_3 = 0,$$

and

$$\alpha_1 + 2\alpha_2 = 0.$$

By the third of these equations, $\alpha_3 = 0$; then the last two equations yield $\alpha_1 = \alpha_2 = 0$. This proves that these vectors form an R_e-li subset of $V_6(R_e)$.

Illustrative
Example

In $C(R_e)$, show that the following are R_e-li: $x_1 = 1$, $x_2 = \sin t$, $x_3 = \cos t$, and $x_4 = \sin 2t$. Assume that

$$\alpha_1 + \alpha_2 \sin t + \alpha_3 \cos t + \alpha_4 \sin 2t = 0.$$

Integration from $t = 0$ to $t = 2\pi$ yields $\alpha_1 = 0$. Setting $t = 0$ yields $\alpha_3 = 0$. We may then infer that $\alpha_2 + 2\alpha_4 \cos t = 0$, since this continuous function must vanish for every t such that $\sin t \neq 0$. Integration gives $\alpha_2 = 0$, and setting $t = 0$ gives $\alpha_4 = 0$. These "vectors" of $C(R_e)$ are, therefore, R_e-li.

We say that a subset S of X is D-ld if it is not D-li. A sequence $x_1, \cdots, x_n$ of vectors of X is D-ld when $x_i = x_j$ for some $i \neq j$ or the set $\{x_i; i = 1, \cdots, n\}$ is D-ld. There is a neat (theoretical) test for D-ld.

TB1. Let $x_1, \cdots, x_n$ be D-li in X and let $x_{n+1}, \cdots, x_m$ be vectors of X such that $x_1, \cdots, x_m$ is D-ld. Then for some $k > n$ we have $x_k \in \langle x_1, \cdots, x_{k-1} \rangle$ and $\langle x_1, \cdots, \hat{x}_k, \cdots, x_m \rangle = \langle x_1, \cdots, x_m \rangle$.

PROOF   If we have $x_i = x_j$ with $i < j$, then $j > n$ and our conclusion is evident. Otherwise there are scalars $\alpha_i \in D$ (where $i = 1, \cdots, m$), not all zero, and such that

(2) $$\alpha_1 x_1 + \cdots + \alpha_m x_m = 0.$$

Let k be the greatest integer such that $\alpha_k \neq 0$. Since $x_1, \cdots, x_n$ are D-li, $k > n$. We may solve (2) for x_k and obtain $x_k \in \langle x_1, \cdots, x_{k-1} \rangle$. The remaining conclusion is then obvious.

Illustrative
Example

Apply TB1 to the sequence

$$x_1 = (1, 0, 1, 0), \qquad x_2 = (0, 1, 1, 1),$$
$$x_3 = (2, -1, 1, -1), \qquad x_4 = (1, 2, 3, 4)$$

in $V_4(R_e)$. Since $x_1 \neq 0$, x_1 is an R_e-li sequence. Now, x_2 in $\langle x_1 \rangle$ means that $x_2 = \alpha x_1$ and $0 = \alpha$, which is impossible. Hence the sequence x_1, x_2 is R_e-li. Now, x_3 in $\langle x_1, x_2 \rangle$ means that $x_3 = \alpha x_1 + \beta x_2$, and $\alpha = 2$, $\beta = -1$ works. Thus we see that the sequence x_1, x_2, x_3, x_4 is R_e-ld and that $\langle x_1, x_2, x_3, x_4 \rangle = \langle x_1, x_2, x_4 \rangle$. Finally, x_4 in $\langle x_1, x_2 \rangle$ means that $x_4 = \gamma x_1 + \delta x_2$ and that $\delta = 2$ and $\delta = 4$, which is impossible. The sequence x_1, x_2, x_4 is R_e-li and has the same span as the given sequence.

Corollary

Let the hypotheses of TB1 hold. Then, by deleting certain x_i with $i > n$, we obtain a D-li subset of X with span $\langle x_1, \cdots, x_m \rangle$.

Most of our study of D vector spaces will be limited to those which fall under the following definition.

Definition

A D vector space X is called finite-dimensional in case $X = \langle x_1, \cdots, x_m \rangle$.

Definition

A subset B of a D vector space X is called a D basis for X in case B is D-li and $\langle B \rangle = X$.

By the corollary to TB1, we see, after first deleting any initial zero vectors from the list $x_1, \cdots, x_m$, that every finite-dimensional D vector space $X \neq 0$ has a D basis: $y_1, \cdots, y_n$. Since bases will serve as our substitute for coordinate systems, the next theorem is of vital importance.

TB2.   Let $y_1, \cdots, y_n$ and $z_1, \cdots, z_r$ be D bases for a D vector space X. Then $r = n$.

PROOF   Suppose that $r > n$ for certain choices of the two bases. Keeping r and $y_1, \cdots, y_n$ fixed, choose the second basis $z_1, \cdots, z_r$ such that $y_i = z_i$ (where $i = 1, \cdots, k$) and k is as great as possible. Then $k < n$, since $k = n$ would yield $z_r \in \langle z_1, \cdots, z_n \rangle$, which is contrary to the D linear independence of $z_1, \cdots, z_r$. Since

$$y_{k+1} \in \langle z_1, \cdots, z_r \rangle = X,$$

the sequence

$$y_1, \cdots, y_{k+1}, z_{k+1}, \cdots, z_r$$

is D-ld, and TB1 gives

$$X = \langle y_1, \cdots, y_{k+1}, z_{k+1}, \cdots, \hat{z}_i, \cdots, z_r \rangle$$

for some $i > k$. By our choice of k, the sequence

$$y_1, \cdots, y_k, z_{k+1}, \cdots, \hat{z}_i, \cdots, z_r, y_{k+1}$$

is D-ld, and TB1 gives

$$y_{k+1} \in \langle y_1, \cdots, y_k, z_{k+1}, \cdots, \hat{z}_i, \cdots, z_r \rangle,$$

from which it follows that

$$X = \langle z_1, \cdots, \hat{z}_i, \cdots, z_r \rangle,$$

contrary to the D linear independence of $z_1, \cdots, z_r$.

SECOND PROOF   Let $y_1, \cdots, y_n$ and $z_1, \cdots, z_r$ be two D bases for X. Since the labels for the vectors are immaterial, we may choose our labelling so that $n \leq r$. (If $n > r$, write y for z and z for y.) Since $X = \langle y_1, \cdots, y_n \rangle$, the sequence $z_1, y_1, \cdots, y_n$ is D-ld and TB1 yields an i_1 such that $X = \langle z_1, y_1, \cdots, \hat{y}_{i_1}, \cdots, y_n \rangle$. Then the sequence $z_1, z_2, y_1, \cdots, \hat{y}_{i_1}, \cdots, y_n$ is D-ld, and TB1 yields an $i_2 \neq i_1$ such that

$$X = \langle z_1, z_2, \cdots, \hat{y}_{i_1}, \cdots, \hat{y}_{i_2}, \cdots, y_n \rangle.$$

We may continue this process of replacing some y_i by a z_j until all the y_i are used up. But then $z_1, \cdots, z_n$ span X and $n = r$ since the sequence $z_1, \cdots, z_r$ is D-li.

Definition of Dimension

Let X be a nonzero finite-dimensional D vector space; then the dimension of X (dim X) is the number of vectors in a D basis for X. If $X = 0$, then dim X is defined as 0.

EXERCISE   Which of the examples of Section 1 are finite-dimensional spaces?

TB3.   If X is a finite-dimensional D vector space and $y_1, \cdots, y_k$ are D-li vectors of X, then $k \le n = \dim X$ and X has a basis of the form $y_1, \cdots, y_k, y_{k+1}, \cdots, y_n$.

PROOF   Let $x_1, \cdots, x_n$ be a D basis for X. Apply the corollary to TB1 to the sequence $y_1, \cdots, y_k, x_1, \cdots, x_n$.

The following theorem permits us to apply our results concerning finite-dimensional D vector spaces to every D subspace of a finite-dimensional space.

TB4.   Every D subspace Y of a finite-dimensional D vector space is finite-dimensional.

PROOF   We may assume that $Y \ne 0$, since $0 = \langle 0 \rangle$. Then Y has a D-li subset, $\{y_1\}$, formed by choosing $y_1 \ne 0$ and in Y. Choose the largest k such that $y_1, \cdots, y_k$ are in Y and are D-li. If $y \in Y$, then $y_1, \cdots, y_k, y$ are D-ld, and TB1 gives $y \in \langle y_1, \cdots, y_k \rangle$. Hence $\langle y_1, \cdots, y_k \rangle = Y$, and Y is finite-dimensional.

Since we have said that a D basis for X will serve as a coordinate system in X, let us close this section by showing how one determines the coordinates of a vector x in X relative to a D basis $x_1, \cdots, x_n$ for X. Since $X = \langle x_1, \cdots, x_n \rangle$ and x is in X, there are scalars $\xi_1, \cdots, \xi_n$ in D such that

$$x = \xi_1 x_1 + \cdots + \xi_n x_n.$$

The scalars $\xi_1, \cdots, \xi_n$ are uniquely determined by x. For if also

$$x = \xi_1'x_1 + \cdots + \xi_n'x_n,$$

then

$$0 = (\xi_1 - \xi_1')x_1 + \cdots + (\xi_n - \xi_n')x_n,$$

and $\xi_1 - \xi_1' = \cdots = \xi_n - \xi_n' = 0$, because the vectors $x_1, \cdots, x_n$ are D-li. We call the scalars $\xi_1, \cdots, \xi_n$ the *coordinates of x relative to the D basis $x_1, \cdots, x_n$*.

It is easy to verify that the vectors $x_1 = (1, 0, \cdots, 0)$, $x_2 = (0, 1, 0, \cdots, 0), \cdots, x_m = (0, 0, \cdots, 1)$ form a basis for $V_m(D)$. We shall call this basis the *usual basis* for $V_m(D)$. One observes that this implies that dim $(V_m(D)) = m$.

Illustrative
Example

Find the coordinates of $x = (\alpha_1, \alpha_2, \alpha_3)$ relative to the R_e basis $x_1 = (1, 2, 3)$, $x_2 = (0, 1, 2)$, and $x_3 = (0, 0, 1)$, for $V_3(R_e)$. The equation

$$x = \xi_1 x_1 + \xi_2 x_2 + \xi_3 x_3$$

yields the equations

$$\alpha_1 = \xi_1, \qquad \alpha_2 = 2\xi_1 + \xi_2, \qquad \alpha_3 = 3\xi_1 + 2\xi_2 + \xi_3,$$

which are easily solved:

$$\xi_1 = \alpha_1, \qquad \xi_2 = \alpha_2 - 2\alpha_1,$$

$$\xi_3 = \alpha_3 - 3\alpha_1 - 2(\alpha_2 - 2\alpha_1), \qquad \xi_3 = \alpha_3 + \alpha_1 - 2\alpha_2.$$

/ 3 / ISOMORPHISM OF VECTOR SPACES

In this section we introduce the concept of isomorphism of two D vector spaces X and X'. We then show that every D vector space X of finite dimension m is isomorphic to $V_m(D)$. It follows that isomorphic finite-dimensional D vector spaces have the same dimension, a fact we shall exploit in the next section.

We say that two D vector spaces X and X' are *isomorphic* when there is a faithful map† $f : X \to X'$ of X *onto* X' which preserves the basic vector space operations. That is, we have

$$f(x + y) = f(x) + f(y) \qquad \text{and} \qquad f(\alpha x) = \alpha f(x)$$

for all x, $y \in X$ and all $\alpha \in D$. If S is a subset of X and $f(S) = \{f(x); x \in S\}$ is the image of S under f, then we see at once that $f(\langle S \rangle) = \langle f(S) \rangle$. Consequently, S is D-li in X if and only if $f(S)$ is D-li in X'. It follows that X is finite-dimensional if and only if X' is. Further, $x_1, \cdots, x_n$ is a D basis for X if and only if $f(x_1), \cdots, f(x_n)$ is a D basis for X'. Hence, isomorphic finite-dimensional D vector spaces have the same dimension. We may illustrate the notion of isomorphism by selecting a D basis $x_1, \cdots, x_m$ for a D vector space X of dimension m. Each $x \in X$ then has coordinates $\xi_1, \cdots, \xi_m \in D$ uniquely determined by

$$x = \xi_1 x_1 + \cdots + \xi_m x_m.$$

Let us write $f(x) = (\xi_1, \cdots, \xi_m) \in V_m(D)$; then we may verify that $f : X \to V_m(D)$ is an isomorphism. For, if also $y \in X$ and

$$y = \eta_1 x_1 + \cdots + \eta_m x_m,$$

then

$$x + y = (\xi_1 + \eta_1) x_1 + \cdots + (\xi_m + \eta_m) x_m$$

and

$$\alpha x = (\alpha \xi_1) x_1 + \cdots + (\alpha \xi_m) x_m$$

for all α in D. Thus,

$$\begin{aligned} f(x + y) &= (\xi_1 + \eta_1, \cdots, \xi_m + \eta_m) \\ &= (\xi_1, \cdots, \xi_m) + (\eta_1, \cdots, \eta_m) = f(x) + f(y) \end{aligned}$$

and

$$f(\alpha x) = (\alpha \xi_1, \cdots, \alpha \xi_m) = \alpha f(x).$$

This proves that f preserves the basic vector space operations. If $f(x) = f(y)$, then $\xi_i = \eta_i$ $(i = 1, \cdots, m)$, $x = y$, so that f is faithful. Given $(\alpha_1, \cdots, \alpha_m) \in V_m(D)$, we see that

$$a = \alpha_1 x_1 + \cdots + \alpha_m x_m$$

is in X and $f(a) = (\alpha_1, \cdots, \alpha_m)$. Hence, f maps X *onto* $V_m(D)$. This completes the proof that, if dim $X = m$, then X is isomorphic

† See the Appendix, Section 2.

to $V_m(D)$. A word of caution is in order. Observe that *every* basis for X yields an isomorphism of X onto $V_m(D)$. These isomorphisms are by no means all the same, and the study of X involves a study of their relationships.

/4/ TRANSLATES OF SUBSPACES AND FACTOR SPACES

If Y is a subspace of a D vector space X and x is a vector of X, then $x + Y = \{x + y; y \in Y\}$ is called a *translate* of Y.

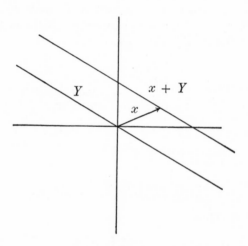

We may add translates and multiply them by scalars of D:

$$(x_1 + Y) + (x_2 + Y) = (x_1 + x_2) + Y,$$

$$\alpha(x_1 + Y) = \alpha x_1 + Y.$$

(One should be careful to observe here that $x_1 + Y = x_1' + Y$ if and only if $x_1 - x_1' \in Y$. Hence, if also $x_2 + Y = x_2' + Y$, then $(x_1 + x_2) - (x_1' + x_2') \in Y$ and $(x_1 + x_2) + Y = (x_1' + x_2') + Y$. Finally, $\alpha(x_1 - x_1') \in Y$ gives $\alpha x_1 + Y = \alpha x_1' + Y$. When extending operations on elements to sets of elements, one frequently encounters this difficulty which must be solved in an analogous way.)

The family of all translates of Y is called the *factor space* of Y in X:

$$X/Y = \{x + Y; x \in X\}.$$

It is easy to verify that X/Y is indeed a D vector space.

If $X = V_3(R_e)$, what is the geometric interpretation of the factor spaces X/Y for subspaces Y of X? We have seen that the subspaces Y of X are 0, lines through the origin, planes through the origin, and X itself. The factor space $X/0$ is essentially X, while X/X has only one vector, zero. If Y is a line through the origin, then the figure shows that X/Y consists of the family of all lines in $V_3(R_e)$ which are parallel to Y. If Y is a plane π through the origin, a similar figure will show that X/Y consists of the family of all planes in $V_3(R_e)$ parallel to π. One sees that the construction of X/Y provides a method of decomposing X into geometrically similar subsets.

If X is a finite-dimensional D vector space and Y is a D subspace of X, then

(1) $\dim (X/Y) = \dim (X) - \dim (Y)$.

PROOF   If $Y = 0$, this is clear. If $Y \neq 0$, let $y_1, \cdots, y_k$ be a basis for Y and let $y_1, \cdots, y_k, x_{k+1}, \cdots, x_n$ be a basis for X (see TB3). Then $x_{k+1} + Y, \cdots, x_n + Y$ is a basis for X/Y, and (1) is true.

When Y, Z are D subspaces of a D vector space X, we write $Y + Z = \langle Y \cup Z \rangle = \{y + z; y \in Y, z \in Z\}$ and we call $Y + Z$ the *sum* of Y and Z. Observe that $Y + Z$ is the least D subspace of X which contains both Y and Z. Factor spaces provide a useful relation between $Y + Z$ and $Y \cap Z$.

Isomorphism Theorem

If Y and Z are D subspaces of a D vector space X, then $(y + z) + Y \rightarrow z + (Y \cap Z)$ for $y \in Y$ and $z \in Z$ establishes a faithful map of $(Y + Z)/Y$ onto $Z/(Y \cap Z)$ which preserves vector addition and scalar multiplication.

PROOF   If $y, y' \in Y$ and $z, z' \in Z$, then $(y + z) + Y = (y' + z') + Y$ iff† $z + Y = z' + Y$ iff $z - z' \in (Y \cap Z)$ iff

† The contraction "iff" of "if and only if" is often used by mathematicians.

$z + (Y \cap Z) = z' + (Y \cap Z)$. This proves that our formula defines a map of $(Y + Z)/Y$ onto $Z/(Y \cap Z)$ which is faithful. The preservation of the operations is immediately evident from the definitions.

Illustrative
Example

In $X = V_3(R_e)$, let $Y = \{(\alpha, \beta, 0); \alpha, \beta \in R_e\}$, and let $Z = \{(\gamma, 0, \delta); \gamma, \delta \in R_e\}$; so that $Y + Z = X$ and $Y \cap Z = \{(\alpha, 0, 0); \alpha \in R_e\}$. The mapping $(y + z) + Y \to z + (Y \cap Z)$ takes a plane parallel to Y into its line of intersection with Z. Thus the planes parallel to Y, which constitute $(Y + Z)/Y$, are matched with the lines in Z parallel to $Y \cap Z$, which constitute $Z/(Y \cap Z)$. See figure below. The vector y in Y is not shown in the figure; PQ is parallel to y and of the same length and sense.

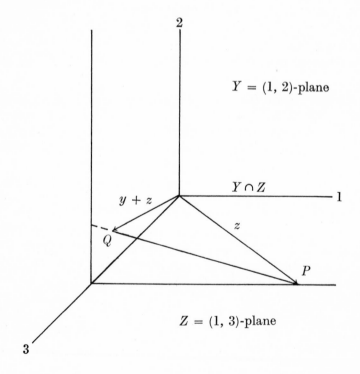

We say that $(Y + Z)/Y$ and $Z/(Y \cap Z)$ are isomorphic D vector spaces. In particular, these spaces must have the same dimension.

Corollary (Fundamental Theorem on Dimension)

If X is a finite-dimensional D vector space and Y, Z are D subspaces of X, then

$$\dim (Y + Z) + \dim (Y \cap Z) = \dim Y + \dim Z.$$

EXERCISES FOR CHAPTER 5

1. Prove TV3.
2. Prove TV4.
3. Is the axiom $1x = x$ a consequence of the other axioms for a D vector space?
4. Find, in $V_3(R_a)$, $\langle(1, -1, 2), (-1, 1, 3), (0, 0, 5), (2, -2, 9)\rangle$.
5. In $V_4(R_e)$, show that $x_1 = (1, 1, 1, 1)$, $x_2 = (1, 1, 1, 0)$, $x_3 = (1, 1, 0, 0)$, and $x_4 = (1, 0, 0, 0)$ form an R_e basis, and find the coordinates of $(\alpha, \beta, \gamma, \delta)$ relative to this basis.
6. From the sequence $(1, 1, -1, 1)$, $(2, 2, -2, 2)$, $(0, 1, 1, 1)$, $(1, 2, 0, 2)$, $(1, 2, 3, 4)$ of vectors of $V_4(R_a)$, select an R_a-li subsequence with the same span.
7. Find the coordinates of $(5, -1, 2)$ relative to the basis $(1, 2, 3)$, $(0, 1, 2)$, $(0, 0, 1)$ for $V_3(R_a)$.
8. In $V_4(R_a)$, let $Y = \langle(1, 0, 1, 0), (2, 1, -1, 0)\rangle$ and $Z = \langle(0, 1, 1, 1), (-1, 2, 1, 0)\rangle$. Find an R_a basis for $Y \cap Z$.
9. Let

$$A = \begin{bmatrix} 1 & 0 & 2 \\ 3 & 1 & -1 \\ 4 & 1 & 1 \end{bmatrix}$$

in $(R_a)_3$. Let Y be the subspace of $V_3(R_a)$ of vectors x such that $xA = 0$. Find the dimension of Y.

10. For the matrix A of Exercise 9, let Z be the subspace of $V_3(R_a)$ of all vectors of the form xA for x in $V_3(R_a)$. Find the dimension of Z.

11. Repeat Exercises 9 and 10 for

$$A = \begin{bmatrix} 0 & 1 & 0 \\ 0 & 1 & 0 \\ 0 & 1 & 0 \end{bmatrix}.$$

12. Show that Y is the zero vector of X/Y.

13. Let Y be a D subspace of a D vector space X. Show that xEx' in case $x - x'$ is in Y defines an equivalence relation in X. What is the corresponding decomposition of X?

14. Find a D basis for $V_2(\mathscr{Q})$, where $\mathscr{Q}$ is the ring of real quaternions, which includes the vector $x_1 = (\mathbf{i}, \mathbf{j})$.

15. What is the dimension, in $V_5(R_e)$, of the subspace W spanned by the vectors $(1, 0, -1, 2, 1)$, $(5, -1, 3, 6, 2)$, $(6, -1, 2, 8, 3)$, $(-4, 1, -4, -4, -1)$, and $(10, -2, 6, 12, 4)$?

16. What is the dimension of $V_5(R_e)/W$ if W is the subspace described in Exercise 15?

17. Find a basis for $V_5(R_e)$ that includes the vectors $(1, 0, -1, 2, 1)$ and $(5, -1, 3, 6, 2)$.

18. Find a basis for $V_5(R_e)/W$, where W is the subspace described in Exercise 15.

19. If $C(R_e)$ is considered as a real vector space, are the "vectors" 1, $\sin t$, $\cos t$, and $\cos^2 t$ R_e-li?

20. Let X be a finite-dimensional D vector space and let V be a subspace of X. Show that there is a subspace W such that $V + W = X$ and $V \cap W = 0$. For which subspaces V of X is W uniquely determined by V?

21. Let W, Y, and Z be D subspaces of a D vector space X with $W \supseteq Y$. Show that $W \cap (Y + Z) = Y + (W \cap Z)$.

22. Find such subspaces W, Y, and Z of $V_2(R_e)$ that $W \cap (Y + Z) \neq Y + (W \cap Z)$.

23. Let E in D_n, where D is a division ring, be idempotent. Define Y and Z as in Exercises 9 and 10. Show that $X = Y + Z$ and $Y \cap Z = 0$.

24. Show that the set of "vectors" $\{1\} \cup \{\sin nx;\ n \in Z_+\} \cup \{\cos nx;\ n \in Z_+\}$ is R_e-li in $C(R_e)$. Here Z_+ denotes the set of positive integers.

25. By Zorn's Lemma,† every D vector space X has maximal D-li subsets M. Show that every such M is a D basis for X.

† See the Appendix, Section 6.

26. Let H be an R_a basis for R_e considered as an R_a vector space. Then every real number has the form

$$x = \sum_{i=1}^{n_x} \alpha_i h_i$$

where $h_i \in H$ and $\alpha_i \in R_a$. If we choose *any* map† $f : H \to R_e$, then we may define

$$f_0(x) = \sum_{i=1}^{n_x} \alpha_i f(h_i).$$

Prove that $f_0(x + y) = f_0(x) + f_0(y)$ for all $x, y \in R_e$. When is the map $f_0 : R_e \to R_e$ continuous?

† See the Appendix, Section 2.

6

RANK AND

LINEAR EQUATIONS

In this chapter we shall apply the basic facts about dimension to a discussion of the rank of a matrix. We first define rank abstractly in Section 1; then we show in Section 2 how one may compute rank by using elementary operations. In the brief Section 3, the results of our study of rank are applied to the solution of systems of linear equations. We include also a derivation of Cramer's Rule in the final Section 4.

/ 1 / ROW RANK

In this section we meet our first definition of the rank of a matrix, as well as of a derived number, the nullity of a matrix, which will be useful in studying the properties of the rank of a matrix.

Throughout this section, D will be a division ring.

Let A be an m-by-n matrix of elements of D. If x is a vector in $V_m(D)$, then xA is a vector in $V_n(D)$. The set $R_A = \{xA\; ; x \in V_m(D)\}$ is a D subspace of $V_n(D)$ since, if x and y are in $V_m(D)$, then $xA + yA = (x + y)A$ and $\alpha(xA) = (\alpha x)A$ for every $\alpha \in D$. If we regard A as decomposed into row vectors $A_1, \cdots, A_m$, then R_A is the span of $A_1, \cdots, A_m$ in $V_n(D)$. Hence we call R_A the *row space* of A and we define the *row rank* of A as the dimension of R_A. The subspace R_A is often also called the *range* of A. There is another important vector space associated with A. The set of vectors x in $V_m(D)$ for which $xA = 0$ is a D subspace $K_A = \{x \in V_m(D); xA = 0\}$ of $V_m(D)$, called the *kernel of A* or *the null-space of A*. It is easy to see that K_A is a D subspace of $V_m(D)$, since $xA = yA = 0$ gives $(x + y)A = 0$ and $(\alpha x)A = \alpha(xA) = 0$ for every $\alpha \in D$. The *nullity of A* is defined as the dimension of the kernel K_A of A.

Illustrative
Example

Let

$$A = \begin{bmatrix} 1 & 2 \\ 0 & 1 \\ 1 & 3 \end{bmatrix}$$

have elements in R_a. Then

$$xA = (\alpha, \beta, \gamma) \begin{bmatrix} 1 & 2 \\ 0 & 1 \\ 1 & 3 \end{bmatrix} = (\alpha + \gamma, 2\alpha + \beta + 3\gamma).$$

It is easy to see that every vector (α_1, α_2) in $V_2(R_a)$ may be expressed in the form $(\alpha + \gamma, 2\alpha + \beta + 3\gamma)$ by the proper choice of α, β, and γ. Thus, R_A equals $V_2(R_a)$ and the row rank of A is 2. Now, $xA = 0$ yields $\alpha + \gamma = 0$ and $\beta + \gamma = 0$, so that $x = (\alpha, \beta, \gamma) = (\alpha, \alpha, -\alpha) = \alpha(1, 1, -1)$. Thus,

$$K_A = \{\alpha(1, 1, -1); \alpha \in R_a\}$$

has dimension 1, and the nullity of A is 1.

The row rank of A and the nullity of A are not independent.

Theorem 1 (Sylvester)

Let A be an m-by-n matrix of elements of a division ring D. Then the row space R_A of A is isomorphic to $V_m(D)/K_A$. Hence the row rank of A is equal to the number of rows of A minus the nullity of A.

PROOF   If $x, x' \in V_m(D)$, then $x + K_A = x' + K_A$ if and only if $x - x' \in K_A$ if and only if $(x - x')A = 0$ if and only if $xA = x'A$. We may therefore define a map of $V_m(D)/K_A$ into† R_A by sending $x + K_A$ into xA. It is easy to check that this is a faithful map of $V_m(D)/K_A$ onto† R_A and one which preserves addition and scalar multiplication:

$$(x + K_A) + (y + K_A) = (x + y) + K_A \rightarrow (x + y)A = xA + yA$$

† See the Appendix, Section 2.

and

$$\alpha(x + K_A) = \alpha x + K_A \rightarrow (\alpha x)A = \alpha(xA).$$

Using our rule for computing the dimension of a factor space, we find

$$\dim (V_m(D)/K_A) = \dim V_m(D) - \dim K_A$$
$$= m - (\text{nullity of } A).$$

By definition, $\dim R_A$ is the row rank of A. Since R_A and $V_m(D)/K_A$ are isomorphic, they have the same dimension and Sylvester's Law of Nullity is proved.

Our proof of the next theorem shows how the nullity is useful in discussions of rank.

Theorem 2

The row rank of a product is less than or equal to the row rank of either factor. If one of the factors of a product is non-singular, then the row rank of the product is the same as the row rank of the other factor.

PROOF   Let A be an m-by-n matrix with elements in D, and let B be an s-by-m matrix with elements in D. The row space of BA is a subset of the row space of A, since $y(BA) = (yB)A$ for every y in $V_s(D)$. Hence the row rank of BA is at most that of A, by TB3 (Section 2, Chapter 5). When B is nonsingular, the row space of A is the same as the row space of BA, since $xA = xB^{-1}(BA)$ for every x in $V_m(D)$ shows that the row space of A is a subset of the row space of BA and, hence, these row spaces are equal. Thus, the row rank of BA and the row rank of A are equal when B is nonsingular.

Now let B be an n-by-t matrix and use Theorem 1. The kernel of A is a subset of the kernel of AB, since $xA = 0$ implies that $x(AB) = (xA)B = 0$. Hence the nullity of AB is at least as great as the nullity of A, and Theorem 1 tells us that the row rank of AB is at most that of A because AB and A have the same number of rows. If B is nonsingular, the kernels of A and of AB are the same, since then $xA = 0$ if and only if $x(AB) = 0$. By Theorem 1, the row ranks of A and of AB are equal when B is nonsingular.

It is possible to define the column rank of A as the row rank of A^T but, as we shall see later, it turns out that the column rank of A and the row rank of A are the same. Recall that A^T has elements in $D°$.

/ 2 / ELEMENTARY OPERATIONS AND THE COMPUTATION OF RANK

In this section we shall give a simple method of computing the rank of a matrix. It will be seen that this convenient computational method has several important theoretical consequences, not the least of which is the fact that a square matrix of elements of a division ring is nonsingular if it has a one-sided inverse.

Throughout this section, D is a division ring.

Let us consider three types of *elementary operations* on an m-by-n matrix A of elements of D.

Type I: interchange of two rows (columns) of A.

Type II: left (right) multiplication of each element of a row (column) of A by a nonzero element c of D.

Type III: addition of a left (right) multiple by c in D of the ith row (column) to the jth row (column) for $i \neq j$.

The inverse of each elementary operation is again an elementary operation. An operation of Type I is its own inverse. In Type II the inverse is obtained by replacing c by c^{-1}. In Type III the inverse is obtained by replacing c by $-c$.

These elementary operations can be effected by matric multiplication. In fact, each elementary row operation results in EA, where E is the result of applying the elementary operation to I_m. It will suffice to illustrate this by the case in which $m = 2$.

$$A = \begin{bmatrix} R_1 \\ R_2 \end{bmatrix}, \qquad \begin{bmatrix} 0 & 1 \\ 1 & 0 \end{bmatrix}\begin{bmatrix} R_1 \\ R_2 \end{bmatrix} = \begin{bmatrix} R_2 \\ R_1 \end{bmatrix},$$

$$\begin{bmatrix} c & 0 \\ 0 & 1 \end{bmatrix}\begin{bmatrix} R_1 \\ R_2 \end{bmatrix} = \begin{bmatrix} cR_1 \\ R_2 \end{bmatrix}, \qquad \begin{bmatrix} 1 & 0 \\ c & 1 \end{bmatrix}\begin{bmatrix} R_1 \\ R_2 \end{bmatrix} = \begin{bmatrix} R_1 \\ R_2 + cR_1 \end{bmatrix}.$$

Each elementary column operation results in AE, E being the result of applying the elementary column operation to I_n. Again we are content to illustrate this by the special case in which $n = 3$ and $A = [C_1, C_2, C_3]$.

$$[C_1, C_2, C_3] \begin{bmatrix} 0 & 0 & 1 \\ 0 & 1 & 0 \\ 1 & 0 & 0 \end{bmatrix} = [C_3, C_2, C_1],$$

$$[C_1, C_2, C_3] \begin{bmatrix} 1 & 0 & 0 \\ 0 & c & 0 \\ 0 & 0 & 1 \end{bmatrix} = [C_1, C_2 c, C_3],$$

$$[C_1, C_2, C_3] \begin{bmatrix} 1 & 0 & c \\ 0 & 1 & 0 \\ 0 & 0 & 1 \end{bmatrix} = [C_1, C_2, C_3 + C_1 c].$$

A matrix E obtained from I by an elementary row or column operation will be called an *elementary matrix* (of course, the column operations actually yield no new elementary matrices). These elementary matrices are all nonsingular. An elementary matrix of Type I is its own inverse, one of Type II has an inverse obtained by replacing c by c^{-1}, and one of Type III has an inverse obtained by replacing c by $-c$.

We are now going to try to "simplify" an m-by-n matrix with elements in D by means of elementary operations. Let us call two m-by-n matrices A and B, with elements in D, *equivalent* when B can be obtained from A by means of a (finite) sequence of elementary operations. We write $A \stackrel{D}{=} B$ when A and B are equivalent. This relation has the following important properties:

E1.   Reflexivity: we have $A \stackrel{D}{=} A$ for every A.
E2.   Symmetry: if $A \stackrel{D}{=} B$, then $B \stackrel{D}{=} A$.
E3.   Transitivity: if $A \stackrel{D}{=} B$ and $B \stackrel{D}{=} C$, then $A \stackrel{D}{=} C$.

The relation $\stackrel{D}{=}$ is then an abstract equivalence relation.† The whole set of m-by-n matrices with elements in D is separated into disjoint maximal subsets of mutually equivalent matrices. These maximal subsets are called equivalence classes relative to $\stackrel{D}{=}$. We shall describe a unique representative of each of these equivalence classes. When such a description has been accomplished,

† See the Appendix, Section 2.

it is customary to call the representative of the equivalence class to which A belongs the *canonical form of A relative to $\stackrel{D}{=}$*.

Theorem 3

Every m-by-n matrix A of elements of D is equivalent to one and only one of the following matrices:

(1) 0 **(2)** $\begin{bmatrix} I_r & 0 \\ 0 & 0 \end{bmatrix}$

where r is the row rank of A and $r = 1, \cdots, \min(m, n)$.

PROOF   We may assume that $A \neq 0$. Operations of Type I place a nonzero element of D in the $(1, 1)$ position. An operation of Type II places 1 in the $(1, 1)$ position. Operations of Type III then yield

$$\begin{bmatrix} 1 & 0 \\ 0 & B \end{bmatrix}.$$

If $B \neq 0$, we repeat the process and ultimately obtain the form (2). The elementary operations employed may be effected by multiplying right or left by nonsingular matrices. According to Theorem 2, these multiplications do not affect row rank. Since the row rank of (2) is evidently r, r is the row rank of A. It is not possible that A be equivalent to two different matrices of these types because no two such have the same row rank. One should note that if $r = m$ ($r = n$) then the last rows (columns) of zeros do not appear in (2). When $r = m = n$, then (2) becomes I_n.

Illustrative
Example

Find the canonical form relative to $\stackrel{2}{=}$ for

$$\begin{bmatrix} \mathbf{i} & \mathbf{j} & \mathbf{k} \\ \mathbf{k} & 1 & -\mathbf{i} \end{bmatrix}.$$

Multiply each element of the first row by $-\mathbf{i}$ on the left, to get

$$\begin{bmatrix} 1 & -\mathbf{k} & \mathbf{j} \\ \mathbf{k} & 1 & -\mathbf{i} \end{bmatrix}.$$

Now multiply each element of the first row by $-\mathbf{k}$ on the left and add the product to the second row to get

$$\begin{bmatrix} 1 & -\mathbf{k} & \mathbf{j} \\ 0 & 0 & 0 \end{bmatrix}.$$

Adding right multiples of the first column to the second and third columns gives the desired canonical form:

$$\begin{bmatrix} 1 & 0 & 0 \\ 0 & 0 & 0 \end{bmatrix}.$$

Illustrative
Example

Find the canonical form for

$$\begin{bmatrix} 1 & 2 & -1 \\ 3 & 6 & -3 \\ 16 & 32 & -16 \end{bmatrix}$$

in $(R_a)_3$. Since R_a is commutative, we need not worry about rights and lefts. Adding multiples of the first row to the second and third rows gives

$$\begin{bmatrix} 1 & 2 & -1 \\ 0 & 0 & 0 \\ 0 & 0 & 0 \end{bmatrix}.$$

Adding multiples of the first column to the others, we find the desired canonical form to be

$$\begin{bmatrix} 1 & 0 & 0 \\ 0 & 0 & 0 \\ 0 & 0 & 0 \end{bmatrix}.$$

A number of useful corollaries flow from Theorem 3.

Theorem 4

Two m-by-n matrices with elements in D are equivalent if and only if they have the same row rank.

Theorem 5

A matrix A in D_m is nonsingular if and only if the row rank of A is m.

PROOF   Let A be nonsingular in D_m. Then the kernel of A is zero, since $xA = 0$ for $x \in V_m(D)$ yields $xAA^{-1} = 0 = x$. By Theorem 1, the row rank of A is m.

Conversely, let the row rank of A be m. By Theorem 3, $A \overset{D}{\sim} I_m$, and we have $E_s \cdots E_1 A F_1 \cdots F_t = I_m$, where E_i and F_j $(i = 1, \cdots, s,$ and $j = 1, \cdots, t)$ are nonsingular, being the elementary matrices which effect the sequence of elementary operations leading from A to I_m. Thus

$$A = E_1^{-1} \cdots E_s^{-1} F_t^{-1} \cdots F_1^{-1}, \qquad A^{-1} = F_1 \cdots F_t E_s \cdots E_1$$

and A is nonsingular.

This proof suggests a method of computing A^{-1} that may be amusing. Form the array

$$I_m$$

$$A \quad I_m$$

and perform elementary operations to replace this array by

$$Q$$

$$I_m \quad P$$

Then $A^{-1} = QP$.

To justify this rule, note that $P = E_s \cdots E_1 I_m$ is the result of applying the elementary row operations in the correct order to I_m, whereas $Q = I_m F_1 \cdots F_t$ is the result of applying the elementary column operations to I_m, again in the correct order. Then $I_m = PAQ$ yields $P^{-1}Q^{-1} = A$, and hence $A^{-1} = QP$.

Illustrative
Example

Find the inverse, in $(R_a)_2$, of $\begin{bmatrix} 1 & 4 \\ 3 & -2 \end{bmatrix}$.

$$\begin{bmatrix} 1 & 0 \\ 0 & 1 \end{bmatrix} \qquad\qquad \begin{bmatrix} 1 & 0 \\ 0 & 1 \end{bmatrix} \qquad\qquad \begin{bmatrix} 1 & -4 \\ 0 & 1 \end{bmatrix}$$

$$\begin{bmatrix} 1 & 4 \\ 3 & -2 \end{bmatrix}\begin{bmatrix} 1 & 0 \\ 0 & 1 \end{bmatrix} \xrightarrow{} \begin{bmatrix} 1 & 4 \\ 0 & -14 \end{bmatrix}\begin{bmatrix} 1 & 0 \\ -3 & 1 \end{bmatrix} \xrightarrow{} \begin{bmatrix} 1 & 0 \\ 0 & 1 \end{bmatrix}\begin{bmatrix} 1 & 0 \\ 3/14 & -1/14 \end{bmatrix}$$

$$QP = \begin{bmatrix} 1 & -4 \\ 0 & 1 \end{bmatrix}\begin{bmatrix} 1 & 0 \\ 3/14 & -1/14 \end{bmatrix} = \begin{bmatrix} 2/14 & 4/14 \\ 3/14 & -1/14 \end{bmatrix} = A^{-1}.$$

Theorem 6

A matrix A in D_m is nonsingular if and only if A is a product of elementary matrices.

PROOF   This follows from 1–9 and the proof of Theorem 5.

Theorem 7

Two m-by-n matrices A and B of elements of D are equivalent if and only if $B = PAQ$ for nonsingular matrices P and Q of elements of D.

PROOF   This follows from Theorem 6 and the argument used in the proof of Theorem 5.

Corollary

If A is a nonzero m-by-n matrix of elements of D of row rank r, then there are nonsingular matrices P and Q of elements of D such that

$$PAQ = \begin{bmatrix} I_r & 0 \\ 0 & 0 \end{bmatrix}.$$

If one desires to find the matrices P and Q of the corollary of Theorem 7 (and, in applications, one frequently *does*), then he may form the array

$$I_n$$

$$A \quad I_m$$

and, as in the computation of A^{-1}, apply elementary operations to obtain

$$Q$$

$$\begin{bmatrix} I_r & 0 \\ 0 & 0 \end{bmatrix} P.$$

Illustrative
Example

For

$$A = \begin{bmatrix} 1 & 0 & 1 \\ 2 & 0 & 2 \end{bmatrix}$$

with elements in R_a, find matrices P and Q effective for the corollary of Theorem 7. A row operation gives

$$\begin{bmatrix} 1 & 0 & 1 \\ 2 & 0 & 2 \end{bmatrix}\begin{bmatrix} 1 & 0 \\ 0 & 1 \end{bmatrix} \rightarrow \begin{bmatrix} 1 & 0 & 1 \\ 0 & 0 & 0 \end{bmatrix}\begin{bmatrix} 1 & 0 \\ -2 & 1 \end{bmatrix}.$$

A column operation then yields

$$\begin{bmatrix} 1 & 0 & 0 \\ 0 & 1 & 0 \\ 0 & 0 & 1 \end{bmatrix} \quad \begin{bmatrix} 1 & 0 & -1 \\ 0 & 1 & 0 \\ 0 & 0 & 1 \end{bmatrix}$$

$$\xrightarrow{}$$

$$\begin{bmatrix} 1 & 0 & 1 \\ 0 & 0 & 0 \end{bmatrix} \quad \begin{bmatrix} 1 & 0 & 0 \\ 0 & 0 & 0 \end{bmatrix}$$

so that

$$P = \begin{bmatrix} 1 & 0 \\ -2 & 1 \end{bmatrix}, \qquad Q = \begin{bmatrix} 1 & 0 & -1 \\ 0 & 1 & 0 \\ 0 & 0 & 1 \end{bmatrix}.$$

It is easy to verify that

$$PAQ = \begin{bmatrix} 1 & 0 & 0 \\ 0 & 0 & 0 \end{bmatrix}.$$

It should be observed that P and Q are by no means uniquely determined by A.

Theorem 8

If A is in D_m and A has a right (left) inverse X, then A is nonsingular and $X = A^{-1}$.

PROOF   Let $AX = I_m$; then the kernel of A is zero and A is nonsingular by Theorems 1 and 5. If $XA = I_m$, then the row space of A is $V_m(D)$, since $x = xXA$ for every $x \in V_m(D)$. Hence A is nonsingular, by Theorem 5.

Appendix I: Column Rank versus Row Rank

We have defined the *column rank* of a matrix A as the row rank of A^T. We may now easily see that the row and column ranks of A are the same. For, if PAQ has the form (2), with P and Q nonsingular matrices of elements of D, then $Q^T A^T P^T$ has an analogous form with the same value of r. Since Q^T and P^T are nonsingular matrices with elements in D^o, it follows that $r =$ the column rank of $A =$ the row rank of A.

Appendix II: Row Rank versus
Determinant Rank

Let $D = F$ be a field, and let A be an m-by-n matrix of elements of F. By a *minor* of A we mean the determinant of a square matrix obtained by deleting some (but not all) of the rows and some (but not all) of the columns of A. If all $(s + 1)$-rowed minors of A vanish while some s-rowed minor of A does not vanish, then s is called the *determinant rank of A*. We shall prove that the determinant rank of A and the row rank of A are the same. Let A have a nonzero s-rowed minor. Using operations of

Type I, which alter neither row nor determinant rank, we may assume that A has the form

$$\begin{bmatrix} A_{11} & A_{12} \\ A_{21} & A_{22} \end{bmatrix},$$

where A_{11} is a nonsingular s-by-s matrix. Elementary operations that certainly do not change row rank will yield

$$\begin{bmatrix} I_s & 0 \\ 0 & B \end{bmatrix},$$

from which it is clear that $s \leq$ row rank of A. Hence the determinant rank of A is at most equal to the row rank of A. On the other hand, with r the row rank of A, let us choose r rows of A which form a basis for the row space of A and delete the remaining rows of A. The column rank of the resulting matrix is also r, and we may choose r of these columns which are F-li. Deleting the other columns, we obtain an r-by-r matrix whose columns are F-li and which is therefore nonsingular (by Theorem 5). Call this matrix C. Since $CC^{-1} = I_r$, then $\det C \neq 0$. Thus C provides us with an r-rowed minor of A which is nonzero. This proves that the determinant rank of A is at least as great as the row rank of A. This completes the proof that the row rank and the determinant rank of A are the same.

A final word: from here on we often use the single word "rank" in place of the phrases "row rank," "column rank," "determinant rank," since all of these phrases mean the same thing.

/ 3 / MATRIC SOLUTION OF

LINEAR EQUATIONS

In this section we shall derive the basic theorems on the solution of linear equations by using matric algebra.

We are not forced to assume that the scalars form a field. All the results of this section are valid for arbitrary division rings.

Let D be a division ring and let $A = [\alpha_{ij}]$, where $i = 1, \cdots, m$ and $j = 1, \cdots, n$, be a matrix with elements in D. We are interested in the following system of linear equations

(1) $$\sum_{i=1}^{m} \xi_i \alpha_{ij} = \gamma_j \ (j = 1, \cdots, n).$$

We assume that $\gamma_j \in D$, where $j = 1, \cdots, n$, and we seek solutions $\xi_i \in D$, where $i = 1, \cdots, m$. Adopting matrix notation,

$$x = [\xi_1, \cdots, \xi_m], \qquad c = [\gamma_1, \cdots, \gamma_n],$$

we write (1) as

(2) $$xA = c.$$

Using Theorems 3 and 7, we obtain

$$PAQ = \begin{bmatrix} I_r & 0 \\ 0 & 0 \end{bmatrix}$$

with r the row rank of A, and with P and Q nonsingular matrices of elements in D. Then (2) is equivalent to

$$xP^{-1}\begin{bmatrix} I_r & 0 \\ 0 & 0 \end{bmatrix} = cQ.$$

Now put $xP^{-1} = [y, z]$ and $cQ = [d, e]$, where y, $d \in V_r(D)$. Then (2) is equivalent to $y = d$ and $0 = e$. If $0 \neq e$, the equation (2) has no solution, but if $0 = e$, then $x = [d, z]P$ gives all solutions as z varies over $V_{m-r}(D)$. If $r = m$, we omit z, and obtain the solution $x = dP$ or no solution according as $e = 0$ or $e \neq 0$. If $r = n$, we omit e, $cQ = d$ and (2) has the solution $x = [d, z]P$.

Illustrative
Example

Solve the following equations in R_a:

$$\begin{aligned}
\xi_1 + \xi_2 - \xi_3 &= 1, \\
\xi_1 + 2\xi_2 + \xi_3 &= 0, \\
3\xi_1 + 5\xi_2 + \xi_3 &= 1.
\end{aligned}$$

Here the matric form is

$$[\xi_1, \xi_2, \xi_3]\begin{bmatrix} 1 & 1 & 3 \\ 1 & 2 & 5 \\ -1 & 1 & 1 \end{bmatrix} = [1, 0, 1].$$

With

$$A = \begin{bmatrix} 1 & 1 & 3 \\ 1 & 2 & 5 \\ -1 & 1 & 1 \end{bmatrix}, \qquad P = \begin{bmatrix} 1 & 0 & 0 \\ -1 & 1 & 0 \\ 3 & -2 & 1 \end{bmatrix},$$

$$Q = \begin{bmatrix} 1 & -1 & -1 \\ 0 & 1 & -2 \\ 0 & 0 & 1 \end{bmatrix},$$

we have

$$PAQ = \begin{bmatrix} 1 & 0 & 0 \\ 0 & 1 & 0 \\ 0 & 0 & 0 \end{bmatrix}.$$

Then $r = 2$, and

$$cQ = [1, 0, 1]\begin{bmatrix} 1 & -1 & -1 \\ 0 & 1 & -2 \\ 0 & 0 & 1 \end{bmatrix} = [1, -1, 0],$$

so that $d = [1, -1]$ and $e = 0$; then $xP^{-1} = [d, z] = [1, -1, \zeta]$
and

$$x = [\xi_1, \xi_2, \xi_3] = [1, -1, \zeta]\begin{bmatrix} 1 & 0 & 0 \\ -1 & 1 & 0 \\ 3 & -2 & 1 \end{bmatrix}$$

$$= [2 + 3\zeta, -1 - 2\zeta, \zeta]$$

so that

$$\xi_1 = 2 + 3\zeta, \qquad \xi_2 = -1 - 2\zeta, \qquad \xi_3 = \zeta$$

yield all solutions of our equations in R_a provided ζ is permitted to take every rational value.

From this discussion we may deduce the usual theorems about the equation (2).

Theorem 9

The equation (2) has a solution x in $V_m(D)$ if and only if the matrices A and $\begin{bmatrix} A \\ c \end{bmatrix}$ have the same (row) rank.

PROOF We have seen that the equation (2) has a solution x in $V_m(D)$ if and only if $e = 0$. But this occurs if and only if

$$\begin{bmatrix} P & 0 \\ 0 & 1 \end{bmatrix}\begin{bmatrix} A \\ c \end{bmatrix}Q = \begin{bmatrix} PAQ \\ cQ \end{bmatrix} = \begin{bmatrix} I_r & 0 \\ 0 & 0 \\ d & 0 \end{bmatrix},$$

that is, if and only if $\begin{bmatrix} A \\ c \end{bmatrix}$ has (row) rank r. (If $r=n$, e is omitted, (2) always has a solution and the condition of our theorem always holds.)

Theorem 10

If $c = 0$, then the equation (2) has a solution $x \neq 0$ if and only if the (row) rank of A is less than m.

Theorem 11

If $c = 0$ and $n < m$, then the equation (2) has a solution $x \neq 0$ in $V_m(D)$.

/4/ CRAMER'S RULE

In many applications, particularly in analysis and in applied mathematics, *theoretical* use is made of determinants in solving systems of linear equations. The purpose of this section is to derive the rule for doing this.

Let R be a commutative ring with identity element 1, and consider the system of linear equations

(1) $$\sum_{j=1}^{n} a_{ij}x_j = c_i \qquad (i = 1, \cdots, n),$$

where a_{ij} and c_i are in R $(i, j = 1, \cdots, n)$. We wish to solve for x_j in R $(j = 1, \cdots, n)$. We write our equations in matric form as

$$AX = C$$

with $A = [a_{ij}]$ $(i, j = 1, \cdots, n)$; $X^T = [x_1, \cdots, x_n]$; and $C^T = [c_1, \cdots, c_n]$. Multiplying on the left by adj A, we obtain

$$(\text{adj } A)AX = (\text{adj } A)C.$$

Now the elements of the ith *row* of adj A are the cofactors of the elements of the ith *column* of A. Thus the ith component of $(\text{adj } A)C$ is the determinant of the matrix C_i obtained by replacing the ith column of A by the column of constant terms, C. Thus we have our rule, as follows.

Cramer's Rule: If A is the matrix of coefficients in (1) and C_i is the matrix obtained from A by replacing the ith column of A by the column $[c_1, \cdots, c_n]^T$, then

$$x_i(\det A) = \det C_i \qquad (i = 1, \cdots, n).$$

If, also, det A is nonsingular in R, then

$$x_i = (\det A)^{-1}(\det C_i) \qquad (i = 1, \cdots, n)$$

is the unique solution of (1) for x_i in R.

Illustrative
Example

Discuss the equations

$$2x_1 - x_2 = 1,$$
$$x_1 + 2x_2 = 0,$$

in Z and in R_a. Here

$$A = \begin{bmatrix} 2 & -1 \\ 1 & 2 \end{bmatrix}, \qquad C_1 = \begin{bmatrix} 1 & -1 \\ 0 & 2 \end{bmatrix}, \qquad C_2 = \begin{bmatrix} 2 & 1 \\ 1 & 0 \end{bmatrix},$$

and Cramer's Rule gives

$$5x_1 = 2, \qquad 5x_2 = -1.$$

Since det $A = 5$ has no inverse in Z, our equations have no solutions in Z. However, det $A = 5$ does have an inverse in R_a, and $x_1 = 2/5$ and $x_2 = -1/5$ are the unique solutions in R_a.

EXERCISES FOR CHAPTER 6

1. For the matrix

$$A = \begin{bmatrix} 1 & 0 & 2 \\ 2 & 0 & 4 \\ 0 & 0 & 0 \\ 1 & 0 & 2 \end{bmatrix}$$

with elements in R_a, find the row rank of A and the nullity of A and test Sylvester's Law.

2. Repeat Exercise 1 for

$$A = \begin{bmatrix} 1 & 0 & 0 \\ 0 & 0 & 1 \end{bmatrix}.$$

3. Repeat Exercise 1 for

$$A = \begin{bmatrix} 1 & 0 \\ 2 & 0 \\ 3 & 0 \end{bmatrix}.$$

4. Repeat Exercise 1 for

$$A = \begin{bmatrix} i & j & k \\ -1 & k & -j \end{bmatrix}$$

of elements of $\mathscr{2}$.

5. Compute the row rank of

$$A = \begin{bmatrix} 1 & 2 & 2 & 0 \\ 0 & 1 & 2 & 3 \\ 0 & 0 & 1 & 2 \end{bmatrix}$$

of elements of R_a.

6. Repeat Exercise 5 for

$$A = \begin{bmatrix} 1 & -1 & 3 & 7 \\ 2 & 3 & 4 & 1 \\ 3 & 2 & 7 & 8 \end{bmatrix}.$$

7. Compute the row rank of the following, in $\mathcal{Q}_3$,

$$A = \begin{bmatrix} 0 & i & j \\ i & 0 & k \\ j & k & 0 \end{bmatrix}.$$

8. Use elementary operations to find A^{-1}, where A has elements in R_a and

$$A = \begin{bmatrix} 1 & 0 & 2 \\ 2 & 2 & 1 \\ -1 & 3 & 4 \end{bmatrix}.$$

9. Repeat Exercise 7 for

$$A = \begin{bmatrix} 1 & -1 & 1 \\ 2 & -2 & 3 \\ 4 & -3 & 4 \end{bmatrix}.$$

10. Suppose one starts with a matrix A which is singular, and tries to find A^{-1} by the method of elementary operations. What happens?

11, 12, 13, 14. Find matrices P and Q effective in the corollary of Theorem 7 for the matrices of Exercises 1, 2, 3, and 4.

15. Solve in the rational field:

$$\xi_1 + 2\xi_2 - \xi_3 + \xi_4 = 3,$$
$$2\xi_1 - \xi_2 + \xi_3 - \xi_4 = 1.$$

16. Repeat Exercise 15 for

$$\xi_1 + \xi_2 = 2, \qquad \xi_1 - \xi_2 = 0,$$
$$3\xi_1 - \xi_2 = 2, \qquad 7\xi_1 - 5\xi_2 = 2.$$

17. Discuss the system

$$\xi_1 \mathbf{i} + \xi_2 \mathbf{j} = \mathbf{k},$$
$$\xi_1 \mathbf{j} + \xi_2 \mathbf{i} = \mathbf{i}.$$

18. Apply Cramer's Rule in Z and in R_a to the equations

$$x_1 - 2x_2 = 2,$$
$$3x_1 - 5x_2 = 4.$$

19. Repeat Exercise 18 for the equations

$$5x_1 - x_2 + 2x_3 = 3,$$
$$x_1 + 2x_2 - x_3 = 1,$$
$$2x_1 + 3x_2 + 4x_3 = -2.$$

20. In Cramer's Rule, is it possible that $\det A$ have no inverse in R and the linear equations still have a unique solution?

21. Show that rank $(A + B) \leq$ rank A + rank B.

22. Show that if rank $(A + B) =$ rank A + rank B, then $R_A \cap R_B = 0$ and $R_A + R_B = R_{A+B}$.

23. Show that, if rank $(A + B) =$ rank A + rank B and if $AB = BA$, then $AB = 0$.

24. Let A be an m-by-n matrix with elements in a division ring D. Show that there is an n-by-m matrix X with elements in D such that $AXA = A$ and $XAX = X$. (Let $C = PAQ$ have the form of Theorem 3. Show that $X = QC^{\mathrm{T}}P$ works.) The matrix X is called a generalized inverse of A.

25, 26, 27. Compute a generalized inverse for the matrix A of Exercises 5, 6, and 7.

28. Show that, if $A^2 = A$ for A in D_n, where D is a division ring, then $V_n(D) = R_A + K_A$ and $R_A \cap K_A = 0$.

29. If A is in D_n, where D is a division ring, and if $V_n(D) = R_A + K_A$ and $R_A \cap K_A = 0$, is it true that $A^2 = A$?

30. Let $A \neq 0$ be an m-by-n matrix with elements in a division ring D. Using row operations alone, show that A may be replaced by a matrix

$$\begin{bmatrix} B_1 \\ 0 \end{bmatrix}$$

such that the rows of B_1 are nonzero, the first nonzero element
of the ith row of B_1 is $b_{ij_i} = 1$, and $j_1 < j_2 < \cdots < j_r$. [*Hint:*
Let the first nonzero column of A be the jth. Permute rows so
that the first row has a nonzero jth entry. Use elementary
operations to obtain

$$\begin{bmatrix} 0 & 1 & C_1 \\ 0 & 0 & C_2 \end{bmatrix}.$$

Repeat the process on C_2.]

31. Let $x_1, \cdots, x_m$ be vectors of $V_n(D)$. Show how the procedure
of Exercise 30 leads to a basis for $\langle x_1, \cdots, x_m \rangle$.

32. Find a basis for $\langle (0, 2, 0, 1), (0, 1, 1, 0), (0, 1, 0, 2), (0, 1, 1, -1) \rangle$
by the procedure of Exercise 31.

7

FINITE GAMES

The applications of matric theory to linear inequalities are varied and extensive. Although we think that a complete discussion of them is not consistent with the aims of this text, the present chapter is included as a brief introduction to this interesting and very useful topic. Our purpose is to present an algorithmic proof of Von Neumann's basic theorem on finite games of strategy. We have chosen to use the proof due to Dantzig (a variant of the simplex method). We make no attempt to discuss more general problems (such as linear programming), for which the interested reader can consult many excellent texts.

/1/ FINITE ZERO-SUM
TWO-PERSON GAMES

Let two players, I and II, engage in a game. Let m moves be available to player I and n moves be available to player II. Let a_{ij} (possibly negative) be the payment to player I if he chooses move i and player II chooses move j. With what probability x_i should player I play the move i to maximize his expectation? If player II plays move j with probability y_j, then

$$E_I = \sum_{i=1}^{m} \sum_{j=1}^{n} x_i a_{ij} y_j$$

is the expectation of player I, while $-E_I$ is the expectation of player II.

For each choice of y_j's made by player II, player I should choose his x_i's so that E_I is a maximum, $y_0(y_1, \cdots, y_n)$, and for each choice of x_i's made by player I, player II should choose his y_j's so that E_I is a minimum, $x_0(x_1, \cdots, x_m)$. Since player I may take $x_i = 1$, clearly

$$\sum_{j=1}^{n} a_{ij} y_j \leq y_0(y_1, \cdots, y_n) \qquad (i = 1, \cdots, m),$$

and, likewise,

$$x_0(x_1, \cdots, x_m) \leq \sum_{i=1}^{m} x_i a_{ij} \qquad (j = 1, \cdots, n).$$

Hence,

$$x_0(x_1, \cdots, x_m) = x_0(x_1, \cdots, x_m) \sum_{j=1}^{n} y_j \leq E_I \leq y_0(y_1, \cdots, y_n) \sum_{i=1}^{m} x_i$$

$$= y_0(y_1, \cdots, y_n).$$

It is an interesting fact (sometimes called the fundamental theorem of game theory) that there are values† $\hat{x}_i$ $(i = 1, \cdots, m)$ and $\hat{y}_j$ $(j = 1, \cdots, n)$ such that the maximum of $x_0(x_1, \cdots, x_m)$ for all choices of the probabilities x_i (the *very* best that player I should expect) is the same as the minimum of $y_0(y_1, \cdots, y_n)$ (the *very* best that player II should expect). This common value is called the value of the game (on the market of a mathematically trained society). The sequence of values $\hat{x}_i$ $(i = 1, \cdots, m)$ is called an *optimal strategy* for player I, while the sequence of values $\hat{y}_j$ $(j = 1, \cdots, n)$ is called an *optimal strategy* for player II.

Consider the old paper, rock, and scissors game:

		Player II		
		P	R	S
	P	0	1	−1
Player I	R	−1	0	1
	S	1	−1	0

A bit of algebra shows that $E_I = 3(x_1 - 1/3)(y_2 - 1/3) - 3(x_2 - 1/3)(y_1 - 1/3)$. If player I chooses $x_1 = x_2 = x_3 = 1/3$, then $E_I = 0$, irrespective of what player II does. But if $x_1 \neq 1/3$, then player II can take $y_1 = 1/3$ and choose y_2 so as to make E_I negative. Player II can also inflict excess punishment on player I if $x_2 \neq 1/3$. It is hoped that the reader has not suffered this excess punishment. The value of the paper, rock, and scissors game is thus 0, and is attained for

$$\hat{x}_1 = \hat{x}_2 = \hat{x}_3 = \hat{y}_1 = \hat{y}_2 = \hat{y}_3 = 1/3.$$

We formulate our theorem mathematically as follows:

† In this chapter *only* we abandon the meaning we attached to the circumflex earlier. The usage adopted in this chapter is customary in game theory.

Von Neumann's Theorem

Let $A = [a_{ij}]$ $(i = 1, \cdots, m; j = 1, \cdots, n)$ be a matrix of real numbers; then among the real numbers $x_0, x_1, \cdots, x_m$, $y_0, y_1, \cdots, y_n$ which satisfy

$$x_i \geq 0 \quad (i = 1, \cdots, m) \qquad \text{and} \qquad y_j \geq 0 \quad (j = 1, \cdots, n),$$

$$\sum_{i=1}^{m} x_i = 1 \qquad \text{and} \qquad \sum_{j=1}^{n} y_j = 1,$$

$$x_0 \leq \sum_{i=1}^{m} x_i a_{ij} \qquad (j = 1, \cdots, n)$$

and

$$\sum_{j=1}^{n} a_{ij} y_j \leq y_0 \qquad (i = 1, \cdots, m),$$

there are two sequences $(\hat{x}_0, \hat{x}_1, \cdots, \hat{x}_m)$ and $(\hat{y}_0, \hat{y}_1, \cdots, \hat{y}_n)$ which satisfy $\hat{x}_0 = \hat{y}_0$.

Various proofs of this theorem are available. We choose to present one which is algorithmic and is suitable for numerical computation. Essential to this proof is a rule for finding the inverse of a matrix embodied in the following lemma.

Lemma

Let B be a nonsingular $(m + 1)$-by-$(m + 1)$ matrix of elements of a division ring partitioned into its columns

$$B = [C_0, C_1, \cdots, C_m]$$

and let β_i $(i = 0, \cdots, m)$ be the rows of B^{-1}. Let B^* be obtained from B by replacing C_r with C, and assume that $v_r = \beta_r C \neq 0$. Then the rows of $(B^*)^{-1}$ are given by

(1) $\beta_i^* = \beta_i - (v_i/v_r)\beta_r$ (where $i \neq r$) and $\beta_r^* = (1/v_r)\beta_r$

with $v_i = \beta_i C$ $(i = 0, \cdots, m)$.

PROOF   Compute the following:

$\beta_r^* C = (1/v_r)\beta_r C = 1,$
$\beta_i^* C = (\beta_i - (v_i/v_r)\beta_r)C = 0,$ where $i \neq r,$
$\beta_r^* C_i = (1/v_r)\beta_r C_i = 0,$ where $i \neq r,$
$\beta_i^* C_k = (\beta_i - (v_i/v_r)\beta_r)C_k = \beta_i C_k,$ where $i \neq r, k \neq r.$

This verifies that (1) defines a matrix X such that $XB^* = I$. It follows that $X = (B^*)^{-1}$.

/ 2 / DANTZIG'S PROOF OF VON NEUMANN'S THEOREM

The first step in our algorithm is to permute the rows of A to attain $a_{m1} \geq a_{i1}$ $(i = 1, \cdots, m)$. We then form the matrix

$$\begin{bmatrix} 0 & U & 0 \\ -U^{\mathrm{T}} & A & I \end{bmatrix} = [P_0, P_1, \cdots, P_{m+n}]$$

where $U = [1, 1, \cdots, 1]$ is a matrix of 1's.

Now it is desirable to introduce an ordering for our vectors. Let us write that $(w_1, \cdots, w_m) > (z_1, \cdots, z_m)$ if the first nonzero component of $(w_1 - z_1, \cdots, w_m - z_m)$ is positive; for example, $(2, 3, 1, 2) > (2, 3, 0, 4)$. Every finite set of vectors has a least vector, in the sense of this ordering, which we call the minimum vector in the set.

A matrix

$$B = [P_0, P_{j_1}, \cdots, P_{j_m}]$$

will be called a basis if B is nonsingular and if

$$B^{-1} = \begin{bmatrix} \beta_0 \\ \beta_1 \\ \vdots \\ \beta_m \end{bmatrix}$$

satisfies $\beta_i > 0$ $(i = 1, \cdots, m)$. Such bases exist, for we may choose

$$B_0 = [P_0, P_1, P_{n+1}, \cdots, P_{n+m-1}] = \begin{bmatrix} 0 & 1 & 0 & \cdots & 0 \\ -1 & a_{11} & 1 & \cdots & 0 \\ \vdots & \vdots & \vdots & & \vdots \\ -1 & a_{(m-1)1} & 0 & \cdots & 1 \\ -1 & a_{m1} & 0 & \cdots & 0 \end{bmatrix}$$

with inverse

$$
B_0{}^{-1} = \begin{bmatrix}
a_{m1} & & 0 & \cdots & 0 & -1 \\
1 & & 0 & \cdots & 0 & 0 \\
a_{m1} - a_{11} & & 1 & \cdots & 0 & -1 \\
\vdots & & \vdots & & \vdots & \vdots \\
a_{m1} - a_{(m-1)1} & & 0 & \cdots & 1 & -1
\end{bmatrix}
$$

for which $\beta_i > 0$ $(i = 1, \cdots, m)$. One may also note that there are only a finite number of such bases.

Suppose we have found a basis B that satisfies $\beta_0 P_j \leq 0$ $(j = 1, \cdots, m + n)$; then define $\hat{x}_0, \hat{x}_1, \cdots, \hat{x}_m$ by

$$
\beta_0 = [\hat{x}_0, -\hat{x}_1, \cdots, -\hat{x}_m]
$$

and let

$$
[\eta_0, \eta_{j_1}, \cdots, \eta_{j_m}]^{\mathrm{T}}
$$

be the 0th column of B^{-1}. Take $\hat{y}_0 = \eta_0$ and $\hat{y}_{j_i} = \eta_{j_i}$ if $j_i \leq n$, $\hat{y}_j = 0$ for all other j. Then these values of $\hat{x}_i$ and $\hat{y}_j$ satisfy our theorem, for

$$
\beta_0 P_0 = 1 \quad \text{is} \quad \sum_{i=1}^{m} \hat{x}_i = 1,
$$

$$
\beta_0 P_j \leq 0 \quad (j = 1, \cdots, n) \quad \text{gives} \quad \hat{x}_0 \leq \sum_{i=1}^{m} \hat{x}_i a_{ij} \quad (j = 1, \cdots, n),
$$

$$
\beta_0 P_j \leq 0 \quad (j = n+1, \cdots, n+m) \quad \text{gives} \quad 0 \leq \hat{x}_i \quad (i = 1, \cdots, m),
$$

$$
\beta_i > 0 \quad (i = 1, \cdots, m) \quad \text{gives} \quad \hat{y}_j \geq 0 \quad (j = 1, \cdots, n),
$$

$$
B \begin{bmatrix} \eta_0 \\ \eta_{j_1} \\ \vdots \\ \eta_{j_m} \end{bmatrix} = \begin{bmatrix} 1 \\ 0 \\ \vdots \\ 0 \end{bmatrix} \quad \text{gives} \quad \sum_{j=1}^{n} \hat{y}_j = 1,
$$

$$
\hat{y}_0 - \sum_{j_i \leq n} a_{kj_i} \hat{y}_{j_i} = \eta_{j_i} \text{ or } 0,
$$

according as $j_i = k + n$ or not; or, since

$$
\eta_{j_i} \geq 0, \quad \sum_{j=1}^{n} a_{ij} \hat{y}_j \leq \hat{y}_0.
$$

If we start with a basis B such that $\beta_0 P_j > 0$ for some $j = 1, \cdots, n + m$, we choose the least s such that $\beta_0 P_s$ is the maximum value of $\beta_0 P_j$ for $1 \le j \le m + n$. Let $V = B^{-1}P_s = (v_0, \cdots, v_m)^{\mathrm{T}}$. Then some $v_i > 0$, where $i = 1, \cdots, m$, for if $v_i \le 0$ $(i = 1, \cdots, m)$, then $P_s = BV = v_0 P_0 + \sum(v_i P_{j_i}; \ i = 1, \cdots, m)$ which, on examination of the initial component, gives $\sum(v_i; \ j_i \le n) = 1$ or 0, according as $s \le n$ or $s > n$. Since $v_i \le 0$ $(i = 1, \cdots, m)$, we must have $s > n$, and all $v_i = 0$ for $j_i \le n$. For $j_i > n$ and $s > n$, examining the $(s - n)$th component gives $1 + v_0 = v_i$ or 0 according as $j_i = s$ or not, which is impossible because $v_0 > 0$ and $v_i \le 0$. We have proved that $v_i > 0$ for some $i = 1, \cdots, m$.

Among those integers $i \ne 0$ for which $v_i > 0$, choose the minimum of the vectors β_i/v_i and let this minimum occur for $i = r$. Note that we have

(1) $$\beta_i - (v_i/v_r)\beta_r > 0, \qquad \text{if } v_i > 0.$$

We now replace column P_{j_r} of B with P_s and obtain a matrix B^* whose inverse, by the lemma, has rows

$$\beta_i^* = \beta_i - (v_i/v_r)\beta_r, \qquad (i \ne r),$$
$$\beta_r^* = (1/v_r)\beta_r.$$

Using (1), we see that $\beta_i^* > 0$, where $i = 1, \cdots, m$, since $\beta_i > 0$, where $i = 1, \cdots, m$. Hence B^* is a new basis. Also $\beta_0^* < \beta_0$ since $r \ne 0$, $v_0 > 0$, $v_r > 0$ and $\beta_r > 0$.

This selection of a sequence of bases with β_0 strictly decreasing cannot go on forever, so that we finally arrive at a basis B such that $\beta_0 P_j \le 0$ $(j = 1, \cdots, m + n)$.

For the case of the rock, paper, and scissors, we construct the matrix

$$P = \begin{bmatrix} 0 & 1 & 1 & 1 & 0 & 0 & 0 \\ -1 & 0 & 1 & -1 & 1 & 0 & 0 \\ -1 & -1 & 0 & 1 & 0 & 1 & 0 \\ -1 & 1 & -1 & 0 & 0 & 0 & 1 \end{bmatrix},$$

$$B_0 = \begin{bmatrix} 0 & 1 & 0 & 0 \\ -1 & 0 & 1 & 0 \\ -1 & -1 & 0 & 1 \\ -1 & 1 & 0 & 0 \end{bmatrix}, \qquad B_0^{-1} = \begin{bmatrix} 1 & 0 & 0 & -1 \\ 1 & 0 & 0 & 0 \\ 1 & 1 & 0 & -1 \\ 2 & 0 & 1 & -1 \end{bmatrix},$$

$$\beta_0 P = [1, 0, 2, 1, 0, 0, -1], \qquad s = 2,$$

$$V = B_0^{-1} P_2 = [2, 1, 3, 3]^T, \qquad r = 2,$$

$$B_0{}^* = \begin{bmatrix} 0 & 1 & 1 & 0 \\ -1 & 0 & 1 & 0 \\ -1 & -1 & 0 & 1 \\ -1 & 1 & -1 & 0 \end{bmatrix},$$

$$(B_0{}^*)^{-1} = \begin{bmatrix} 1/3 & -2/3 & 0 & -1/3 \\ 2/3 & -1/3 & 0 & 1/3 \\ 1/3 & 1/3 & 0 & -1/3 \\ 1 & -1 & 1 & 0 \end{bmatrix},$$

$$\beta_0{}^* P = [1, 0, 0, 1, -2/3, 0, -1/3], \qquad s = 3,$$

$$V^* = (B_0{}^*)^{-1} P_3 = [1, 1, 0, 3]^T, \qquad r = 3,$$

$$B_0{}^{**} = \begin{bmatrix} 0 & 1 & 1 & 1 \\ -1 & 0 & 1 & -1 \\ -1 & -1 & 0 & 1 \\ -1 & 1 & -1 & 0 \end{bmatrix},$$

$$(B_0{}^{**})^{-1} = \begin{bmatrix} 0 & -1/3 & -1/3 & -1/3 \\ 1/3 & 0 & -1/3 & 1/3 \\ 1/3 & 1/3 & 0 & -1/3 \\ 1/3 & -1/3 & 1/3 & 0 \end{bmatrix},$$

$$\beta_0{}^{**} P = [1, 0, 0, 0, -1/3, -1/3, -1/3].$$

Hence, $\hat{x}_i = 1/3$ and $\hat{y}_j = 1/3$ give probabilities for which $\hat{x}_0 = \hat{y}_0 = 0$.

It may be worth while to work through a less trivial illustrative example. Let

$$A = \begin{bmatrix} 4 & -1 & 0 & 2 & 1 \\ 2 & -2 & 3 & 2 & -1 \\ -1 & 0 & -4 & 2 & 2 \end{bmatrix}.$$

Permuting the rows of A, we construct

$$P = \begin{bmatrix} 0 & 1 & 1 & 1 & 1 & 1 & 0 & 0 & 0 \\ -1 & -1 & 0 & -4 & 2 & 2 & 1 & 0 & 0 \\ -1 & 2 & -2 & 3 & 2 & -1 & 0 & 1 & 0 \\ -1 & 4 & -1 & 0 & 2 & 1 & 0 & 0 & 1 \end{bmatrix}.$$

Here we have

$$B_0 = \begin{bmatrix} 0 & 1 & 0 & 0 \\ -1 & -1 & 1 & 0 \\ -1 & 2 & 0 & 1 \\ -1 & 4 & 0 & 0 \end{bmatrix}, \quad B_0^{-1} = \begin{bmatrix} 4 & 0 & 0 & -1 \\ 1 & 0 & 0 & 0 \\ 5 & 1 & 0 & -1 \\ 2 & 0 & 1 & -1 \end{bmatrix},$$

$$\beta_0 P = [1, 0, 5, 4, 2, 3, 0, 0, -1], \quad s = 2,$$

$$V = B_0^{-1} P_2 = [5, 1, 6, 1]^{\mathrm{T}}, \quad r = 2,$$

$$B_0^* = \begin{bmatrix} 0 & 1 & 1 & 0 \\ -1 & -1 & 0 & 0 \\ -1 & 2 & -2 & 1 \\ -1 & 4 & -1 & 0 \end{bmatrix},$$

$$(B_0^*)^{-1} = \begin{bmatrix} -1/6 & -5/6 & 0 & -1/6 \\ 1/6 & -1/6 & 0 & 1/6 \\ 5/6 & 1/6 & 0 & -1/6 \\ 7/6 & -1/6 & 1 & -5/6 \end{bmatrix},$$

$$\beta_0^* P = [1, 0, 0, 19/6, -13/6, -12/6, -5/6, 0, -1/6], \quad s = 3,$$

$$V^* = (B_0^*)^{-1} P_3 = [19/6, 5/6, 1/6, 29/6]^{\mathrm{T}}, \quad r = 1.$$

$$B_0^{**} = \begin{bmatrix} 0 & 1 & 1 & 0 \\ -1 & -4 & 0 & 0 \\ -1 & 3 & -2 & 1 \\ -1 & 0 & -1 & 0 \end{bmatrix},$$

$$(B_0^{**})^{-1} = \begin{bmatrix} -4/5 & -1/5 & 0 & -4/5 \\ 1/5 & -1/5 & 0 & 1/5 \\ 4/5 & 1/5 & 0 & -1/5 \\ 1/5 & 4/5 & 1 & -9/5 \end{bmatrix},$$

$$\beta_0{}^{**}P = [1, \ -19/5, \ 0, \ 0, \ -14/5, \ -2, \ -1/5, \ 0, \ -4/5].$$

Hence, $(\hat{x}_1, \hat{x}_2, \hat{x}_3) = (1/5, 0, 4/5)$, $\hat{y}_3 = 1/5$, $\hat{y}_2 = 4/5$, and all other $\hat{y}_j = 0$, and so $(\hat{y}_1, \hat{y}_2, \hat{y}_3, \hat{y}_4, \hat{y}_5) = (0, 4/5, 1/5, 0, 0)$. The value of E_I (the expectation of player I) is $\hat{x}_0 = \hat{y}_0 = -4/5$. The probabilities $(\hat{x}_1, \hat{x}_2, \hat{x}_3)$ refer to the game after permutation of the rows of A. The optimal probabilities in terms of the original matrix are $(4/5, 0, 1/5)$ for player I.

EXERCISES FOR CHAPTER 7

1, 2, 3, 4. For the following matrices, A, compute the optimal strategies.

$$A = \begin{bmatrix} 1 & 0 & -2 \\ 2 & -3 & 1 \end{bmatrix}$$

$$A = \begin{bmatrix} 1 & -1 & 1 & -1 \\ -1 & 0 & 1 & 1 \end{bmatrix}$$

$$A = \begin{bmatrix} 1 & 1 & 1 & 1 \\ 2 & -3 & 2 & -4 \end{bmatrix}$$

$$A = \begin{bmatrix} 1 & 0 & 0 & -1 & 2 \\ 0 & 1 & 1 & -1 & -1 \\ 1 & 0 & 1 & 2 & 3 \end{bmatrix}.$$

8

LINEAR TRANSFORMATIONS AND MATRICES

In this chapter we shall connect matrices with maps of one finite-dimensional vector space into another; the maps are linear in that they preserve the vector space structure. We then discuss transformation of coordinates in a finite-dimensional vector space and find the relationship between two matrices that describe the same linear map relative to different coordinate systems.

/ 1 /   LINEAR

TRANSFORMATIONS

In this section we define and illustrate the concept of linear transformation. We then show how this concept is related to matric theory when the vector spaces involved are finite-dimensional.

Let X and Y be D vector spaces, D a division ring, and let L be a map of X into Y; that is, for each vector x in X there is a uniquely determined vector $y = L(x)$ in Y. We call L a D *linear transformation*, a D-lt, of X *into* Y whenever L preserves the vector space operations in the sense that

(1) $L(x + x') = L(x) + L(x'), \qquad L(\alpha x) = \alpha L(x)$

for every x and x' in X and every α in D.

Let us give a few examples of D linear transformations. We may observe first that an isomorphism f of a D vector space X onto a D vector space X' is automatically a D-lt of X into X'.

Example 1   Let A be an m-by-n matrix of elements of D. Then xA is in $V_n(D)$ for every x in $V_m(D)$ and $L(x) = xA$ defines a D-lt L of $V_m(D)$ into $V_n(D)$.

Example 2   Let $X = Y = R_e$, regarded as an R_a vector space. Let c be a fixed real number and define $L(x) = cx$ for every x in R_e. Then L is an R_a-lt of R_e into R_e.

Example 3   Let $X = C(R_e)$ and $Y = R_e$ be regarded as R_e vector spaces. Define $L(f) = \int_0^1 f(t) \, dt$ where $f(t)$ is in $C(R_e)$. Then L is an R_e-lt of $C(R_e)$ into R_e.

Example 4   Let $X = C'(R_e)$ and $Y = C(R_e)$, and, for $f(t)$ in $C'(R_e)$, define $L(f) = f'$. Then L is an R_e-lt of $C'(R_e)$ into $C(R_e)$.

Example 5   Let $X = C''(R_e)$ and $Y = C(R_e)$, and, for $f(t)$ in $C''(R_e)$, define $L(f) = f'' + g(t)f' + h(t)f$, where $g(t)$ and $h(t)$ are fixed elements in $C(R_e)$. Then $L(f)$ is an R_e-lt of $C''(R_e)$ into $C(R_e)$.

Our next task is to relate linear transformations to matrices, when the D vector spaces X and Y are finite-dimensional (true in only the first of the examples we have given).

When the D vector spaces X and Y are finite-dimensional and L is a D-lt of X into Y, let us choose D bases $x_1, \cdots, x_m$ and $y_1, \cdots, y_n$, of X and Y respectively. Then each vector $L(x_i)$ $(i = 1, \cdots, m)$, being in Y, is a D linear combination of the vectors y_j $(j = 1, \cdots, n)$, as follows:

$$(2) \qquad L(x_i) = \sum_{j=1}^{n} \alpha_{ij} y_j \qquad (i = 1, \cdots, m).$$

Thus L and the D bases $x_1, \cdots, x_m$ and $y_1, \cdots, y_n$ produce a matrix $A = [\alpha_{ij}]$ $(i = 1, \cdots, m; j = 1, \cdots, n)$. We call A the *matrix of L relative to the D bases $x_1, \cdots, x_m$ and $y_1, \cdots, y_n$ of X and Y*. One should note especially that the *order* of the vectors in the D bases $x_1, \cdots, x_m$ and $y_1, \cdots, y_n$ is vital. For example, interchanging x_1 and x_2 has the effect of interchanging the first and second rows of the matrix A. Since coordinates are uniquely determined by a basis, we see that the matrix A is uniquely determined by L and the two bases of X and of Y. In the last section of this chapter we shall discuss the effect on A of changing bases in X and in Y.

Let us determine the relation between the coordinates of x and $L(x)$. If $x = \xi_1 x_1 + \cdots + \xi_m x_m$, we may use (2) to see that

$$L(x) = \sum(\xi_i \alpha_{ij} y_j; \quad i = 1, \cdots, m, \quad j = 1, \cdots, n).$$

Thus, if the coordinates of x are $\xi = (\xi_1, \cdots, \xi_m)$, then the coordinates of $L(x)$ are $\eta = (\eta_1, \cdots, \eta_n)$ where

$$\eta = \xi A.$$

Illustrative
Example

Let $L((1, 2)) = (1, 0, 2)$ and $L((2, 1)) = (1, -1, 1)$. What is the matrix of L relative to the bases $(1, 0)$, $(0, 1)$, and $(1, 0, 0)$, $(0, 1, 0)$, $(0, 0, 1)$? Since $(1, 0) = (-1/3)(1, 2) + (2/3)(2, 1)$, we find that $L((1, 0)) = (-1/3)(1, 0, 2) + (2/3)(1, -1, 1) = (1/3, -2/3, 0)$. Similarly, $(0, 1) = (2/3)(1, 2) - (1/3)(2, 1)$ and $L((0, 1)) = (2/3)(1, 0, 2) - (1/3)(1, -1, 1) = (1/3, 1/3, 1)$. The required matrix is, therefore,

$$A = \begin{bmatrix} 1/3 & -2/3 & 0 \\ 1/3 & 1/3 & 1 \end{bmatrix}.$$

Conversely, two D bases $x_1, \cdots, x_m$ and $y_1, \cdots, y_n$ of X and Y respectively, together with an m-by-n matrix A of elements of D, uniquely determine a D-lt of X into Y. First we define $L(x_i)$ by (2). Then, since every x in X has the form

$$x = \sum_{i=1}^{m} \xi_i x_i,$$

where the coordinates ξ_i are elements of D uniquely determined by x, we define

$$L(x) = \sum_{i, j} \xi_i \alpha_{ij} y_j.$$

It is easy to verify that the resulting map L of X into Y is a D-lt.

The case in which the matrix A of a D-lt of X into Y is nonsingular is covered by the following useful theorem.

Theorem 1

Let X and Y be finite-dimensional D vector spaces of the same dimension n. Let L be a D-lt of X into Y and let A be the matrix of L relative to D bases $x_1, \cdots, x_n$ and $y_1, \cdots, y_n$, of X

and Y respectively. Then the following statements are all equivalent.

(3)	L	is an isomorphism of X onto Y.
(4)	L	is faithful.
(5)	L	is onto.
(6)	A	is nonsingular.
(7)	A	has a right inverse.
(8)	A	has a left inverse.

PROOF   Using coordinates, we see that (4) holds if and only if $\xi A = 0$ implies $\xi = 0$; that is, if and only if the kernel of A is zero. Next, (5) holds if and only if every vector of Y has the form ξA for some $\xi \in V_n(D)$; that is, the row space of A is Y. Hence (4) and (5) are equivalent to the statement "rank $A = n$." It follows from our study of rank that all the statements (4) to (8) are equivalent. Since (3) is clearly equivalent to the conjunction of (4) and (5), the proof is complete.

/2/ SOURCE OF THE DEFINITION OF MATRIC MULTIPLICATION

In this section we shall finally explain why matrices must be multiplied as defined in Chapter 1. Once we have this reason clearly in mind we will be prepared to discuss transformation of coordinates (change of basis) in a finite-dimensional vector space.

Let D be a division ring, let L be a D-lt of a D vector space X into a D vector space Y, and let M be a D-lt of Y into a D vector space Z. Then, for each x in X, $M(L(x))$ is a uniquely defined vector in Z and there is a map, $M \circ L$ of X into Z, defined by $(M \circ L)(x) = M(L(x))$ for every x in X. The map $M \circ L$ is a D-lt of X into Z, since

$$(M \circ L)(x + x') = M(L(x + x')) = M(L(x) + L(x'))$$
$$= M(L(x)) + M(L(x'))$$
$$= (M \circ L)(x) + (M \circ L)(x')$$

and

$$(M \circ L)(\alpha x) = M(L(\alpha x)) = \alpha M(L(x)) = \alpha((M \circ L)(x)),$$

for every x and x' in X and every α in D. It is customary to call $M \circ L$ the *composite* of the maps M and L, and we have proved that the composite of two D-lt's is again a D-lt.

Now assume that the spaces X, Y, and Z of the preceding paragraph are finite-dimensional and that D bases $x_1, \cdots, x_m$, $y_1, \cdots, y_n$, and $z_1, \cdots, z_s$ are chosen for X, Y, and Z respectively. Let

$$L(x_i) = \sum_{j=1}^{n} \alpha_{ij} y_j \qquad (i = 1, \cdots, m),$$

$$M(y_j) = \sum_{k=1}^{s} \beta_{jk} z_k \qquad (j = 1, \cdots, n),$$

so that $A = [\alpha_{ij}]$ is the matrix of L relative to the bases $x_1, \cdots, x_m$ and $y_1, \cdots, y_n$, while $B = [\beta_{jk}]$ is the matrix of M relative to the bases $y_1, \cdots, y_n$ and $z_1, \cdots, z_s$. We seek the matrix of $M \circ L$ relative to the bases $x_1, \cdots, x_m$ and $z_1, \cdots, z_s$. We find that

$$(M \circ L)(x_i) = M(L(x_i)) = M\left(\sum_{j=1}^{n} \alpha_{ij} y_j \right) = \sum_{j=1}^{n} \alpha_{ij} M(y_j)$$

$$= \sum_{k=1}^{s} \sum_{j=1}^{n} \alpha_{ij} \beta_{jk} z_k \qquad (i = 1, \cdots, m),$$

from which it is clear that AB is the matrix of $M \circ L$ relative to the bases $x_1, \cdots, x_m$ and $z_1, \cdots, z_s$.

We now see that matric multiplication is naturally associated with the composition of two D-lt's, just as a single matrix is naturally associated with a single D-lt.

It may be well to record the discussion of this section in a diagram. Let the following diagram

$$
\begin{array}{ccc}
X & \xrightarrow{\quad\quad L \quad\quad} & Y \\
x_1, \cdots, x_m & A & y_1, \cdots, y_n
\end{array}
$$

indicate the D-lt L of X into Y, whose matrix, relative to the bases $x_1, \cdots, x_m$ of X and $y_1, \cdots, y_n$ of Y is A. Then we have the very useful diagram

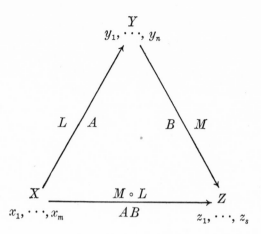

/ 3 / TRANSFORMATION OF COORDINATES

We shall use the results of the preceding section to find the relationship between two different bases of the same finite-dimensional vector space. This will also permit us to find the effect of a change of basis on the matrix of a D-lt.

Let $x_1, \cdots, x_n$ and $x_1', \cdots, x_n'$ be two D bases of the D vector space X. If we set $e_X(x) = x$ for every x in X, it is easy to see that e_X is a D-lt of X into X. It is customary to call e_X the *identity map of X into X*. As a D-lt of X into X, e_X has a matrix P relative to the bases $x_1, \cdots, x_n$ and $x_1', \cdots, x_n'$. Moreover, e_X has a matrix Q relative to the bases $x_1', \cdots, x_n'$ and $x_1, \cdots, x_n$. By the result of the preceding section, $e_X \circ e_X = e_X$ has the matrix PQ relative to the bases $x_1, \cdots, x_n$ and $x_1, \cdots, x_n$ of X. But, since

$$e_X(x_i) = \sum_{j=1}^{n} \delta_{ij} x_j \qquad (i = 1, \cdots, n)$$

where $\delta_{ii} = 1$, $\delta_{ij} = 0$, $i \neq j$, and $i, j = 1, \cdots, n$, the matrix of e_X relative to the bases $x_1, \cdots, x_n$ and $x_1, \cdots, x_n$ is just I_n. Hence, $PQ = I_n$, P is nonsingular, and $Q = P^{-1}$. It will be useful to determine the formulas connecting the coordinates of a vector x

in X relative to the two bases $x_1, \cdots, x_n$ and $x_1', \cdots, x_n'$. These coordinates are determined uniquely by the equations

$$x = \sum_{i=1}^{n} \xi_i x_i = \sum_{j=1}^{n} \xi_j' x_j'.$$

Since

$$e_X(x_i) = \sum_{j=1}^{n} p_{ij} x_j' \qquad (i = 1, \cdots, n),$$

we obtain

$$e_X(x) = \sum_{i,j=1}^{n} \xi_i p_{ij} x_j'.$$

But also

$$e_X(x) = x = \sum_{j=1}^{n} \xi_j' x_j'.$$

Hence, since coordinates relative to $x_1', \cdots, x_n'$ are unique,

$$\xi_j' = \sum_{i=1}^{n} \xi_i p_{ij} \qquad (j = 1, \cdots, n).$$

Introducing the matrices

$$\xi = [\xi_1, \cdots, \xi_n] \qquad \text{and} \qquad \xi' = [\xi_1', \cdots, \xi_n'],$$

we have the convenient formulas for transformation of coordinates:

$$\xi' = \xi P \qquad \text{and} \qquad \xi = \xi' P^{-1}.$$

Illustrative
Example

Let

$$x_1 = (1, -1, 0), \qquad x_2 = (0, 1, -1), \qquad x_3 = (1, 0, 1)$$

and

$$x_1' = (1, 1, 1), \qquad x_2' = (1, 1, 0), \qquad x_3' = (1, 0, 1)$$

be bases for $X = V_3(R_a)$. Find the formula for transformation of coordinates from x_1, x_2, x_3 to x_1', x_2', x_3'. Let P be the matrix of e_X relative to x_1, x_2, x_3 and x_1', x_2', x_3'; then

$$\begin{aligned}
e_X(x_1) &= x_1 = (1, -1, 0) = -2x_1' + x_2' + 2x_3', \\
e_X(x_2) &= x_2 = (0, 1, -1) = x_2' - x_3', \\
e_X(x_3) &= x_3 = (1, 0, 1) = x_3',
\end{aligned}$$

from which we find

$$P = \begin{bmatrix} -2 & 1 & 2 \\ 0 & 1 & -1 \\ 0 & 0 & 1 \end{bmatrix}.$$

Thus,

$$(\xi_1', \xi_2', \xi_3') = (\xi_1, \xi_2, \xi_3) \begin{bmatrix} -2 & 1 & 2 \\ 0 & 1 & -1 \\ 0 & 0 & 1 \end{bmatrix}$$

gives the required formulas:

$$\xi_1' = -2\xi_1,$$
$$\xi_2' = \xi_1 + \xi_2,$$
$$\xi_3' = 2\xi_1 - \xi_2 + \xi_3.$$

It is natural to inquire whether there is any restriction on P (other than nonsingularity) in these formulas. It may be seen that there is not. For, if P is any nonsingular matrix in D_n and $x_1', \cdots, x_n'$ is a D basis for X, then

$$x_i = \sum_{j=1}^{n} p_{ij} x_j' \qquad (i = 1, \cdots, n)$$

is also a basis for X. For, if $\sum_{i=1}^{n} \alpha_i x_i = 0$, then $[\alpha_1, \cdots, \alpha_n]$ is in the kernel of P, since $x_1', \cdots, x_n'$ are D-li. But the kernel of P is zero, and it follows that $x_1, \cdots, x_n$ are D-li. By TB3 (Chapter 5), $x_1, \cdots, x_n$ is a second D basis for X, and P is the matrix of e_X relative to the bases $x_1, \cdots, x_n$ and $x_1', \cdots, x_n'$.

Again a diagram is helpful:

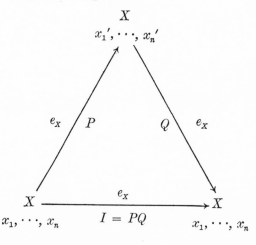

We are now ready to find the effect of a change of basis on the matrix of a D-lt. Let L be a D-lt of a D vector space X into a D vector space Y, let $x_1, \cdots, x_m$ and $y_1, \cdots, y_n$ be D bases of X and Y respectively, and let A be the matrix of L relative to these bases. Let $x_1', \cdots, x_m'$ and $y_1', \cdots, y_n'$ be also D bases of X and Y, respectively. Let P be the matrix of e_X relative to the bases $x_1, \cdots, x_m$ and $x_1', \cdots, x_m'$. We have seen that then P^{-1} is the matrix of e_X relative to the bases $x_1', \cdots, x_m'$ and $x_1, \cdots, x_m$. Let Q be the matrix of e_Y relative to the bases $y_1, \cdots, y_n$ and $y_1', \cdots, y_n'$; then $P^{-1}AQ$ is the matrix of $e_Y \circ L \circ e_X = L$ relative to the bases $x_1', \cdots, x_m'$ and $y_1', \cdots, y_n'$. Thus, the effect of a change of basis in both X and in Y is one of replacing the matrix A by the equivalent matrix $B = P^{-1}AQ$.

To summarize by means of a diagram,

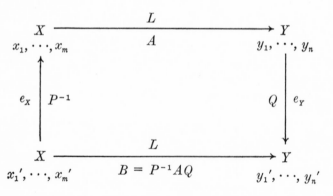

When L is a D-lt of X into X, the result given in the previous paragraph is not an appropriate one. A single D basis $x_1, \cdots, x_m$ of X will yield the matrix A which we have previously called the matrix of L relative to the bases $x_1, \cdots, x_m$ and $x_1, \cdots, x_m$. The matrix of L relative to the single basis $x_1, \cdots, x_m$ is obtained from the equations

$$L(x_i) = \sum_{j=1}^{m} \alpha_{ij}x_j \qquad (i = 1, \cdots, m).$$

Now let $x_1', \cdots, x_m'$ be a second basis of X and let P be the matrix of e_X relative to the bases $x_1, \cdots, x_m$ and $x_1', \cdots, x_m'$. We have seen that P^{-1} is the matrix of e_X relative to the bases $x_1', \cdots, x_m'$ and

$x_1, \cdots, x_m$. Hence $P^{-1}AP$ is the matrix of $e_X \circ L \circ e_X = L$ relative to the bases $x_1', \cdots, x_m'$ and $x_1', \cdots, x_m'$, or what we have decided to call the matrix of L relative to the new basis $x_1', \cdots, x_m'$. Thus we see that two matrices A and B in D_m represent the same D-lt L relative to two different bases of X if and only if $B = P^{-1}AP$ for a nonsingular matrix P in D_m. When this is true, we call A and B *similar in D*.

The appropriate diagram to cover similarity is

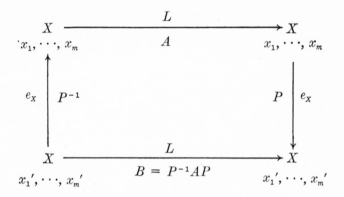

Illustrative
Example

Let L be defined by

$$L((1, 0, 0)) = (2, 1, 3),$$
$$L((0, 1, 0)) = (-1, 0, 0),$$
$$L((0, 0, 1)) = (0, 0, 0),$$

so that the matrix of L relative to the basis $x_1 = (1, 0, 0)$, $x_2 = (0, 1, 0)$, and $x_3 = (0, 0, 1)$ is

$$A = \begin{bmatrix} 2 & 1 & 3 \\ -1 & 0 & 0 \\ 0 & 0 & 0 \end{bmatrix}.$$

Let $x_1' = (1, 1, 1)$, $x_2' = (1, 1, 0)$, and $x_3' = (1, 0, 0)$. Then $L(x_1') = (1, 1, 3)$, $L(x_2') = (1, 1, 3)$, and $L(x_3') = (2, 1, 3)$. Since

$L(x_1') = 3x_1' - 2x_2' = L(x_2')$ and $L(x_3') = 3x_1' - 2x_2' + x_3'$, the matrix of L relative to the basis x_1', x_2', x_3' is

$$B = \begin{bmatrix} 3 & -2 & 0 \\ 3 & -2 & 0 \\ 3 & -2 & 1 \end{bmatrix}.$$

The matrix P of e_X relative to the bases x_1, x_2, x_3 and x_1', x_2', x_3' is computed as follows:

$$e_X(x_1) = (1, 0, 0) = x_3',$$
$$e_X(x_2) = (0, 1, 0) = x_2' - x_3',$$
$$e_X(x_3) = (0, 0, 1) = x_1' - x_2'.$$

Hence

$$P = \begin{bmatrix} 0 & 0 & 1 \\ 0 & 1 & -1 \\ 1 & -1 & 0 \end{bmatrix}$$

and

$$PB = \begin{bmatrix} 3 & -2 & 1 \\ 0 & 0 & -1 \\ 0 & 0 & 0 \end{bmatrix} = AP,$$

which verifies the general requirement $B = P^{-1}AP$.

The relation "A is similar to B in D" is an equivalence relation, as is easily seen, and there is a corresponding separation of D_m into disjoint maximal subsets of mutually similar matrices. Each of these subsets consists of matrices that define the same D-lt of X into X provided a suitable basis is used. The problem of classification of D-lt's of X into X (ignoring the particular basis used to define the D-lt) then reduces to the problem of finding a canonical representative of each of the equivalence classes under the similarity relation. We shall solve this problem in this text only for the case in which D is commutative and hence a field. As a start on the solution of this classification problem, we prove the following simple theorem.

Theorem 2

Let A and B be in D_m, where D is a division ring. Then B is similar to A in D if and only if $xI - B = P(x)(xI - A)Q(x)$, where $P(x)$ and $Q(x)$ are nonsingular elements of $D_m[x]$.

PROOF   If B is similar to A in D, then $B = P^{-1}AP$ with P nonsingular in D_m. Then $xI - B = P^{-1}(xI - A)P$ and we may choose $P(x) = P^{-1}$ and $Q(x) = P$ as nonsingular (constant) polynomials in x with coefficients in D_m. Conversely, let $xI - B = P(x)(xI - A)Q(x)$ with $P(x)$ and $Q(x)$ nonsingular polynomials in $D_m[x]$. Then $R(x) = (P(x))^{-1}$ is in $D_m[x]$, and $R(x)(xI - B) = (xI - A)Q(x)$. By the Factor Theorem (Corollary 3 of the Substitution Theorem, (3-2), in Chapter 3): $((xI - A)Q(x))_\rho(B) = 0$, and (3-2) then gives $Q_\rho(B)B - AQ_\rho(B) = 0$. Define $P = Q_\rho(B)$ and get $PB = AP$. We have only to show that P is nonsingular in D_m. To do this, set $S(x) = [Q(x)]^{-1}$. Since $S(x)$ is in $D_m[x]$, we may write $S(x) = C_0 + C_1x + \cdots + C_tx^t$. We have $[S(x)][Q(x)] - I = 0$ and, hence, $[S(x)Q(x)]_\rho(B) = I$. Using (3-2) again gives $C_0Q_\rho(B) + \cdots + C_tQ_\rho(B)B^t = C_0P + C_1PB + \cdots + C_tPB^t = I$. Using the commutation rule $PB = AP$, we readily conclude that $(C_0 + C_1A + \cdots + C_tA^t)P = I$. By Theorem 8 of Chapter 6, P is nonsingular and the proof is complete.

EXERCISES FOR CHAPTER 8

1. Let $L((1, 2)) = (-3, 0, 1)$ and $L((2, 1)) = (0, -1, 0)$. With $x_1 = (1, 0)$, $x_2 = (0, 1)$, and $y_1 = (1, 0, 0)$, $y_2 = (0, 1, 0)$, $y_3 = (0, 0, 1)$ as bases of $V_2(R_a)$ and $V_3(R_a)$, find the matrix A of L. (We call such bases the *usual* bases in this problem set.)

2. Let $M(1, 1, 0) = (2, 0, 1, 5)$, $M(0, 1, 0) = (3, 1, 4, -2)$, and $M(1, 0, 1) = (1, 0, -1, 0)$; find the matrix B of M relative to the usual bases.

3. Verify that AB is the matrix of $M \circ L$ with M and L as given in Exercises 1 and 2.

4. Find the square matrix P associated with a change of basis from the usual basis to $x_1' = (1, 1, 1)$, $x_2' = (1, 1, 0)$, $x_3' = (1, 0, 0)$.

5. Find the transformation of coordinates associated with the change from the basis $x_1 = (1, 1, 1)$, $x_2 = (1, 1, 0)$, $x_3 = (1, 0, 0)$ to the basis $x_1' = (1, 0, 2)$, $x_2' = (2, 1, 0)$, $x_3' = (0, 2, 1)$ in $V_3(R_a)$.

6. With L as in Exercise 1, let $x_1' = (1, 2)$, $x_2' = (2, 1)$, and $y_1' = (2, 1, 1)$, $y_2' = (0, 2, 1)$, $y_3' = (1, 0, 1)$. Find the matrix B of L relative to these new bases and verify that $B = P^{-1}AQ$.

7. In $V_3(R_e)$, let $L(1, 2, 1) = (0, 0, 0)$, $L(1, 0, 1) = (2, 1, 0)$, and $L(1, 1, 0) = (1, 0, 0)$. Find the matrices A and B of L relative to the usual basis and that of Exercise 4. Verify that $B = P^{-1}AP$.

8. In $V_2(R_a)$, let $L(1, 2) = (0, 0)$ and $L(2, 1) = (1, 1)$. Let A be

/ 144 /

the matrix of L relative to the usual basis and B be the matrix of L relative to the basis $x_1' = (1, 2)$, $x_2' = (2, 1)$. Verify that $B = P^{-1}AP$.

9. Let V be an F vector space, F being a field, and define V^* as the set of all F-lt L of V into F. Define $(L + M)(x) = L(x) + M(x)$ and $(\alpha L)(x) = \alpha(L(x))$, and verify that $L + M$ and αL are in V^* for L and M in V^* and α in F. Verify that V^* is an F vector space. Show that, if $x_1, \cdots, x_n$ is a basis for V, there is a dual basis for V^*: a basis $L_1, \cdots, L_n$, such that $L_i(x_j) = 1$ if $i = j$ and $L_i(x_j) = 0$ for $i \neq j$.

10. Find the dual basis for $[V_3(R_e)]^*$ corresponding to the basis $x_1 = (1, 1, 1)$, $x_2 = (1, 1, 0)$, $x_3 = (1, 0, 0)$.

11. Let X and Y be F vector spaces, F a field, and let $Hom_F(X, Y)$ be the set of all F-lt of X into Y. Show that $Hom_F(X, Y)$ is an F vector space.

12. Show that if X is an F vector space, where F is a field, then $Hom_F(X, X)$ is a ring under the multiplication $M \circ L$.

13. Show that in Exercise 11, $Hom_F(X, X)$ is isomorphic to F_n, provided that dim $X = n$.

14. Let L be a D-lt of X into Y and let A be the matrix of L relative to the bases $x_1, \cdots, x_m$ and $y_1, \cdots, y_n$ for X and Y, respectively. Show that $R_A \cong L(X)$ and that the kernel of $A \cong \{x \in X; L(x) = 0\}$. If new bases are chosen in X and Y and if B is the matrix of L relative to these new bases, how are R_B and the kernel of B related to R_A and the kernel of A? (In this exercise, the sign $\cong$ denotes vector space isomorphism.)

9

SIMILARITY OF MATRICES

In this chapter we solve one of the principal problems of matric theory, the problem of normal and canonical forms under the relation of similarity. The solution is effected by a preliminary study of an equivalence problem more delicate than that studied in Chapter 6. In Sections 1 to 3 this new equivalence problem is treated by means of minor variations of the technique used in Chapter 6. This leads at once to the rational canonical form, Section 4, and to a related normal form, Section 5. In Section 6 the Jordan normal form for algebraically closed fields is quickly derived. The characteristic and minimum polynomials are introduced and studied in Section 7. The last section of the chapter is devoted to the much easier problem of finding a simultaneous triangular form for a set of commuting matrices.

/ 1 / $F_n[x]$ VERSUS $(F[x])_n$

There is a natural ismorphism between the rings $F_n[x]$ and $(F[x])_n$. If $g(x) = A_0 + A_1x + \cdots + A_tx^t$ is in $F_n[x]$, with $A_q = [a_{ijq}]$, where $i, j = 1, \cdots, n$ for $q = 0, \cdots, t$, then the matrix

$$g\varphi = \left[\sum_{q=0}^{t} a_{ijq}x^q \right] \qquad (i = 1, \cdots, n; j = 1, \cdots, n)$$

is in $(F[x])_n$. It is evident that φ maps $F_n[x]$ faithfully onto $(F[x])_n$ and preserves addition and multiplication. Thus, the concepts of a matrix of polynomials and a polynomial with matric coefficients are essentially the same. We exploit the isomorphism φ by using whichever of the two concepts seems most convenient in a given discussion. (We met the isomorphism φ first in Chapter 4.)

/ 2 / EQUIVALENCE OF MATRICES OF POLYNOMIALS

From the final theorem of Chapter 8 we see that we may translate the problem of similarity into one which concerns polynomials with matric coefficients. In this section we present the solution (due to H. J. S. Smith†) of the derived problem. It is convenient to transform the polynomials with matric coefficients into matrices of polynomials using the isomorphism φ of Section 1. Throughout this section, F is a field.

Let A be an m-by-n matrix of elements of $F[x]$. We propose to simplify A by means of the following $F[x]$ *elementary operations*.

Type I: interchanging two rows (columns) of A.

Type II: multiplying the ith row (column) of A by a nonzero scalar of F.

Type III: adding $f(x) \in F[x]$ times the jth row (column) of A to the kth row (column) of A, where $j \neq k$.

As in Chapter 6, these $F[x]$ elementary operations can be effected by matric multiplication. Thus EA is the result of applying the $F[x]$ elementary row operation to A, and AE is the result of applying the $F[x]$ elementary column operation to A, provided that E is the result of applying the same $F[x]$ operation to I. The $F[x]$ *elementary matrices* are those obtained by applying $F[x]$ elementary operations to I, and all such matrices are nonsingular in $(F[x])_n$. Note especially that the $F[x]$ elementary operations of Type II permit multiplication only by nonzero constant polynomials of $F[x]$, and these are precisely the nonsingular polynomials of $F[x]$.

Let us call two m-by-n matrices A and B, of polynomials of $F[x]$, $F[x]$ *equivalent* whenever B can be obtained from A by a (finite) sequence of $F[x]$ elementary operations. It is easy to see that we have defined a third equivalence relation, and we seek a canonical form under $F[x]$ equivalence.

Theorem 1 (H. J. S. Smith)

Every m-by-n matrix of elements of $F[x]$ is $F[x]$ equivalent to one and only one of the matrices

(1) $\quad 0,$ $\qquad\qquad$ **(2)** $\quad \begin{bmatrix} \text{diag } (f_1, \cdots, f_s) & 0 \\ 0 & 0 \end{bmatrix},$

where each f_i is a monic polynomial of $F[x]$ and f_i divides f_{i+1} $(i = 1, \cdots, s - 1)$, and $s = 1, \cdots, \min (m, n)$.

---

† H. J. S. Smith was an English mathematician who worked in the latter part of the nineteenth century. This theorem of his appeared in 1861.

PROOF   We may clearly assume that $A \neq 0$. Of the monic polynomials that appear as elements in matrices B which are $F[x]$ equivalent to A, choose one, f_1, of least degree. (The subsequent arguments will provide a method of computing f_1.) By operations of Type I, we may assume that f_1 is in the $(1, 1)$ position of B. Then f_1 must divide every element of B.

First, if f_1 fails to divide some element g in the first row or first column of B, then $g = qf_1 + r$ with $\deg r < \deg f_1$ and $r \neq 0$. An $F[x]$ elementary operation of Type III will produce a matrix $F[x]$ equivalent to A, in which r appears; we need only add $-q$ times the first row (or column) to the row (or column) in which g appears. Thus f_1 must divide every element of the first row and first column of B. Operations of Type III will then replace B by a matrix,

$$B_1 = \begin{bmatrix} f_1 & 0 \\ 0 & C \end{bmatrix}$$

in which the elements of C differ from the corresponding elements of B by multiples of f_1.

Now suppose that f_1 fails to divide some b_{ij} with $i, j > 1$. Then f_1 fails to divide c_{ij}. Adding the ith row of B_1 to the first row of B_1 yields a matrix which is $F[x]$ equivalent to A with f_1 in the $(1, 1)$ position and for which f_1 fails to divide an element in the first row. But, as we have seen in the previous paragraph, this is impossible. Hence, f_1 divides every element of B and therefore divides every element of C. If $C = 0$, we have the form (2), with $s = 1$. If $C \neq 0$, repetition of the process, starting with C, gives an $F[x]$ equivalent of A, $B_2 = \text{diag} (f_1, f_2, D)$, in which f_2 is monic and f_1 divides f_2. Continuing in this way we reach the desired form, (2).

Illustrative
Example

Let

$$A = \begin{bmatrix} x & 0 & 0 \\ 0 & x + 1 & x \end{bmatrix}$$

with elements in $R_a[x]$. Since x does not divide $x + 1$, we add the second row to the first and get

$$\begin{bmatrix} x & x + 1 & x \\ 0 & x + 1 & x \end{bmatrix}.$$

Subtracting the first column from the second column gives

$$\begin{bmatrix} x & 1 & x \\ 0 & x + 1 & x \end{bmatrix}.$$

Interchanging columns, we have

$$\begin{bmatrix} 1 & x & x \\ x + 1 & 0 & x \end{bmatrix}.$$

A row operation yields

$$\begin{bmatrix} 1 & x & x \\ 0 & -x^2 - x & -x^2 \end{bmatrix},$$

and column operations give

$$\begin{bmatrix} 1 & 0 & 0 \\ 0 & x^2 + x & x^2 \end{bmatrix}.$$

Since $x^2 + x$ does not divide x^2, we subtract the second column from the third and have

$$\begin{bmatrix} 1 & 0 & 0 \\ 0 & x^2 + x & -x \end{bmatrix}.$$

Column operations then produce the desired form:

$$\begin{bmatrix} 1 & 0 & 0 \\ 0 & x & 0 \end{bmatrix}.$$

To prove the uniqueness of the form (2), we resort to determinants. By an *i-rowed minor* of a matrix A we mean the determinant of an i-rowed square submatrix of A. For each m-by-n matrix A of elements of $F[x]$, we denote by $d_i(A)$ the greatest common divisor of all of the i-rowed minors of A, provided

A has some nonzero i-rowed minor. For notational convenience, we also define $d_0(A)$ to be 1 when $A \neq 0$. We shall now prove that these *determinantal divisors of A* are not affected by $F[x]$ equivalence.

Lemma 1

If A and B are $F[x]$ equivalent, then A has a nonzero i-rowed minor if and only if B does; and then $d_i(A) = d_i(B)$.

PROOF   If B is obtained from A by an operation of Type I or II, one easily sees that every i-rowed minor of B is merely a multiple (by some nonzero element of F) of some i-rowed minor of A. The lemma needs proof, then, only for operations of Type III. Let B be obtained from A by an operation of Type III. By D1 of Section 3, Chapter 2, each i-rowed minor of B has the form $M = M_1 + pM_2$, where M_1 and M_2 are i-rowed minors of A and p is in $F[x]$. For, if M is obtained by deleting both the kth and jth rows (columns), then M is a minor of A; the same is true if M is obtained by selecting both the kth and jth rows (columns) or if the kth row (column) is deleted and the jth row (column) is selected. If, however, the kth row (column) is selected and the jth deleted, then $M = M_1 \pm fM_2$, where M_1 is the minor of A corresponding to M and M_2 is a minor of A obtained by replacing the kth row (column) of A by the jth row (column) of A and interchanging certain rows (columns).

We now see that if every i-rowed minor of A is zero, then the same is true for B. Because the relation of $F[x]$ equivalence is symmetric, it follows that A has a nonzero i-rowed minor if and only if B does.

We also see that $d_i(A)$ divides every i-rowed minor of B so that $d_i(A)$ divides $d_i(B)$. Again, appealing to the symmetry of the relation of $F[x]$ equivalence, we see that $d_i(B)$ divides $d_i(A)$. Both being monic polynomials, it follows that $d_i(A) = d_i(B)$ and the proof of the lemma is complete.

A brief comment on the number s of (2) is in order. Since we may embed $F[x]$ in the field of all rational functions $f(x)/g(x)$ with coefficients in F and $g(x) \neq 0$, we may, but we do not, regard A as a matrix of elements of a field. Were we to so regard A, it would be proper to call s the rank of A. Since we have given a separate proof that s is uniquely determined by A, we shall abuse our language only slightly when we define s as the *rank of* A, and from now on we adopt this definition.

COMPLETION OF THE PROOF OF THEOREM 1   To show that A is $F[x]$ equivalent to only one matrix of the form (2), we use the lemma. If B is the matrix defined by (2), then B has a nonzero i-rowed minor if and only if $i \leq s$. It is very easy to see, by using the fact that f_i divides f_{i+1}, that

$$d_i(B) = f_1 f_2 \cdots f_i \qquad (i = 1, \cdots, s).$$

But $d_i(B) = d_i(A)$ is uniquely determined by A $(i = 1, \cdots, s)$, and hence so is f_i $(i = 1, \cdots, s)$, since

$$f_i = d_i(A)/d_{i-1}(A) \qquad (i = 1, \cdots, s).$$

This completes the proof of Theorem 1.

We call the monic polynomials $f_1, \cdots, f_s$, which appear in the canonical form (2) for A under $F[x]$ equivalence, *the invariant factors of A*.

Because the determinantal divisors of A are unaffected by enlargement of the field F, being greatest common divisors of polynomials in $F[x]$ (see Page 50), the invariant factors of A are also unaffected by enlargement of the field F. In fact, the invariant factors of A are polynomials with coefficients in the least field which contains the coefficients of all the polynomials which are elements of A.

Theorem 2

Two nonzero m-by-n matrices with elements in $F[x]$ are $F[x]$ equivalent if and only if they have the same list of invariant factors.

As in Chapter 6, we may use our canonical form for A to discuss nonsingularity in $(F[x])_n$.

Theorem 3

An n-by-n matrix $P(x)$ in $(F[x])_n$ is nonsingular if and only if $P(x)$ is a product of $F[x]$ elementary matrices.

PROOF   Since $F[x]$ elementary matrices are nonsingular, every product of $F[x]$ elementary matrices is nonsingular. Conversely, let $P(x)$ be nonsingular. As in the proof of Theorem 5 of Chapter 6, $A(x)P(x)B(x) = S(x)$ has the form (2) for nonsingular matrices $A(x)$ and $B(x)$ in $(F[x])_n$ which are products of $F[x]$ elementary matrices. Then $S(x)$ is nonsingular in $(F[x])_n$ and det $S(x)$ is nonsingular in $F[x]$. But the only nonsingular elements in $F[x]$ are nonzero constants in F; hence $s = n$ and $f_i = 1$ (where $i = 1, \cdots, n$), $S(x) = I_n$, so that $P(x) = [A(x)]^{-1}[B(x)]^{-1}$ is a product of $F[x]$ elementary matrices.

Corollary

Two m-by-n matrices A and B of elements of $F[x]$ are $F[x]$ equivalent if and only if $B = P(x)AQ(x)$, where $P(x)$ and $Q(x)$ are nonsingular matrices of elements of $F[x]$.

We complete this section by noting the following immediate consequence of Theorem 3 and Theorem 2 of Chapter 8.

Theorem 4

Two matrices A and B in F_n are similar if and only if the matrices $xI - A$ and $xI - B$ have the same list of invariant factors.

/ 3 / ELEMENTARY DIVISORS

AND $F[x]$ EQUIVALENCE

It is sometimes useful to have still another criterion for $F[x]$ equivalence. In this section the elementary divisors of the invariant factors are employed to produce such a criterion.

Let F be a field and let A be an m-by-n matrix of polynomials of $F[x]$. Let $f_k, \cdots, f_s$ be the nonconstant invariant factors of A. Let

$$f_i = p_{i1}^{e_{i1}} \cdots p_{iq_i}^{e_{iq_i}} \qquad (i = k, \cdots, s)$$

be the factorization of f_i into a product of powers of distinct irreducibles of $F[x]$. Recall that we have named $p_{ij}^{e_{ij}}$, where $j = 1, \cdots, q_i$, the elementary divisors of f_i. We call the complete list $p_{ij}^{e_{ij}}$, where $j = 1, \cdots, q_i$, and $i = k, \cdots, s$, the *list of elementary divisors of A*. Given the rank s, it is easy to reconstruct the list of invariant factors of A from the list of elementary divisors of A. Since every f_i divides f_s, then f_s is the product of the highest power of each of the irreducibles appearing in the list of elementary divisors of A. Discard these and obtain f_{s-1} similarly from what remains of the list. For example, let

$$(x - 1)^2, \qquad x - 1, \qquad x - 1, \qquad x, \qquad (x^2 + 1)^2,$$
$$(x^2 + 1)^2, \qquad x^2 + 1$$

be the list of elementary divisors, and let $s = 5$. Then $f_5(x) = (x - 1)^2 x (x^2 + 1)^2$, $f_4(x) = (x - 1)(x^2 + 1)^2$, $f_3(x) = (x - 1)(x^2 + 1)$, and $f_2 = f_1 = 1$.

Theorem 5

Two nonzero m-by-n matrices of polynomials in $F[x]$ are $F[x]$ equivalent if and only if they have the same rank and the same list of elementary divisors.

Theorem 6

Two matrices A and B in F_n (where F is a field) are similar in F if and only if $xI - A$ and $xI - B$ have the same list of elementary divisors.

/ 4 / THE RATIONAL CANONICAL FORM

In this section we shall apply the results of Section 2 to obtain a canonical form for A in F_n (where F is a field) under the equivalence relation of similarity in F. We first introduce, for each monic nonconstant polynomial f in $F[x]$, a companion matrix $C(f)$ for which f is the only nonconstant invariant factor of $xI - C(f)$. Then it is easy to show that A is similar to the matrix diag $(C(f_k), \cdots, C(f_n))$ where $f_k, \cdots, f_n$ are the nonconstant invariant factors of $xI_n - A$.

Let F be a field and let

$$f(x) = x^t + c_{t-1}x^{t-1} + \cdots + c_1 x + c_0$$

be a monic nonconstant polynomial in $F[x]$. Define the matrix

$$
C(f) = \begin{bmatrix}
0 & 1 & 0 & 0 & \cdots & 0 & 0 & 0 \\
0 & 0 & 1 & 0 & \cdots & 0 & 0 & 0 \\
0 & 0 & 0 & 1 & \cdots & 0 & 0 & 0 \\
\vdots & \vdots & \vdots & \vdots & & \vdots & \vdots & \vdots \\
0 & 0 & 0 & 0 & \cdots & 0 & 1 & 0 \\
0 & 0 & 0 & 0 & \cdots & 0 & 0 & 1 \\
-c_0 & -c_1 & -c_2 & -c_3 & \cdots & -c_{t-3} & -c_{t-2} & -c_{t-1}
\end{bmatrix}.
$$

We call $C(f)$ the *companion of f*. We wish to compute the invariant factors of

$$
xI - C(f) = \begin{bmatrix}
x & -1 & 0 & 0 & \cdots & 0 & 0 & 0 \\
0 & x & -1 & 0 & \cdots & 0 & 0 & 0 \\
0 & 0 & x & -1 & \cdots & 0 & 0 & 0 \\
\vdots & \vdots & \vdots & \vdots & & \vdots & \vdots & \vdots \\
0 & 0 & 0 & 0 & \cdots & x & -1 & 0 \\
0 & 0 & 0 & 0 & \cdots & 0 & x & -1 \\
c_0 & c_1 & c_2 & c_3 & \cdots & c_{t-3} & c_{t-2} & x + c_{t-1}
\end{bmatrix}.
$$

Let M be the $(t-1)$-rowed minor of $xI - C(f)$ given by the determinant of the matrix obtained by deleting the first column and the last row of $xI - C(f)$. Since M is the determinant of a triangular matrix, $M = (-1)^{t-1}$. It follows that $d_{t-1}(xI - C(f)) = 1$. Hence $xI - C(f)$ has only one nonconstant invariant factor $f_t = \det(xI - C(f))$. To compute f_t, add x times the tth column to the $(t-1)$th column, then x times the $(t-1)$th column to the $(t-2)$th column, etc. These operations yield a matrix,

$$\begin{bmatrix} 0 & -1 & 0 & 0 & \cdots & 0 & 0 & 0 \\ 0 & 0 & -1 & 0 & \cdots & 0 & 0 & 0 \\ 0 & 0 & 0 & -1 & \cdots & 0 & 0 & 0 \\ \vdots & \vdots & \vdots & \vdots & & \vdots & \vdots & \vdots \\ 0 & 0 & 0 & 0 & \cdots & 0 & -1 & 0 \\ 0 & 0 & 0 & 0 & \cdots & 0 & 0 & -1 \\ f(x) & * & * & * & \cdots & * & * & * \end{bmatrix}$$

whose determinant is f_t. (The values of the last $t - 1$ elements of the last row are immaterial, as we shall see.) Successive expansions on the first $t - 1$ rows then give $f_t = \det(xI - C(f)) = f(x)$. This proves that f is the single nonconstant invariant factor of $xI - C(f)$.

Let A be in F_n, then $d_n(xI - A) = \det(xI - A) \neq 0$, so that $xI - A$ has invariant factors $f_1, \cdots, f_n$ in $F[x]$. Let f_k be the first $f_i \neq 1$ in the list $f_1, \cdots, f_n$; and define $t_i = \deg f_i$ for $i = k, \cdots, n$. Because $d_n(xI - A) = f_k \cdots f_n$ we see that $n = t_k + \cdots + t_n$.

Theorem 7

Every matrix A in F_n (where F is a field) is similar to the matrix $R = \operatorname{diag}(C(f_k), \cdots, C(f_n))$, where $f_k, \cdots, f_n$ are the nonconstant invariant factors of $xI - A$. The matrix A is similar to one and only one matrix of the form R.

PROOF   It will suffice to show that $xI_n - R$ and $xI_n - A$ have the same invariant factors. Now,

$$xI_n - R = \operatorname{diag}(xI_{t_k} - C(f_k), \cdots, xI_{t_n} - C(f_n))$$

where $t_i = \deg f_i$, for $i = k, \cdots, n$. By Theorem 1 and the remarks preceding the statement of Theorem 7, $F[x]$ elementary operations will replace $M = xI_{t_i} - C(f_i)$ by $\operatorname{diag}(1, 1, \cdots, 1, f_i)$, since f_i is the single nonconstant invariant factor of M. It follows that $F[x]$ elementary operations will replace $xI_n - R$ by $\operatorname{diag}(1, \cdots, 1, f_k, \cdots, f_n)$. By Theorem 1, $xI_n - R$ and

$xI_n - A$ have the same list of invariant factors, and R is similar to A in F by Theorem 2. Since R is uniquely determined by the polynomials $f_k, \cdots, f_n$ and since these polynomials are uniquely determined by A, it follows that R is uniquely determined by A and that A can be similar to only one matrix of the form R. We call R the *rational canonical form for A under similarity in F*.

Illustrative
Example

Find the rational canonical form for the matrix

$$A = \begin{bmatrix} 1 & 0 & -1 \\ 2 & 3 & 1 \\ 1 & 0 & -2 \end{bmatrix}$$

in $(R_a)_3$. Here

$$\det (xI - A) = \det \begin{bmatrix} x - 1 & 0 & 1 \\ -2 & x - 3 & -1 \\ -1 & 0 & x + 2 \end{bmatrix}$$
$$= (x - 3)(x^2 + x - 1) = x^3 - 2x^2 - 4x + 3.$$

One sees that $-2x - 4 - 1 = -2x - 5$ and $-x + 1 + 2 = -x + 3$ are two-rowed minors of $xI - A$, and hence $d_2(xI - A) = 1$. Thus $f(x) = x^3 - 2x^2 - 4x + 3$ is the only nonconstant invariant factor of $xI - A$ and the rational canonical form of A is $C(f)$:

$$R = \begin{bmatrix} 0 & 1 & 0 \\ 0 & 0 & 1 \\ -3 & 4 & 2 \end{bmatrix}.$$

Illustrative
Example

Find the rational canonical form R for

$$A = \begin{bmatrix} 1 & -1 \\ 2 & 3 \end{bmatrix}$$

in $(R_a)_2$ and find a nonsingular matrix P in $(R_a)_2$ such that $R = P^{-1}AP$. Here

$$\det (xI - A) = \det \begin{bmatrix} x - 1 & 1 \\ -2 & x - 3 \end{bmatrix} = x^2 - 4x + 5 = f(x)$$

and, clearly, $d_1(xI - A) = 1$; hence $R = C(f)$,

$$R = \begin{bmatrix} 0 & 1 \\ -5 & 4 \end{bmatrix},$$

the desired canonical form. To find P we use the proof of the final theorem of Chapter 8, which shows that, if $xI - R = P(x)(xI - A)Q(x)$, with $P(x)$ and $Q(x)$ nonsingular in $(R_a[x])_2$, then $P = Q_\rho(R)$ is effective. We first apply the Smith reduction to $xI - A$, recording the column operations as in Chapter 6. A row operation on $xI - A$ gives

$$\begin{bmatrix} x - 1 & 1 \\ -f(x) & 0 \end{bmatrix},$$

and another gives

$$\begin{bmatrix} x - 1 & 1 \\ f(x) & 0 \end{bmatrix}.$$

A column operation, which we record, produces

$$\begin{bmatrix} 0 & 1 \\ 1 & 0 \end{bmatrix}$$

$$\begin{bmatrix} 1 & x - 1 \\ 0 & f(x) \end{bmatrix},$$

and another yields the Smith form for $xI - A$:

$$\begin{bmatrix} 0 & 1 \\ 1 & -x + 1 \end{bmatrix}$$

$$\begin{bmatrix} 1 & 0 \\ 0 & f(x) \end{bmatrix}.$$

Now we must apply the Smith reduction to

$$xI - R = \begin{bmatrix} x & -1 \\ 5 & x - 4 \end{bmatrix}.$$

Adding x times the second column to the first gives

$$\begin{bmatrix} 1 & 0 \\ x & 1 \end{bmatrix}$$

$$\begin{bmatrix} 0 & -1 \\ f(x) & x - 4 \end{bmatrix},$$

and now row operations produce

$$\begin{bmatrix} 0 & 1 \\ f(x) & 0 \end{bmatrix}.$$

A final column operation,

$$\begin{bmatrix} 0 & 1 \\ 1 & x \end{bmatrix}$$

$$\begin{bmatrix} 1 & 0 \\ 0 & f(x) \end{bmatrix},$$

gives the Smith form for $xI - R$. To find the desired $Q(x)$ we start with

$$\begin{bmatrix} 0 & 1 \\ 1 & -x + 1 \end{bmatrix}$$

and apply the inverses of the column operations which led from $xI - R$ to

$$\begin{bmatrix} 1 & 0 \\ 0 & f(x) \end{bmatrix}$$

in *reverse* order. Interchanging columns we have

$$\begin{bmatrix} 1 & 0 \\ -x + 1 & 1 \end{bmatrix}.$$

Subtracting x times the second column from the first gives

$$Q(x) = \begin{bmatrix} 1 & 0 \\ -2x+1 & 1 \end{bmatrix} = \begin{bmatrix} 0 & 0 \\ -2 & 0 \end{bmatrix} x + \begin{bmatrix} 1 & 0 \\ 1 & 1 \end{bmatrix}.$$

Thus

$$P = Q_\rho(R) = \begin{bmatrix} 0 & 0 \\ -2 & 0 \end{bmatrix} \begin{bmatrix} 0 & 1 \\ -5 & 4 \end{bmatrix} + \begin{bmatrix} 1 & 0 \\ 1 & 1 \end{bmatrix}$$

$$= \begin{bmatrix} 1 & 0 \\ 1 & -1 \end{bmatrix},$$

for which

$$PR = \begin{bmatrix} 1 & 0 \\ 1 & -1 \end{bmatrix} \begin{bmatrix} 0 & 1 \\ -5 & 4 \end{bmatrix} = \begin{bmatrix} 0 & 1 \\ 5 & -3 \end{bmatrix}$$

and

$$AP = \begin{bmatrix} 1 & -1 \\ 2 & 3 \end{bmatrix} \begin{bmatrix} 1 & 0 \\ 1 & -1 \end{bmatrix} = \begin{bmatrix} 0 & 1 \\ 5 & -3 \end{bmatrix},$$

as required.

/5/ A NORMAL FORM

UNDER SIMILARITY

We may employ the elementary divisors of $xI - A$ to obtain a very useful normal form for A under similarity. We shall prove in this section that, if $g_1, \cdots, g_q$ is the list of elementary divisors of $xI - A$, then A is similar to the matrix diag $(C(g_1), \cdots, C(g_q))$. Since the order of the elementary divisors $g_1, \cdots, g_q$ is not prescribed, this form fails to be uniquely determined by A. For this reason we use the phrase *normal form* since "canonical form" implies a description of a unique representative of the equivalence class to which A belongs.

Theorem 8

If F is a field and A is in F_n, then A is similar to the matrix $N = $ diag $(C(g_1), \cdots, C(g_q))$ where $g_1, \cdots, g_q$ is the list of elementary divisors of $xI - A$. Apart from the order of the diagonal blocks $C(g_i)$, where $i = 1, \cdots, q$, the matrix N is uniquely determined by A.

PROOF   It will suffice to show that $xI - A$ and $xI - N$ have the same list of elementary divisors. As in the proof of Theorem 7, $xI - N$ is $F[x]$ equivalent to the matrix diag $(1, 1, \cdots, 1, g_1, \cdots, g_q)$. The theorem then follows at once from the following useful lemma.

Lemma 2

If g_j are nonconstant monic polynomials of $F[x]$, then the list of elementary divisors of $D = $ diag $(g_1, \cdots, g_q)$ is the same as the list of elementary divisors of all of the g_j, where $j = 1, \cdots, q$.

PROOF   Let p be an irreducible of $F[x]$ which divides some g_i. Let p^{e_j} be the highest power of p that divides g_j, where $j = 1, \cdots, q$. By operations of Type I applied to D, we may assume that $0 = e_1 = e_2 = \cdots = e_{k-1} < e_k \leq \cdots \leq e_q$. Then it is easily seen that the highest power of p that divides $d_j(D)$ is

$$r_j = e_1 + \cdots + e_j \qquad (j = 1, \cdots, q).$$

Recalling that the invariant factors of D have the form $f_j = d_j(D)/d_{j-1}(D)$, for $j = 1, \cdots, q$, we see that p^{e_j} is the highest power of p that divides f_j, where $j = 1, \cdots, q$. The list of elementary divisors of the f_j that are powers of p is then $p^{e_k}, \cdots, p^{e_q}$, which corresponds exactly with the portion of the list of elementary divisors of g_j, $(j = 1, \cdots, q)$ that are powers of p. Varying p over the irreducibles of $F[x]$ which divide some g_j, we see that the complete list of elementary divisors of D coincides with the list of elementary divisors of all the g_j $(j = 1, \cdots, q)$.

Illustrative
Example

Find the invariant factors of

$$\begin{bmatrix} x^3 - 1 & 0 & 0 \\ 0 & x^4 - 1 & 0 \\ 0 & 0 & (x - 1)^3 \end{bmatrix}$$

in $(R_a[x])_3$. For $x - 1$, we have $e_1 = e_2 = 1$ and $e_3 = 3$. For $x + 1$, we have $e_1 = e_2 = 0$ and $e_3 = 1$. For $x^2 + 1$ and $x^2 + x + 1$, we have $e_1 = e_2 = 0$ and $e_3 = 1$. Hence $f_1 = x - 1$, $f_2 = x - 1$, and $f_3 = (x - 1)^3(x + 1)(x^2 + 1)(x^2 + x + 1)$.

/6/ THE JORDAN
NORMAL FORM

In this section we assume that F is an algebraically closed field. We recall that this means that all the irreducible polynomials of $F[x]$ have the form $x - \alpha$ for $\alpha \in F$. The field K of all complex numbers is the primordial example of an algebraically closed field. However, it is proved in more advanced courses in algebra that every field F is a subfield of an algebraically closed field, and this fact makes the normal form discussed in this section quite useful.

When F is an algebraically closed field we may simplify the normal form of Section 5 considerably. This simplification ends our treatment of the problem of canonical and normal forms under similarity.

Our first task is to simplify the matrix $C((x - \alpha)^e)$, as in the following lemma.

Lemma 3

Let F be a field, α be in F, and e be a positive integer. Then the matrix $C((x - \alpha)^e)$ is similar in F to the matrix

$$
J_e(\alpha) = \begin{bmatrix}
\alpha & 1 & 0 & \cdots & 0 & 0 \\
0 & \alpha & 1 & \cdots & 0 & 0 \\
\vdots & \vdots & \vdots & & \vdots & \vdots \\
0 & 0 & 0 & \cdots & \alpha & 1 \\
0 & 0 & 0 & \cdots & 0 & \alpha
\end{bmatrix}.
$$

PROOF   We easily compute the invariant factors of

$$xI_e - J_e(\alpha) = \begin{bmatrix} x-\alpha & -1 & 0 & \cdots & 0 & 0 \\ 0 & x-\alpha & -1 & \cdots & 0 & 0 \\ \vdots & \vdots & \vdots & & \vdots & \vdots \\ 0 & 0 & 0 & \cdots & x-\alpha & -1 \\ 0 & 0 & 0 & \cdots & 0 & x-\alpha \end{bmatrix},$$

since $d_e(xI_e - J_e(\alpha)) = (x - \alpha)^e$, while deletion of the first column and the last row of $xI_e - J_e(\alpha)$ yields an $(e-1)$-rowed minor $M = (-1)^{e-1}$. Hence $d_{e-1}(xI_e - J_e(\alpha)) = 1$ and $(x - \alpha)^e$ is the only nonconstant invariant factor of $xI_e - J_e(\alpha)$. Since $(x - \alpha)^e$ is also the only nonconstant invariant factor of $xI_e - C((x - \alpha)^e)$, the similarity asserted in the lemma follows at once from Theorem 4.

Theorem 9

Let F be an algebraically closed field and let A be in F_n. Let the list of elementary divisors of $xI - A$ be $(x - \alpha_1)^{e_1}, \cdots,$ $(x - \alpha_q)^{e_q}$. Then A is similar in F to $J = \text{diag } (J_{e_1}(\alpha_1), \cdots,$ $J_{e_q}(\alpha_q))$. Aside from the order of the diagonal blocks, the matrix J is uniquely determined by A.

PROOF   By the lemmas of this and the preceding sections we easily see that the lists of elementary divisors of $xI - J$ and $xI - A$ are precisely the same. Hence J is similar to A in F by Theorem 6. We call J the *Jordan normal form* for A.

Illustrative
Example

Determine the Jordan normal form for

$$A = \begin{bmatrix} 1 & 0 & -1 \\ 2 & 3 & 1 \\ 1 & 0 & -2 \end{bmatrix}$$

in K_3. We have seen that $xI - A$ has only one invariant factor, $f(x) = (x - 3)(x^2 + x - 1)$, whose elementary divisors are $x - 3$, $x - (-1 + \sqrt{5})/2$, and $x - (-1 - \sqrt{5})/2$. Hence

$$J = \operatorname{diag}(3, [-1 + \sqrt{5}]/2, [-1 - \sqrt{5}]/2).$$

Illustrative
Example

Determine the Jordan normal form for

$$A = \begin{bmatrix} 1 & 0 & 0 & 0 \\ 2 & 1 & 0 & 0 \\ 3 & 2 & 1 & 0 \\ 4 & 3 & 2 & 1 \end{bmatrix}$$

in K_4. Here $\det(xI - A) = (x - 1)^4$. A three-rowed minor of $xI - A$ is

$$\det \begin{bmatrix} -2 & x-1 & 0 \\ -3 & -2 & x-1 \\ -4 & -3 & -2 \end{bmatrix} = g(x)$$

with $g(1) = -8 \neq 0$. Since $(x - 1)^3$ is also a three-rowed minor of $xI - A$, we see that $d_3(xI - A) = 1$, and that the list of invariant factors of $xI - A$ is $1, 1, 1, (x - 1)^4$. Thus the desired Jordan normal form is

$$\begin{bmatrix} 1 & 1 & 0 & 0 \\ 0 & 1 & 1 & 0 \\ 0 & 0 & 1 & 1 \\ 0 & 0 & 0 & 1 \end{bmatrix}.$$

/ 7 / CHARACTERISTIC AND MINIMUM POLYNOMIALS

In this section we use the theory of similarity to introduce and study two very useful polynomials associated with a matrix A

in F_n. These polynomials are $d_n(xI - A) = \det(xI - A)$, which is called the *characteristic polynomial*† of A, and the monic polynomial $m(x)$ of least degree such that $m(A) = 0$, which will be called the *minimum polynomial* of A. When F is algebraically closed, the roots of $\det(xI - A) = 0$ are in F, and we call them *characteristic roots* of A. This section is devoted to the derivation of the important basic properties which involve the characteristic and minimum polynomials.

Let F be a field, and let A be in F_n and $g(x)$ in $F[x]$. Since each element of F commutes with A, we write $g(A)$ for the common value of $g_\rho(A)$ and $g_\lambda(A)$. Our first theorem is old but still famous and useful.

Theorem 10

If F is a field, A is in F_n, and $f(x) = \det(xI - A)$, then $f(x)$ is in $F[x]$ and $f(A) = 0$. (This theorem was also stated and proved in Chapter 4, page 61.)

PROOF   This is immediate from the Factor Theorem, since $(xI - A)\,\mathrm{adj}\,(xI - A) = f(x)I_n$.

The characteristic polynomial $f(x) = \det(xI - A)$ of A in F_n is a monic nonconstant polynomial in $F[x]$ such that $f(A) = 0$. But there may be polynomials $p(x)$ in $F[x]$ of lower degree such that $p(A) = 0$. As an extreme example, if $A = I_n$, then $f(x) = (x - 1)^n$, while A satisfies $p(A) = 0$ for $p(x) = x - 1$. There is a monic polynomial $m_A(x)$ in $F[x]$ of least degree such that $m_A(A) = 0$, which we call the *minimum polynomial* of A. This polynomial is uniquely determined by A. For, if also $p(A) = 0$ for $p(x)$ in $F[x]$, then we have $p = m_A q + r$ with $\deg r < \deg m_A$. It is not possible that $r \neq 0$, since this would lead at once to a monic polynomial $\alpha r(A) = 0$, contrary to our choice of m_A. Thus a rival m for the position of minimum polynomial of A must be divisible by m_A and, reversing the roles of m and m_A, m must divide m_A. Since the rivals are monic and each divides the other, they must be equal. This proves that the minimum polynomial

† We met the characteristic polynomial for the first time in Chapter 4.

m_A is uniquely determined by A and that m_A divides every polynomial $p(x)$ in $F[x]$ for which $p(A) = 0$.

Our next theorem relates the minimum polynomial of A to an invariant factor of $xI - A$.

Theorem 11

Let F be a field and let A be in F_n. Then the last invariant factor of $xI - A$ is the minimum polynomial of A.

PROOF   We have

$$f_n = d_n(xI - A)/d_{n-1}(xI - A) = \det (xI - A)/d_{n-1}(xI - A).$$

From the definitions, we see that $d_{n-1}(xI - A)$ is the greatest common divisor of the elements of the matrix adj $(xI - A)$. Let us write

$$\text{adj } (xI - A) = d_{n-1}(xI - A)H(x),$$

where $H(x)$ is a matrix of polynomials of $F[x]$ for which $d_1(H(x)) = 1$. We may then write the equation [adj $(xI - A)](xI - A) = [\det (xI - A)]I$ in the form

(1) $H(x)(xI - A) = f_n(x)I.$

By the Factor Theorem, $f_n(A) = 0$. Now let $p(x)$ be any polynomial in $F[x]$ such that $p(A) = 0$. Again by the Factor Theorem, we know that $xI - A$ is a left factor of $p(x)I$:

(2) $(xI - A)Q(x) = p(x)I,$

where $Q(x)$ is a matrix of polynomials in $F[x]$. Hence also

$$H(x)(xI - A)Q(x) = f_n(x)Q(x) = p(x)H(x).$$

It follows that f_n divides every element of the matrix $p(x)H(x)$. Hence f_n divides $d_1(p(x)H(x)) = p(x)d_1(H(x)) = p(x)$. In particular, $\deg f_n \le \deg p$. This proves that f_n is the monic polynomial in $F[x]$ of least degree such that $m(A) = 0$. Hence f_n is the minimum polynomial of A.

Illustrative
Example

Find the minimum polynomial of

$$A = \begin{bmatrix} 0 & 1 & 1 \\ -1 & 2 & 1 \\ 0 & 0 & 1 \end{bmatrix}$$

in $(R_a)_3$. Here

$$\det(xI - A) = \det \begin{bmatrix} x & -1 & -1 \\ 1 & x-2 & -1 \\ 0 & 0 & x-1 \end{bmatrix} = (x-1)(x^2 - 2x + 1)$$

and $d_3(xI - A) = (x-1)^3$. Now

$$\text{adj}(xI - A) = \begin{bmatrix} (x-1)(x-2) & x-1 & x-1 \\ -(x-1) & x(x-1) & x-1 \\ 0 & 0 & (x-1)^2 \end{bmatrix}$$

shows that $d_2(xI - A) = x - 1$ and $(x-1)^2$ is the minimum polynomial for A. This result may be checked by computing

$$(A - I)^2 = \begin{bmatrix} -1 & 1 & 1 \\ -1 & 1 & 1 \\ 0 & 0 & 0 \end{bmatrix} \begin{bmatrix} -1 & 1 & 1 \\ -1 & 1 & 1 \\ 0 & 0 & 0 \end{bmatrix} = \begin{bmatrix} 0 & 0 & 0 \\ 0 & 0 & 0 \\ 0 & 0 & 0 \end{bmatrix}.$$

Corollary

Every irreducible of $F[x]$ that divides the characteristic polynomial of A also divides the minimum polynomial of A. When the field F is algebraically closed, every characteristic root of A is a root of the minimum polynomial (with, possibly, lower multiplicity).

PROOF   On taking determinants in equation (1) we see that every irreducible p of $F[x]$ that divides $\det(xI - A)$ also divides $(f_n(x))^n$ and, consequently, also $f_n(x) = m_A(x)$.

In later chapters we shall have frequent occasion to use the characteristic and minimum polynomials, and we shall have a few words to say about computation of the characteristic roots of A.

/ 8 / SIMULTANEOUS TRIANGULAR FORM

FOR A SET OF COMMUTING MATRICES

The normal and canonical forms we have discussed thus far are much more precise than needed for certain important applications. In this section we indicate how one may directly derive a certain useful form without resorting to the theory of similarity presented in Sections 1 to 7.

Theorem 12

Let F be an algebraically closed field and let $\mathscr{A}$ be a set of commuting matrices of F_n; that is, if A and B are in $\mathscr{A}$, $AB = BA$. Then there is a nonsingular matrix P in F_n such that PAP^{-1} is a triangular matrix for every A in $\mathscr{A}$.

Remark. If $A = \alpha I$ with $\alpha \in F$, then $PAP^{-1} = A = \alpha I$ for all nonsingular P in F_n and A is evidently triangular. We may assume, then, that no matrix A in $\mathscr{A}$ has the form $A = \alpha I$ with $\alpha \in F$.

PROOF   If $n = 1$, there is nothing to prove. We use induction on n. Choose a particular matrix A in $\mathscr{A}$. Let α be a characteristic root of A in F. Then the kernel K of $\alpha I - A$ is nonzero, by Theorem 1 of Chapter 6, since det $(\alpha I - A) = 0$. Furthermore, if x is in K and B is in $\mathscr{A}$, then $xB(\alpha I - A) = x(\alpha I - A)B = 0$, and it follows that xB is in K for every x in K and every B in $\mathscr{A}$. Define $L_B(x) = xB$ for x in $V_n(F)$ and B in $\mathscr{A}$. Then L_B is an F linear transformation of $V_n(F)$ into $V_n(F)$. Choose a basis $x_1, \cdots, x_s$ for K and extend it to a basis $x_1, \cdots, x_n$ for $V_n(F)$. Since $L_B(x_i)$ is in K for $i = 1, \cdots, s$, the matrix of L_B relative to the basis $x_1, \cdots, x_n$ of $V_n(F)$ has the form

$$\begin{bmatrix} C_B & 0 \\ X_B & D_B \end{bmatrix}.$$

But, by our inductive hypothesis, there is a new basis for $\langle x_1, \cdots, x_s \rangle$ relative to which every C_B takes triangular form; and there is a new basis for $\langle x_{s+1}, \cdots, x_n \rangle$ relative to which every D_B takes triangular form. It follows that there is a new basis for $V_n(F)$ relative to which every one of the matrices A in $\mathscr{A}$ takes triangular form. This completes the proof of Theorem 12.

Alternatively, one may use the inductive hypothesis to secure nonsingular matrices $Q \in F_s$ and $R \in F_{n-s}$ such that both QC_BQ^{-1} and RD_BR^{-1} are triangular for every B in $\mathscr{A}$. If

$$P = \begin{bmatrix} Q & 0 \\ 0 & R \end{bmatrix},$$

then P is nonsingular in F_n and PBP^{-1} is triangular for every B in $\mathscr{A}$.

Remark. If $\mathscr{A}$ consists of just one matrix $A \in F_n$, then $\mathscr{A}$ is a commuting set of matrices. Theorem 12 then yields the fact that if $A \in F_n$, there is a nonsingular $P \in F_n$ such that PAP^{-1} is triangular. One may also observe that F need not be algebraically closed; it suffices that F contain all the roots of the characteristic polynomial of every $A \in \mathscr{A}$.

Illustrative
Example

The matrices

$$A = \begin{bmatrix} 1 & 3 \\ 2 & 2 \end{bmatrix}, \qquad B = \begin{bmatrix} -1 & 6 \\ 4 & 1 \end{bmatrix}$$

commute. Find a nonsingular matrix P for which $P^{-1}AP$ and $P^{-1}BP$ are triangular. We have $\det(xI - A) = x^2 - 3x - 4 = (x - 4)(x + 1)$. Let K be the kernel of

$$4I - A = \begin{bmatrix} 3 & -3 \\ -2 & 2 \end{bmatrix}$$

and choose $x_1 = (2, 3)$ as a basis for K and $x_1 = (2, 3)$, $x_2 = (0, 1)$ as a basis for $V_2(R_a)$. Let P be the matrix which transforms the basis $x_1' = (1, 0)$, $x_2' = (0, 1)$ into x_1 and x_2, so that

$$P = \begin{bmatrix} 1/2 & -3/2 \\ 0 & 1 \end{bmatrix} \quad \text{and} \quad P^{-1} = \begin{bmatrix} 2 & 3 \\ 0 & 1 \end{bmatrix}.$$

Then

$$P^{-1}AP = \begin{bmatrix} 4 & 0 \\ 1 & -1 \end{bmatrix} \quad \text{and} \quad P^{-1}BP = \begin{bmatrix} 5 & 0 \\ 2 & -5 \end{bmatrix}.$$

EXERCISES FOR CHAPTER 9

1, 2, 3, 4, 5. Find the Smith canonical form for the following matrices.

$$A = \begin{bmatrix} x & x + 4 \\ x - 1 & 3 \end{bmatrix}.$$

$$A = \begin{bmatrix} x & x & 1 \\ x - 1 & x^2 - 1 & x^3 - 1 \end{bmatrix}.$$

$A = \operatorname{diag}(x, \quad x + 1, \quad x^2[x + 1]).$

$$A = \begin{bmatrix} -x & x + 1 & x - 1 & 2 \\ 2 - x & 1 & x + 2 & -4 \\ -3 - 2x & x + 1 & x & x + 4 \\ -x^2 + x + 1 & 2x + 1 & x^2 + 3x - 1 & -4x + 3 \end{bmatrix}.$$

$A = \operatorname{diag}(x^2[x - 1], \quad x[x - 1]^3, \quad x^3[x - 1]^5).$

6. Let D_t denote differentiation with respect to t. Consider the system of differential equations

$$D_t f + (D_t + 4)g = 0,$$
$$(D_t - 1)f + 3g = 0.$$

Observe that the elementary operations which lead to the Smith canonical form (with $x = D_t$) are such that they produce an equivalent system. Using the result of Exercise 1, solve the given system.

7. Generalize the method of Exercise 6 to the system

$$\sum_{j=1}^{n} F_{ij}(D_t)f_j = 0 \qquad (i = 1, \cdots, n)$$

in which $F_{ij}(D_t)$ are polynomials in D_t with constant (real) coefficients.

8. Show that the number of independent arbitrary constants in the solution of the system given in Exercise 7 is equal to the sum of the degrees of the invariant factors of the matrix $[F_{ij}(D_t)]$.

9. Let A be an m-by-n matrix of integers. Introduce elementary operations and show that there are square matrices P and Q of integers with $\det P = \pm 1$ and $\det Q = \pm 1$ such that

$$PAQ = 0 \qquad \text{or} \qquad PAQ = \begin{bmatrix} \text{diag } (i_1, \cdots, i_s) & 0 \\ 0 & 0 \end{bmatrix},$$

where each i_j is a positive integer and i_j divides i_{j+1} $(j = 1, \cdots, s - 1)$.

10. Find nonsingular matrices P and Q of integers such that PAQ has the form given in Exercise 9 if

$$A = \begin{bmatrix} 2 & -3 & 4 & 3 \\ 1 & 2 & 0 & 1 \\ -1 & 4 & 2 & -1 \end{bmatrix}.$$

11. The *free* abelian group A generated by elements $g_1, \cdots, g_n$ consists of all integral linear combinations

$$x = \sum_{i=1}^{n} k_i g_i$$

of $g_1, \cdots, g_n$. Subgroups S of A may be singled out by specifying certain relations

$$\sum_{j=1}^{n} a_{ij}g_j = 0 \qquad (i = 1, \cdots, m)$$

on the generators $g_1, \cdots, g_n$, where the a_{ij} are integers. Using the result of Exercise 9, show that one may choose new generators $h_1, \cdots, h_n$ for A such that the relations on the generators $h_1, \cdots, h_n$ take the form

$$b_j h_j = 0 \qquad (j = 1, \cdots, m).$$

12. Let A be the free abelian group generated by g_1, g_2, and g_3. Let S be the subgroup of A defined by the relations

$$
\begin{aligned}
2g_1 + g_2 - g_3 &= 0, \\
-3g_1 + 2g_2 + 4g_3 &= 0, \\
4g_1 + 2g_3 &= 0, \\
3g_1 + g_2 - g_3 &= 0.
\end{aligned}
$$

Find generators h_1, h_2, and h_3 for A such that the relations become $b_1 h_1 = b_2 h_2 = b_3 h_3 = 0$.

13. The list of nontrivial invariant factors of $xI - A$ ($A \in F_n$) are x, x^2, $x^2(x-1)$, $x^2(x-1)$, $x^2(x-1)$. Write down the rational canonical form for A.

14. The list of elementary divisors of $xI - A$ are x, x, x, x^2, $(x-1)$, $(x-1)^5$, $x^2 + 1$. What is the rational canonical form for A?

15, 16. Write down the normal form of Theorem 8 for the matrices A of Exercises 13 and 14, assuming that $F = R_e$.

17, 18. Write down the Jordan normal form for the matrices A of Exercises 13 and 14, assuming that $F = K$.

19. One may write $J_e(\alpha)$ as $\alpha I + N_e$ where $(N_e)^e = 0$. If $f(x) \in F[x]$, prove that

$$
f(J_e(\alpha)) = f(\alpha)I + f'(\alpha)N_e + \frac{f''(\alpha)}{2!} N_e{}^2 + \cdots.
$$

20. Find all matrices B such that $BJ_3(\alpha) = J_3(\alpha)B$.

21, 22, 23. Find the minimum polynomials for the following matrices.

$$
A = \begin{bmatrix} 4 & 6 & 0 \\ -1 & -1 & 0 \\ 0 & 0 & 1 \end{bmatrix}.
$$

$$
A = \begin{bmatrix} 7 & 4 & -1 \\ 4 & 7 & -1 \\ -4 & -4 & 4 \end{bmatrix}.
$$

$$
A = \begin{bmatrix} 4 & -5 & -2 \\ -5 & 4 & -2 \\ -2 & -2 & -8 \end{bmatrix}.
$$

24, 25, 26. Using the minimum polynomial in place of the characteristic polynomial, compute e^A for A as in Exercises 21, 22, and 23.

27. If $A = \operatorname{diag}(B, C)$ and $g, h \in F[x]$ are the minimum polynomials of B and C respectively, show that the minimum polynomial of A is the least common multiple of g and h.

28. Let

$$A = \begin{bmatrix} B & 0 \\ D & C \end{bmatrix}$$

have elements in a field F, and let the characteristic polynomials of B and C be relatively prime. Show that A is similar to $\operatorname{diag}(B, C)$.

29. Let $A \in K_n$ and assume that no nonzero polynomial in A is nilpotent (that is, $(p(A))^n \neq 0$ if $p(A) \neq 0$). Show that the Jordan form for A is a diagonal matrix.

10

EUCLIDEAN
SPACES

In this chapter we shall define the concept of euclidean space and study some of the elementary properties of such spaces in the finite-dimensional case. We introduce the dual space and the adjoint of a linear transformation of a finite-dimensional euclidean space. The important self-adjoint linear transformations are then classified by finding a normal form for a real symmetric matrix under orthogonal similarity.

/1/ BASIC CONCEPTS OF

EUCLIDEAN GEOMETRY

In this section we first derive two fundamental inequalities for euclidean spaces. Cartesian coordinate systems are then described and constructed in the finite-dimensional case. Finally we discuss the matrices that effect changes from one cartesian coordinate system to another.

A real vector space X is called a *euclidean space* if the following axioms are valid in X.

ES1.   To each ordered pair (x, y) of vectors of X there corresponds a unique real number† $(x \mid y)$ called the inner product of x and y.

ES2.   We have $(x \mid y) = (y \mid x)$ for every $x, y \in X$.

ES3.   If $x, y, z \in X$ and c is a real number, then $(cx \mid y) = c(x \mid y)$ and $(x + y \mid z) = (x \mid z) + (y \mid z)$.

ES4.   If x is a nonzero vector of X, then $(x \mid x) > 0$.

We offer three examples of euclidean spaces.

Example   1   Let $V_m(R_e) = X$ and   define $(x \mid y) = xy^T$. Throughout this chapter, whenever we consider $V_n(R_e)$ as a euclidean space, we shall assume that the inner product of x and y is given by xy^T.

† The customary notation for the inner product of x and y is (x, y), conflicting with the notation for an ordered pair. We follow S. K. Berberian, *Introduction to Hilbert Space*, Academic Press, New York, 1963, in his use of $(x \mid y)$.

Example 2   Let X be the set of real-valued continuous functions $f(t)$ defined on the interval $0 \le t \le 1$, and define $(f | g) = \int_0^1 f(t)g(t) \, dt$.

Example 3   Let X be the set of sequences $x = (c_i; i = 1, 2, \cdots)$ of real numbers such that $\sum_{i=1}^{\infty} c_i^2 < +\infty$. We define $(x | y) = \sum_{i=1}^{\infty} c_i d_i$ for $y = (d_i; i = 1, 2, \cdots)$ in X, and then X becomes a euclidean space.

The following lemma lists some immediate consequences of ES1 to ES4.

Lemma 1

Let X be a euclidean space, let $x, y, z \in X$, and let c be a real number. Then first, $(x|x) = 0$ if and only if $x = 0$; second, $(x|cy) = c(x|y)$ and $(x|y + z) = (x|y) + (x|z)$; third, $(x|0) = (0|x) = 0$; fourth, every R_e subspace of X is a euclidean space.

In view of Lemma 1, one customarily calls the inner product *symmetric* because $(y|x) = (x|y)$, *bilinear* because $(x|y)$ is linear in both x and y, and *positive* because $(x|x)$ is positive unless $x = 0$.

We define the *length* of a vector x in a euclidean space X by† $|x| = \sqrt{(x|x)}$. This agrees with the convention adopted for $V_2(R_e)$ and $V_3(R_e)$ in analytic geometry.

The next lemma is easy, but it has a very important consequence.

Lemma 2

Let X be a euclidean space and let $x, y \in X$. Then $(x|y) \le |x| \, |y|$ and equality holds if and only if $|y| \, x = |x| \, y$.

PROOF   If either $x = 0$ or $y = 0$, there is nothing to prove. We assume that both x and y are nonzero, and apply ES4 to the vector $|y| \, x - |x| \, y$. A bit of computation yields the lemma.

† Many writers use $\|x\|$ for the length of x, but we feel that the present notation is easier to read and write.

Corollary (Schwarz's Inequality)

If x and y are two vectors of a euclidean space X, then $|(x|y)| \leq |x|\,|y|$, and equality holds if and only if $|y|\,x = \pm |x|\,y$.

PROOF   This follows by applying the lemma to the two pairs x, y and $-x$, y.

Corollary (Triangle Inequality)

Let X be a euclidean space and let x, $y \in X$. Then $|x + y| \leq |x| + |y|$, and equality holds if and only if $|y|\,x = |x|\,y$.

PROOF   Expand $|x + y|^2 = ([x + y][x + y])$ and use the lemma.

Remark. If x is a vector of a euclidean space X and c is a real number, then $|cx| = |c|\,|x|$, and $|x| > 0$ unless $x = 0$.

We may use the inequality of Schwarz to define the *angle* θ between two nonzero vectors x and y of a euclidean space X, by setting $\cos \theta = (x|y)/(|x|\,|y|)$. In particular, we call x and y *orthogonal (perpendicular)*, and write $x \perp y$ in case $(x|y) = 0$. A subset S of X will be called *orthogonal* when every two distinct vectors of S are orthogonal. When S is orthogonal and every vector of S has length 1, we call S an *orthonormal* subset of X. An orthonormal subset S of X is automatically R_e-li. (The proof of this is left as an exercise.) If B is an orthonormal basis for X, we call B a *cartesian coordinate system* for X. Every euclidean space of finite dimension has a cartesian coordinate system. To facilitate the proof of this fact, we make one more definition. If T is a subset of a euclidean space X, we define

$$T^{\perp} = \{z \in X;\, z \perp y \quad \text{for every} \quad y \in T\}.$$

It is easy to verify that $T^{\perp}$ is an R_e subspace of X, and we leave the verification to the reader. By ES4, $T^{\perp} \cap T = 0$ for every R_e subspace T of X.

Illustrative
Example

Find the cosine of the angle between the vectors $x = (1, 2, -1, 4)$ and $y = (2, 1, 4, -3)$. Here $|x| = \sqrt{22}$, $|y| = \sqrt{30}$, $(x|y) = 2 + 2 - 4 - 12 = -12$, and $\cos\theta = -12/(\sqrt{22}\,\sqrt{30})$.

Illustrative
Example

In $V_3(R_e)$, let $Y = \langle(1, 0, 1), (0, 1, 2)\rangle$. Find $Y^\perp$. We have $x = (\alpha, \beta, \gamma)$ in $Y^\perp$ if and only if $\alpha + \gamma = \beta + 2\gamma = 0$, so that $x = (\alpha, 2\alpha, -\alpha) = \alpha(1, 2, -1)$ and $Y^\perp = \langle(1, 2, -1)\rangle$.

Illustrative
Example

Find $|f|$ in the euclidean space of Example 2 if $f(t) = \sin\pi t$. We have $|f|^2 = \int_0^1 f^2(t)\,dt = \int_0^1 (\sin^2 \pi t)\,dt = (1/2)$.

Theorem 1

Let X be a nonzero finite-dimensional euclidean space. Then X has an orthonormal basis.

PROOF   We use induction on $\dim X$. If $\dim X = 1$, select $x \neq 0$ in X and verify that $x_1 = x/|x|$ is an orthonormal basis for X. Now let $\dim X$ be greater than 1, and assume the theorem for euclidean spaces of dimension less than $\dim X$. Select $y \neq 0$ in X and let x_1 be an orthonormal basis for $Y = \langle y \rangle$. Then Y is an R_e subspace of X, and $Y \cap Y^\perp = 0$ shows that $Y^\perp \subset X$ since y is not in $Y^\perp$. Hence $\dim Y^\perp < \dim X$, and the fourth statement of Lemma 1 and our inductive hypothesis show that $Y^\perp$ has an orthonormal basis $x_2, \cdots, x_m$. If x is in X, then $x - (x|x_1)x_1$ is in $Y^\perp$, since $([x - (x|x_1)x_1]|x_1) = 0$. Thus x is in the span of $x_1, x_2, \cdots, x_m$, and the elements $x_1, \cdots, x_m$ span X. It is clear that $x_1, \cdots, x_m$ is an orthonormal subset of X and it follows that it is an orthonormal basis for X.

Illustrative
Example

In $X = V_4(R_e)$, let $Y = \langle(1, 1, -1, 2), (1, 1, 1, -2)\rangle$. Find an orthonormal basis for Y and extend it to an orthonormal basis for X. Take $y_1 = (1, 1, -1, 2)$ and $y_2 = y_1 + \alpha(1, 1, 1, -2)$. Choose α so that $(y_2 | y_1) = 0$. This equation becomes $7 - 3\alpha = 0$, or $\alpha = 7/3$ and $y_2 = (10/3, 10/3, 4/3, -8/3)$. We then have $y_1 \perp y_2$ and $Y = \langle y_1, y_2 \rangle$. Thus $y_1' = (1/\sqrt{7})y_1$ and $y_2' = (1/\sqrt{280})(10, 10, 4, -8)$ is an orthonormal basis for Y. Now, $x = (\alpha, \beta, \gamma, \delta) \in Y^\perp$ if and only if $\alpha + \beta - \gamma + 2\delta = \alpha + \beta + \gamma - 2\delta = 0$ if and only if $\beta = -\alpha$ and $\gamma = 2\delta$. It follows that $Y^\perp = \langle(1, -1, 0, 0), (0, 0, 2, 1)\rangle$ and that $y_3 = (1/\sqrt{2})(1, -1, 0, 0)$ and $y_4 = (1/\sqrt{5})(0, 0, 2, 1)$ is an orthonormal basis for $Y^\perp$. The required orthonormal basis for X is, then, y_1', y_2', y_3, y_4.

Remark. Coordinates of a vector x in X relative to an orthonormal basis $x_1, \cdots, x_m$ of X are easy to compute. For, from

$$x = \sum_{i=1}^{m} c_i x_i$$

we get $(x | x_k) = c_k$ for $k = 1, \cdots, m$. In other words, every vector x in X has the form

$$x = \sum_{i=1}^{m} (x | x_i)x_i.$$

Illustrative
Example

Let $x = (\alpha, \beta, \gamma, \delta) \in V_4(R_e)$. Find the coordinates of x relative to the orthonormal basis constructed in the previous example. We have

$$\xi_1 = (x | y_1') = (1/\sqrt{7})(\alpha + \beta - \gamma + 2\delta),$$
$$\xi_2 = (x | y_2') = (1/\sqrt{280})(10\alpha + 10\beta + 4\gamma - 8\delta),$$
$$\xi_3 = (x | y_3) = (1/\sqrt{2})(\alpha - \beta),$$
$$\xi_4 = (x | y_4) = (1/\sqrt{5})(2\gamma + \delta).$$

Corollary 1

If Y is an R_e subspace of a finite-dimensional euclidean space X, then $Y + Y^\perp = X$ and $Y \cap Y^\perp = 0$.

PROOF   The corollary is trivial if $Y = 0$. If $Y \neq 0$, let $y_1, \cdots,$ y_q be an orthonormal basis for Y. For each x in X, $x - \sum_{j=1}^{q} (x\,|\,y_j)y_j$ is in $Y^\perp$. Hence $X \subseteq Y + Y^\perp \subseteq X$.

Corollary 2

Every orthonormal subset S of a finite-dimensional euclidean space X has at most dim X elements, and S is a part of an orthonormal basis for X.

PROOF   The first conclusion follows from TB3 (Chapter 5). To prove the second conclusion, put $Y = \langle S \rangle$. If $Y = X$, then S is an orthonormal basis for X; otherwise, $Y^\perp \neq 0$ and it has an orthonormal basis T. Then $S \cup T$ is an orthonormal set which spans X, since $Y + Y^\perp = X$.

Corollary 3

If Y is an R_e subspace of a finite-dimensional euclidean space X, then $Y^{\perp\perp} = (Y^\perp)^\perp = Y$.

PROOF   Clearly, $Y \subseteq Y^{\perp\perp}$. Suppose that $Y \subset Y^{\perp\perp}$. Then $Y \neq 0$, since $0^{\perp\perp} = X^\perp = 0$. Select an orthonormal basis $y_1, \cdots,$ y_m for Y and extend it to an orthonormal basis $y_1, \cdots, y_t$ for $Y^{\perp\perp}$. Then $y_t \in Y^\perp \cap Y^{\perp\perp} = 0$, which is impossible.

We call two R_e subspaces Y and Z of a euclidean space orthogonal, and write $Y \perp Z$ when $y \perp z$ for every y in Y and every z in Z. If Y and Z are orthogonal subspaces with orthonormal bases S and T respectively, then it is easy to see that $S \cup T$ is an orthonormal basis for $Y + Z$.

To conclude this section we shall find the special property of the matrix P of e_X relative to two orthonormal bases $x_1, \cdots, x_n$

and $x_1', \cdots, x_n'$ for X. This will yield formulas for the *transformation of cartesian coordinates* in X. The definition of P is provided by the equations

$$e_X(x_i) = x_i = \sum_{j=1}^{n} p_{ij} x_j' \qquad (i = 1, \cdots, n).$$

(We have seen that $p_{ij} = (x_i | x_j')$ $(i, j = 1, \cdots, n)$.) Hence we also have

$$x_k = \sum_{l=1}^{n} p_{kl} x_l' \qquad (k = 1, \cdots, n).$$

Then

$$(x_i | x_k) = \sum_{j,l} p_{ij} p_{kl} (x_j' | x_l') = \sum_{j} p_{ij} p_{kj} \qquad (i, k = 1, \cdots, n).$$

We translate these equations into the statement that the element in the ith row and kth column of I_n is equal to the element in the corresponding position of PP^T or, more briefly, $PP^T = I_n$. A matrix P in $(R_e)_n$ is called *orthogonal* when $PP^T = I_n$ (and then, of course, also $P^T P = I_n$ since $P^T = P^{-1}$). The reason for the term *orthogonal* is clear when we realize that $PP^T = I$ means that the rows of P form an orthonormal subset of $V_n(R_e)$. These orthogonal matrices effect changes from one orthonormal basis to another. They correspond to the matrices encountered in elementary analytic geometry when rotation (and reflection) of coordinate axes is discussed.

Illustrative
Example

Find the formulas for the transformation of coordinates from $x_1 = (1, 0, 0)$, $x_2 = (0, 1, 0)$, and $x_3 = (0, 0, 1)$ to $x_1' = (1/3)(1, 2, -2)$, $x_2' = (1/3)(2, 1, 2)$, and $x_3' = (1/3)(2, -2, -1)$. To find P we use $p_{ij} = (x_i | x_j')$, where $i, j = 1, 2, 3$, and we get

$$P = (1/3) \begin{bmatrix} 1 & 2 & 2 \\ 2 & 1 & -2 \\ -2 & 2 & -1 \end{bmatrix}.$$

Since always $[\xi_1', \xi_2', \xi_3'] = [\xi_1, \xi_2, \xi_3]P$, we find that

$$\xi_1' = (1/3)(\xi_1 + 2\xi_2 - 2\xi_3),$$
$$\xi_2' = (1/3)(2\xi_1 + \xi_2 + 2\xi_3),$$
$$\xi_3' = (1/3)(2\xi_1 - 2\xi_2 - \xi_3).$$

/2/ ADJOINT OF A REAL

LINEAR TRANSFORMATION

In this section we first introduce the dual of a finite-dimensional euclidean space. This permits us to discuss the adjoint of a real linear transformation. We conclude the section by finding the special property of the matrix of a self-adjoint real linear transformation.

We begin our discussion by finding a formula for real linear transformations of a euclidean space X into R_e.

Lemma 3

Let f be an R_e-lt of a finite-dimensional euclidean space X into $V_1(R_e) = R_e$. Then there is a unique vector u^f in X such that $f(x) = (x|u^f)$ for every x in X.

PROOF Let $x_1, \cdots, x_n$ be an orthonormal basis for X. Then, if any u^f with the desired property exists, we must have

$$u^f = \sum_{i=1}^{n} (u^f|x_i)x_i = \sum_{i=1}^{n} f(x_i)x_i.$$

That this value of u^f actually works is shown by

$$f(x) = f\left(\sum_{i=1}^{n} (x|x_i)x_i \right) = \sum_{i=1}^{n} (x|x_i)f(x_i)$$
$$= \left(x| \sum_{i=1}^{n} f(x_i)x_i \right) = (x|u^f)$$

for every x in X. If also $f(x) = (x|v)$ for every $x \in X$, then $v - u^f \in X^\perp = 0$ and $v = u^f$.

The set X^* of all R_e-lt of X into R_e is called the *dual of the space* X. For f and g in X^* and c a real number, we define

$$(f + g)(x) = f(x) + g(x), \qquad (cf)(x) = cf(x)$$

for every x in X. It is easily verified that X^* thus becomes a real vector space. Using Lemma 3, we may also define $(f|g) = (u^f|u^g)$ and check that then X^* is a euclidean space. In fact, the mapping $f \to u^f$ is a faithful map of X^* onto X for which

$$u^f + u^g = u^{f+g}, \qquad u^{cf} = cu^f, \qquad |f| = |u^f|$$

for every f and g in X^* and every $c \in R_e$. We say that X^* and X are *isomorphic* and *isometric*. In this sense a finite-dimensional euclidean space is *self-dual*.

Let us consider an R_e-lt $L(x)$ of a finite-dimensional euclidean space X into X. For each fixed y in X, the equation $f(x) = (L(x)|y)$ defines an R_e-lt of X into R_e. By Lemma 3, there is a vector u^f in X which is uniquely determined by y and is such that $(L(x)|y) = (x|u^f)$ for every x in X. Permitting y to vary in X, we obtain a map L^* of X into X for which $(L(x)|y) = (x|L^*(y))$ for every x and y in X. It is easy to verify that L^* is an R_e-lt of X into X. We call L^* the *adjoint*† of L. If one defines, for L and M R_e-lt's of X into X and for c a real number, $(L + M)(x) = L(x) + M(x)$ and $(cL)(x) = cL(x)$ for every x in X, then cL and $L + M$ are also R_e-lt's of X into X. Using these definitions, we have the following rules for adjoints:

$$(cL)^* = cL^*, \qquad (L + M)^* = L^* + M^*,$$
$$(M \circ L)^* = L^* \circ M^*.$$

It will now be interesting to find the relation between the matrices of L and L^* relative to the same orthonormal basis $x_1, \cdots, x_n$ for X. The equations

$$L(x_i) = \sum_{j=1}^{n} a_{ij} x_j \qquad (i = 1, \cdots, n)$$

---

† We used the same word "adjoint" earlier in a quite different sense and in a different context. Such usages abound in mathematics. They merely reflect its growth on the one hand and the permanence of its nomenclature on the other.

define the matrix $A = [a_{ij}]$ of L relative to the basis $x_1, \cdots, x_n$ of X. Then we may compute

$$(L(x_i)|x_k) = \sum_{j=1}^{n} a_{ij}(x_j|x_k) = a_{ik},$$

$$(x_i|L^*(x_k)) = a_{ik} = (L^*(x_k)|x_i),$$

$$L^*(x_k) = \sum_{i=1}^{n} a_{ik}x_i,$$

where $i, k = 1, \cdots, n$. We now see that the matrix of L^* relative to the basis $x_1, \cdots, x_n$ for X is A^T.

We call an R_e-lt L of a finite-dimensional euclidean space X into X *self-adjoint* whenever $L = L^*$. We shall devote the remainder of this chapter to the study of such self-adjoint R_e-lt's. Relative to an orthonormal basis for X, the matrix of a self-adjoint R_e-lt of X into X is *symmetric* in that $A = A^T$. Two real symmetric matrices A and B represent the same self-adjoint R_e-lt relative to two different orthonormal bases for X if and only if $B = P^T A P$ for an orthogonal real matrix P $(P^T = P^{-1})$. We shall call A and B *orthogonally similar* when this relation holds. Here the real square matrices A and B need not be symmetric. Since the product of two real orthogonal matrices is again a real orthogonal matrix, it is evident that orthogonal similarity is still another equivalence relation. We shall derive a normal form for a real symmetric matrix A under orthogonal similarity in the next section.

/ 3 / EVERY REAL SYMMETRIC MATRIX

IS ORTHOGONALLY SIMILAR TO A

REAL DIAGONAL MATRIX

In this section we apply our simple geometric considerations as well as some results of the previous chapter to prove the statement just made. This result has many applications in applied mathematics and for this reason it is sometimes called the *principal axes theorem*. Very special cases of the theorem constitute a considerable portion of elementary analytic geometry.

We base our proof on the following three lemmas about real symmetric matrices.

Lemma 4

The roots of the characteristic polynomial of a real symmetric matrix are real.

PROOF   Let A be in $(R_e)_n$ and let $A = A^T$. Then $f(x) = \det (xI - A)$ is in $R_e[x]$. Using the fact that the complex field K is algebraically closed, we find that $f(x)$ is a product of linear factors $(x - \alpha_i)$ in $K[x]$, where $i = 1, \cdots, n$. Let α be one of α_i. Since $\det (\alpha I - A) = 0$, there is a nonzero vector z of $V_n(K)$ which is in the kernel of $\alpha I - A$. Thus $z(\alpha I - A) = 0$ or $zA = \alpha z$. Let $z = [\zeta_1, \cdots, \zeta_n]$ and put $\bar{z} = [\bar{\zeta}_1, \cdots, \bar{\zeta}_n]$. Then we may obtain $zA\bar{z}^T = \alpha z\bar{z}^T$. Since $z \neq 0$, $z\bar{z}^T$ is a nonzero real number. But then $zA\bar{z}^T$ is a complex number whose conjugate is given by

$$\overline{zA\bar{z}^T} = \bar{z}Az^T = (\bar{z}Az^T)^T = zA\bar{z}^T.$$

Hence $zA\bar{z}^T$ is real and so is $\alpha = (zA\bar{z}^T)/(z\bar{z}^T)$.

Lemma 5

The minimum polynomial of a real symmetric matrix has distinct real roots.

PROOF   Let $A = A^T$ be in $(R_e)_n$ and let $m(x)$ be the minimum polynomial of A. Of course, $m(x) \in R_e[x]$ and $m(A) = 0$.

The roots of $m(x) = 0$ are real by Lemma 4 and the Corollary of Theorem 11 of Chapter 9. Suppose that c is a real number and that $(x - c)^2$ divides $m(x)$. Set $p(x) = m(x)/(x - c)$. Then $(p(A))^2 = 0$ but $p(A) \neq 0$. Thus $B = p(A)$ satisfies $B^2 = 0$, $B^T = B$, and $B \neq 0$. But this is impossible, for it implies that $BB^T = 0$, while the diagonal elements of BB^T are the sums of the squares of the elements of the rows of B.

When $A = A^T$ is in $(R_e)_n$ and c is a root of $f(x) = \det (xI - A) = 0$, we call c a *characteristic root* of A. The kernel of $cI - A$ is then a nonzero R_e subspace of $V_n(R_e)$, which is called the *characteristic subspace* of A corresponding to the characteristic root c. Each nonzero vector of a characteristic subspace is called a *characteristic vector* of A.

Lemma 6

Two distinct characteristic subspaces of a real symmetric matrix are orthogonal.

PROOF   Let $A = A^T$ be in $(R_e)_n$, $c, d \in R_e$, $y, z \in V_n(R_e)$, and $y(cI - A) = z(dI - A) = 0$, and let $c \neq d$. Then $yA = cy$, $zA = dz$, $Az^T = dz^T$, $yAz^T = cyz^T = dyz^T$, and $yz^T = 0$, since $c \neq d$ and hence $y \perp z$.

Lemma 7

Let $A = A^T$ be in $(R_e)_n$. Then the sum of the characteristic subspaces of A is $V_n(R_e)$.

PROOF   We use the resolution of the identity

$$I = E_1 + \cdots + E_k$$

as derived (for the special case at hand) in Section 2 of Chapter 4. Then each x in $V_n(R_e)$ has the form $x = xE_1 + \cdots + xE_k$. But, by the definition of the idempotents E_i (refer to Chapter 4), $xE_i(A - c_iI) = 0$. It follows that xE_i is zero or a characteristic vector for A, and that every x in $V_n(R_e)$ is a sum of characteristic vectors.

SECOND PROOF   Let Y be the sum of the characteristic subspaces of A and suppose that $Y \neq V_n(R_e)$. Note that $yA \in Y$ for all $y \in Y$. Choose an orthonormal basis $x_1, \cdots, x_s$ for Y and extend it to an orthonormal basis $x_1, \cdots, x_n$ for $V_n(R_e)$. With $L(x) = xA$ for $x \in V_n(R_e)$, A is the matrix of L relative to the usual basis while the matrix of L relative to $x_1, \cdots, x_n$ is

$$P^T A P = \begin{bmatrix} B & 0 \\ 0 & C \end{bmatrix}$$

with $B \in (R_e)_s$. Since $C \in (R_e)_{n-s}$ and $C^T = C$, we may choose u as a characteristic vector of C in $V_{n-s}(R_e)$. But then $[0, u]P^T$ is a characteristic vector for A and must have the form $[y, 0]P^T$ with $y \in V_s(R_e)$, a contradiction.

We are now ready to prove the main theorem of the chapter.

Theorem 2

Every real symmetric matrix A is orthogonally similar to a real diagonal matrix $D = \text{diag}(c_1, \cdots, c_n)$ where $\det(xI - A) = (x - c_1)\cdots(x - c_n)$, so that each c_i is a characteristic root of A and so that the distinct characteristic roots of A appear in D according to their multiplicities as roots of the characteristic equation $\det(xI - A) = 0$.

PROOF   Choose an orthonormal basis B_i for each characteristic subspace of A, where $i = 1, \cdots, k$. By Lemmas 6 and 7, $B_1 \cup B_2 \cup \cdots \cup B_k$ is an orthonormal basis for $V_n(R_e)$. Write $x_1, \cdots, x_n$ for $B_1 \cup B_2 \cup \cdots \cup B_k$. Then $x_i A = c_i x_i$ for $i = 1, \cdots, n$ and c_i a characteristic root of A. Hence

(1)
$$\begin{bmatrix} x_1 \\ x_2 \\ \vdots \\ x_n \end{bmatrix} A = \begin{bmatrix} x_1 A \\ x_2 A \\ \vdots \\ x_n A \end{bmatrix} = \begin{bmatrix} c_1 x_1 \\ c_2 x_2 \\ \vdots \\ c_n x_n \end{bmatrix} = \text{diag}(c_1, c_2, \cdots, c_n)\begin{bmatrix} x_1 \\ x_2 \\ \vdots \\ x_n \end{bmatrix}.$$

Setting

$$P = \begin{bmatrix} x_1 \\ x_2 \\ \vdots \\ x_n \end{bmatrix}^T$$

we obtain $PP^T = I_n$, since $x_1, \cdots, x_n$ is an orthonormal basis for $V_n(R_e)$. Using this definition of P, equation (1) becomes $P^T A = (\text{diag}(c_1, c_2, \cdots, c_n))P^T$, from which we get $P^T A P = \text{diag}(c_1, c_2, \cdots, c_n)$, and the proof is complete.

Illustrative
Example

Find a real diagonal matrix which is orthogonally similar to

$$A = \begin{bmatrix} 4 & -5 & -2 \\ -5 & 4 & -2 \\ -2 & -2 & -8 \end{bmatrix}.$$

First solution. We find the idempotents for A. We have

$$\det (xI - A) = \det \begin{bmatrix} x-4 & 5 & 2 \\ 5 & x-4 & 2 \\ 2 & 2 & x+8 \end{bmatrix} = x^3 - 81x.$$

The characteristic roots are 0, 9, -9, and $1/(x^3 - 81x) = a_1/x + a_2/(x-9) + a_3/(x+9)$ with $a_1 = -1/(81)$, $a_2 = 1/(162)$, and $a_3 = 1/(162)$. Hence

$$E_1 = (-1/81)(A^2 - 81I) = -(1/9)\begin{bmatrix} -4 & -4 & 2 \\ -4 & -4 & 2 \\ 2 & 2 & -1 \end{bmatrix},$$

$$E_2 = (1/162)(A^2 + 9A) = (1/2)\begin{bmatrix} 1 & -1 & 0 \\ -1 & 1 & 0 \\ 0 & 0 & 0 \end{bmatrix},$$

$$E_3 = (1/162)(A^2 - 9A) = (1/18)\begin{bmatrix} 1 & 1 & 4 \\ 1 & 1 & 4 \\ 4 & 4 & 16 \end{bmatrix}.$$

Characteristic vectors of unit length are then $x_1 = (1/3)(2, 2, -1)$, $x_2 = (1/\sqrt{2})(1, -1, 0)$, and $x_3 = (1/\sqrt{18})(1, 1, 4)$; and

$$\begin{bmatrix} x_1 \\ x_2 \\ x_3 \end{bmatrix} A = \begin{bmatrix} x_1 A \\ x_2 A \\ x_3 A \end{bmatrix} = \begin{bmatrix} 0 \\ 9x_2 \\ -9x_3 \end{bmatrix} = \begin{bmatrix} 0 & 0 & 0 \\ 0 & 9 & 0 \\ 0 & 0 & -9 \end{bmatrix}\begin{bmatrix} x_1 \\ x_2 \\ x_3 \end{bmatrix}.$$

With $P = [x_1^T, x_2^T, x_3^T]$, we have $P^T P = I$ and $P^T A P = $ diag $(0, 9, -9)$.

Second solution. It is not necessary to compute the idempotents, since only the characteristic subspaces are required. For the characteristic root 0, we need a nonzero vector x_1' such that $x_1'A = 0$. Taking $x_1' = (\xi_1, \xi_2, \xi_3)$ we see that $4\xi_1 - 5\xi_2 - 2\xi_3 = -5\xi_1 + 4\xi_2 - 2\xi_3 = -2\xi_1 - 2\xi_2 - 8\xi_3 = 0$. Now, $9\xi_1 - 9\xi_2 = 0$ and $\xi_2 = -2\xi_3$, and we may choose $x_1' = (2, 2, -1)$. A characteristic vector for 0 of unit length is then $x_1 = (1/3)(2, 2, -1)$.

For the characteristic root 9, we take $x_2' = (\eta_1, \eta_2, \eta_3)$ and require that $x_2'(A - 9I) = 0$, and we get

$$-5\eta_1 - 5\eta_2 - 2\eta_3 = -5\eta_1 - 5\eta_2 - 2\eta_3$$
$$= -2\eta_1 - 2\eta_2 - 17\eta_3 = 0,$$

$$\eta_1 + \eta_2 = 0 \quad \text{and} \quad \eta_3 = 0,$$

$$x_2' = (1, -1, 0) \quad \text{and} \quad x_2 = (1/\sqrt{2})(1, -1, 0).$$

Finally, for the characteristic root -9, we take $x_3' = (\xi_1, \xi_2, \xi_3)$ and require that $x_3'(A + 9I) = 0$, and we get

$$13\xi_1 - 5\xi_2 - 2\xi_3 = -5\xi_1 + 13\xi_2 - 2\xi_3$$
$$= -2\xi_1 - 2\xi_2 + \xi_3 = 0,$$

$$18\xi_1 - 18\xi_2 = 0, \qquad 8\xi_1 = 2\xi_3,$$

$$x_3' = (1, 1, 4), \qquad x_3 = (1/\sqrt{18})(1, 1, 4).$$

EXERCISES FOR CHAPTER 10

1. Find an orthonormal basis x_1, x_2, x_3 in $V_3(R_e)$, with $x_1 = (1/3, -2/3, 2/3)$.

2. Let $Y = \langle (1, -1, 0), (1, 2, -1) \rangle$ in $V_3(R_e)$. Find $Y^\perp$. Find an orthonormal basis for Y and extend it to an orthonormal basis for X.

3. Show that the vectors

    $$x_1 = (1/\sqrt{3})(1, 1, 1),$$
    $$x_2 = (1/\sqrt{2})(1, -1, 0),$$
    $$x_3 = (1/\sqrt{6})(-1, -1, 2)$$

    form an orthonormal basis for $V_3(R_e)$ and find the coordinates of $x = (\alpha, \beta, \gamma)$ relative to this basis.

4. Show that, in Example 2, Section 1, $x_{2n+1} = \sin 2n\pi t$ and $x_{2n} = \cos 2n\pi t$ are orthogonal vectors.

5. Let $x_1, \cdots, x_m$ be orthonormal vectors in a euclidean space. Show that

    $$\left| x - \sum_{i=1}^m (x|x_i)x_i \right|^2 = |x|^2 - \sum_{i=1}^m [(x|x_i)]^2.$$

6.† Prove that in a euclidean space

    $$|x + y + z| + |x| + |y| + |z|$$
    $$\geq |x + y| + |y + z| + |x + z|.$$

† This is *not* an easy exercise.

7. In $V_3(R_e)$, let $L(1, 1, 0) = (0, 1, 0)$, $L(2, 1, -1) = (1, 0, 0)$ and $L(0, 0, 1) = (0, 0, 1)$. Find the matrix A of L relative to the usual basis and verify that A^T is the matrix of L^* relative to the usual basis.

8. Let Y be a subspace of $X = V_n(R_e)$. If $x \in X$, show that there is a unique vector $P(x) \in Y$ such that $x - P(x) \in Y^\perp$. [*Hint:* Let $y_1, \cdots, y_s$ be an orthonormal basis for Y so that $P(x) = \eta_1 y_1 + \cdots + \eta_s y_s$.] Show that the correspondence $x \to P(x)$ is a linear transformation of X into X such that $P(P(x)) = P(x)$ for all $x \in X$. Show that P is self-adjoint. [*Hint:* $(x - P(x) | P(z)) = 0$ for all x, z in X. We call P the *orthogonal projection* of X onto Y.]

9. Find the minimum polynomial of the real symmetric matrix

$$A = \begin{bmatrix} 0 & -1 & 1 \\ -1 & 0 & -1 \\ 1 & -1 & 0 \end{bmatrix}.$$

10. Do Exercise 9 with

$$A = \begin{bmatrix} 0 & 1 & 1 \\ 1 & 0 & 1 \\ 1 & 1 & 0 \end{bmatrix}.$$

11. Do Exercise 9 with

$$A = \begin{bmatrix} 0 & 1 & 1 \\ 1 & -3 & 2 \\ 1 & 2 & -3 \end{bmatrix}.$$

12, 13, 14. For the matrices of Exercises 9, 10, and 11, find an orthogonal matrix P such that $B = P^T A P$ is diagonal.

15. Let $L = L^*$ be a self-adjoint linear transformation of $V_n(R_e)$ into $V_n(R_e)$. Call L *positive semidefinite* when $(L(x) | x) \geq 0$ for all x in $V_n(R_e)$. Show that L is positive semidefinite if and only if $xAx^T \geq 0$ for all x in $V_n(R_e)$ where A is the matrix of L relative to an orthonormal basis for $V_n(R_e)$. Show that L is positive semidefinite if and only if all the characteristic roots of A are nonnegative.

16. Let P and Q be self-adjoint linear transformations of $X = V_n(R_e)$ into X such that $P^2 = P$ and $Q^2 = Q$. Assume that

$P - Q$ is positive semidefinite so that $(P(x) - Q(x)|x) \geq 0$ for all $x \in X$. Show that $Q \circ P = Q$.

17. Let P be a self-adjoint linear transformation of $X = V_n(R_e)$ into X, such that $P^2 = P$. Find a subspace Y of X for which P is the orthogonal projection of X onto Y. (See Exercise 8.)

18. Call a matrix $S \in (R_e)_n$ *real skew* if $A^T = -A$. Show that the characteristic roots of a real skew matrix are pure imaginaries.

19. Find a canonical form for real skew matrices under orthogonal similarity.

11

UNITARY
SPACES

In many applications it is convenient to use the complex number field, K, instead of the real number field. In this chapter we introduce and study the elementary properties of the complex analog of euclidean spaces. These spaces are called unitary spaces. As in Chapter 10, we confine our discussion to the finite-dimensional case. The dual space leads us to discuss the adjoint of a complex linear transformation and to the study of self-adjoint and skew linear transformations. We conclude the chapter with a discussion of the important class of normal transformations.

/1/ BASIC CONCEPTS OF
UNITARY GEOMETRY

This section introduces the reader to the concept of unitary spaces and develops their elementary properties. The parallel with euclidean geometry is so close that many of the proofs are quite analogous to those of Section 1 in Chapter 10. Such proofs will be omitted.

A K vector space X (K the complex field) is called a *unitary space* when the following axioms are valid in X.

U1.   To each ordered pair (x, y) of vectors of X there corresponds a unique complex number $(x\,|\,y)$ called the inner product of x and y.

U2.   We have $(y\,|\,x) = \overline{(x\,|\,y)}$ for every $x, y \in X$.

U3.   If x, y, $z \in X$ and $c \in K$, then $(cx\,|\,y) = c(x\,|\,y)$ and $(x + y\,|\,z) = (x\,|\,z) + (y\,|\,z)$.

U4.   If x is a nonzero vector of X, then $(x\,|\,x)$ (which is real by U2) is positive.

We offer three examples of unitary spaces.

Example 1   Let $X = V_n(K)$ and, for $y = (c_1, \cdots, c_n)$ in X, define $\bar{y} = (\bar{c}_1, \cdots, \bar{c}_n)$ and $(x\,|\,y) = x\bar{y}^{\mathrm{T}}$ whenever $x \in X$.

Example 2   Let X be the set of complex-valued continuous functions $f(t)$ defined on the real interval $0 \le t \le 1$, and define $(f\,|\,g) = \int_0^1 f(t)\overline{g(t)}\,\mathrm{d}t$.

Example 3   Let X be the set of sequences $x = (c_i; \; i = 1, 2, \cdots)$ of complex numbers such that $\sum_{i=1}^{\infty} |c_i|^2 < +\infty$. For $y = (d_i; \; i = 1, 2, \cdots)$ in X, define $(x|y) = \sum_{i=1}^{\infty} c_i \bar{d_i}$. Then X becomes a unitary space.

Lemma 1

Let X be a unitary space, let $x, y \in X$, and let $c \in K$. Then: first, $(x|x) = 0$ if and only if $x = 0$; second, $(x|cy) = \bar{c}(x|y)$ and $(x|y + z) = (x|y) + (x|z)$; third, $(x|0) = (0|x) = 0$; fourth, every K subspace of X is a unitary space.

For a vector x of a unitary space X, we define $|x| = \sqrt{(x|x)}$ and note that $|x| > 0$ unless $x = 0$ and that $|cx| = |c||x|$ for every complex number c.

Lemma 2

Let X be a unitary space and let $x, y \in X$. Then $Re(x|y) \leq |x||y|$, and equality holds if and only if $|y|x = |x|y$.

Remark. For a complex number c, we define $Re(c) = (c + \bar{c})/2$ and $Im \, c = Re(-ic) = (c - \bar{c})/2i$.

Corollary 1 (Schwarz's Inequality)

If x and y are two vectors of a unitary space X, then $|(x|y)| \leq |x||y|$, and equality holds if and only if $|y|x = e^{i\theta}|x|y$ for some $\theta \in R_e$.

PROOF   Apply Lemma 2 to $e^{-i\theta}x, y$, where θ is so chosen that $(x|y) = e^{i\theta}|(x|y)|$.

Corollary 2 (The Triangle Inequality)

Let X be a unitary space and let $x, y \in X$. Then $|x + y| \leq |x| + |y|$, and equality holds if and only if $|y|x = |x|y$.

The definitions of perpendicularity and of orthonormal sets and bases, given in Chapter 10, could now be repeated. We assume these concepts, then, as well as the analogs of Theorem 1 of Chapter 10 and its corollaries.

There is a slight difference in the special property of a matrix U which effects a transformation of coordinates from the orthonormal basis $x_1, \cdots, x_n$ to the orthonormal basis $x_1', \cdots, x_n'$ in a unitary space X. By definition,

$$e_X(x_i) = x_i = \sum_{j=1}^{n} u_{ij} x_j' \qquad (i = 1, \cdots, n).$$

Hence also

$$x_k = \sum_{l=1}^{n} u_{kl} x_l' \qquad (k = 1, \cdots, n).$$

Then

$$(x_i | x_k) = \sum_{j,l} u_{ij} \bar{u}_{kl} (x_j' | x_l')$$
$$= \sum_{j} u_{ij} \bar{u}_{kj} \qquad (i, k = 1, \cdots, n).$$

In matrix notation, this condition reads $U\bar{U}^T = I_n$. A matrix $U \in K_n$ for which $U\bar{U}^T = I_n$ (and hence also $\bar{U}^T U = I_n$) is called a *unitary* matrix. A matrix $U \in K_n$ is then unitary if and only if its rows (or columns) form an orthonormal basis for $V_n(K)$. It is the unitary matrices which effect changes from one orthonormal basis of a unitary space to another orthonormal basis.

Illustrative
Example

In $V_2(K)$, find the formulas for transformation of coordinates from those relative to $x_1 = (i, 0)$ and $x_2 = (0, i)$ to those relative to $x_1' = (1/\sqrt{2})(i, 1)$ and $x_2' = (1/\sqrt{2})(i, -1)$. We have

$$\xi_j' = \sum_{i=1}^{n} \xi_i u_{ij} \qquad (j = 1, \cdots, n),$$
$$u_{ij} = (x_i | x_j') \qquad (i, j = 1, \cdots, n).$$

We find

$$U = \begin{bmatrix} 1/\sqrt{2} & 1/\sqrt{2} \\ i/\sqrt{2} & -i/\sqrt{2} \end{bmatrix},$$

so that

$$\xi_1' = (1/\sqrt{2})\xi_1 + (i/\sqrt{2})\xi_2,$$
$$\xi_2' = (1/\sqrt{2})\xi_1 - (i/\sqrt{2})\xi_2,$$

are the desired formulas.

/ 2 / ADJOINT OF A COMPLEX

LINEAR TRANSFORMATION

In this section we introduce the dual of a finite-dimensional unitary space and the adjoint of a complex linear transformation. These concepts permit us to describe the important classes of self-adjoint and of skew complex linear transformations.

Lemma 3

Let f be a K-lt of a finite-dimensional unitary space X into $V_1(K) = K$. Then there is a unique vector u^f in X such that $f(x) = (x|u^f)$ for every $x \in X$.

We omit the proof.

The set X^* of all K-lt of X into K is called the *dual of the space* X. As in Section 2, Chapter 10, we may see that X^* is a unitary space if we define $(f|g) = (u^g|u^f)$ for $f, g \in X^*$. However, the mapping $f \to u^f$ of X^* onto X is no longer a vector space isomorphism because $u^{cf} = \bar{c}u^f$.

For a K-lt L of a finite-dimensional unitary space X into X, we may use Lemma 3 to define the adjoint L^* of L. We find that L^* is the unique K-lt of X into X for which

$$(L(x)|y) = (x|L^*(y))$$

for every $x, y \in X$. The rules for computation with adjoints are the same as in Chapter 10 except that $(cL)^* = \bar{c}L^*$ replaces the rule $(cL)^* = cL^*$. If A is the matrix of L relative to the ortho-normal basis $x_1, \cdots, x_n$ of X, then we may see (as in Chapter 10) that $\bar{A}^{\mathrm{T}}$ is the matrix of L^* relative to the same basis. It is customary to simplify the notation by defining $A^* = \overline{A}^{\mathrm{T}}$ for A in K_n. Then the rules for adjoints imply that

$$I^* = I, \qquad (cA)^* = \bar{c}A^*,$$
$$(A + B)^* = A^* + B^*, \qquad (AB)^* = B^*A^*$$

for A and B in K_n and c in K.

We observe that two matrices A and B in K_n represent the same K-lt relative to two different orthonormal bases of $V_n(K)$ if and only if $B = U^*AU$, where U is unitary in K_n. We call A and B *unitarily similar* when this condition holds.

Let us again call a K-lt L of X into X *self-adjoint* in case $L^* = L$. Then L is self-adjoint if and only if the matrix A of L relative to some orthonormal basis of X satisfies $A^* = A$. It is customary to say that a matrix A in K_n is *hermitian* when $A^* = A$. We call L *skew* when $L^* = -L$, and we note that L is skew if and only if $A^* = -A$, in which case we call A *skew* also. Every L is a sum of a self-adjoint K-lt and a skew K-lt, since $L = (L + L^*)/2 + (L - L^*)/2$. In the next section we shall obtain normal forms for the matrices of self-adjoint and of skew complex linear transformations under unitary similarity.

Illustrative
Example

Let L be the K-lt of $V_2(K)$ into $V_2(K)$ such that

$$L((1, 0)) = (i, 2) \qquad \text{and} \qquad L((0, 1)) = (i, 0).$$

Find L^*. For $x_1, \cdots, x_n$ any orthonormal basis for $V_n(K)$, we have

$$(L(x_i)|x_j) = (x_i|L^*(x_j)) = \overline{(L^*(x_j)|x_i)} \qquad (i, j = 1, \cdots, n).$$

Since $(L^*(x_j)|x_i)$ are the coordinates of $L^*(x_j)$ relative to $x_1, \cdots, x_n$, we see that

$$L^*(x_j) = \sum_{i=1}^{n} \overline{(L(x_i)|x_j)}x_i \qquad (j = 1, \cdots, n).$$

For the example at hand, with $x_1 = (1, 0)$, $x_2 = (0, 1)$,

$$L^*(x_1) = \overline{(L(x_1)|x_1)}x_1 + \overline{(L(x_2)|x_1)}x_2$$
$$= -ix_1 - ix_2 = (-i, -i),$$
$$L^*(x_2) = \overline{(L(x_1)|x_2)}x_1 + \overline{(L(x_2)|x_2)}x_2$$
$$= 2x_1 + 0x_2.$$

Note that the matrix of L relative to x_1 and x_2 is

$$A = \begin{bmatrix} i & 2 \\ i & 0 \end{bmatrix},$$

while the matrix of L^* relative to x_1 and x_2 is

$$A^* = \begin{bmatrix} -i & -i \\ 2 & 0 \end{bmatrix}.$$

/ 3 / MATRICES OF K_n WHICH ARE UNITARILY SIMILAR TO A DIAGONAL MATRIX

In this section we first show that every matrix of K_n which represents a self-adjoint or skew K-lt of $V_n(K)$ into $V_n(K)$ is unitarily similar to a diagonal matrix. It is an easy consequence of this result that A in K_n is unitarily similar to a diagonal matrix if and only if $AA^* = A^*A$.

Lemma 4

The characteristic roots of a hermitian matrix A in K_n are real. The characteristic roots of a skew matrix A in K_n are pure imaginaries.

PROOF   We give the proof of only the second assertion. Let c in K be a characteristic root of $A = -A^*$ in K_n. Choose $z \neq 0$ in $V_n(K)$ such that $zA = cz$. Then $zAz^* = czz^*$ and $(zAz^*)^* = zA^*z^* = -zAz^* = \bar{c}zz^* = -czz^*$. Hence $c + \bar{c} = 0$, and c is a pure imaginary.

Lemma 5

Let $m(x)$ be the minimum polynomial of A in K_n and assume that $A^* = A$ or that $A^* = -A$. Then the roots of $m(x)$ are distinct.

PROOF   We give the proof only for the case in which $A^* = -A$. Suppose that $c \in K$ and that $(x - c)^2$ divides $m(x)$. Set $p(x) = m(x)/(x - c)$ and $B = p(A)(p(A))^*$. Since $A^* = -A$, then $(p(A))^* = q(A)$ where q is in $K[x]$. Then $BB^* = (p(A))^2(q(A))^2 = 0$. Hence $B = 0$, since the diagonal elements of BB^* are the squares of the lengths of the rows of B. But, for the same reason, $p(A) = 0$, a contradiction.

Lemma 6

If A is in K_n and $A^* = A$ or $A^* = -A$, then two distinct characteristic subspaces of A are orthogonal.

PROOF   We give the proof only for $A^* = -A$. Let $c \neq d$ be in K and let y and z be in $V_n(K)$ and satisfy $yA = cy$ and $zA = dz$. Then $yAz^* = cyz^*$, $A^*z^* = \bar{d}z^*$, $-Az^* = -dz^*$ (by Lemma 4), $yAz^* = dyz^* = cyz^*$, and $yz^* = 0$.

Lemma 7

Let $\mathscr{A}$ be a set of commuting matrices of K_n. Then there is a unitary matrix U in K_n such that U^*AU is triangular for every A in $\mathscr{A}$.

Remark.   If $A = \alpha I$ with $\alpha \in K$ then $U^*AU = A = \alpha I$ for all unitary U in K_n and A is evidently triangular. We may assume, then, that no matrix A in $\mathscr{A}$ has the form $A = \alpha I$ with $\alpha \in K$.

PROOF   We use induction on n, noting that the lemma is trivial for $n = 1$. Let c be a characteristic root of a particular B in $\mathscr{A}$ and let Z be the kernel of $cI - B$. If $z \in Z$, then $zA \in Z$ for every A in $\mathscr{A}$, since $zA(cI - B) = z(cI - B)A = 0$. Choose an orthonormal basis $x_1, \cdots, x_k$ for Z and extend it to an orthonormal basis $x_1, \cdots, x_n$ for $V_n(K)$. Define $L_A(x) = xA$, for A in $\mathscr{A}$ and $x \in V_n(K)$. Relative to the orthonormal basis $x_1, \cdots, x_n$ for $V_n(K)$, L_A has a matrix of the form

$$\begin{bmatrix} C_A & 0 \\ G_A & D_A \end{bmatrix},$$

with C_A in K_k and D_A in K_{n-k}. By our inductive hypothesis, there are unitary matrices S in K_k and T in K_{n-k} such that S^*C_AS and T^*D_AT are triangular for every A in $\mathscr{A}$; for one easily sees that the sets $\{C_A; A \in \mathscr{A}\}$ and $\{D_A; A \in \mathscr{A}\}$ are commuting sets of matrices. Then the matrix

$$U = \begin{bmatrix} S & 0 \\ 0 & T \end{bmatrix}$$

satisfies the requirement of the lemma.

Remark. Lemma 7 applies especially to the case in which the set $\mathscr{A}$ has but one element, A. Thus every A in K_n is unitarily similar to a triangular matrix.

Lemma 8

If A is in K_n, is triangular, and satisfies $AA^* = A^*A$, then A is diagonal.

PROOF We use induction on n, noting that the lemma is trivial if $n = 1$. Equating the elements in the (n, n) position of AA^* and A^*A yields

$$|a_{n1}|^2 + \cdots + |a_{nn-1}|^2 + |a_{nn}|^2 = |a_{nn}|^2$$

and consequently $a_{nj} = 0$ for $j \neq n$. Hence

$$A = \begin{bmatrix} A_1 & 0 \\ 0 & a_{nn} \end{bmatrix},$$

and $AA^* = A^*A$ yields $A_1A_1^* = A_1^*A_1$. By induction, A_1 is a diagonal matrix and so is A.

Theorem 1

If A in K_n satisfies $A^* = A$ or $A^* = -A$, then A is unitarily similar to a diagonal matrix $D = \text{diag}(c_1, \cdots, c_n)$ where $\det(xI - A) = (x - c_1)\cdots(x - c_n)$ so that each c_i is a characteristic root of A and so that the distinct characteristic roots of A

appear in D according to their multiplicities as roots of the characteristic equation det $(xI - A) = 0$.

The proof is omitted. In addition to Lemmas 4, 5, 6 of this chapter, one will need analogs of Lemma 7 of Chapter 10. These are easy to prove using spectral theory (Chapter 4). Analogs of our Second Proof of Lemma 7 of Chapter 10 are readily available to the reader who skipped Chapter 4.

Illustrative
Example

Find a unitary matrix U such that U^*AU is diagonal if

$$A = \begin{bmatrix} 0 & i & 1 \\ i & 0 & i \\ -1 & i & 0 \end{bmatrix}.$$

Here

$$\det (xI - A) = \begin{bmatrix} x & -i & -1 \\ -i & x & -i \\ 1 & -i & x \end{bmatrix} = x^3 + 3x.$$

The characteristic roots of A are 0, $\sqrt{3}i$, $-\sqrt{3}i$. We determine $x_1' = (\xi_1, \xi_2, \xi_3)$ such that $x_1'A = 0$; $i\xi_2 - \xi_3 = 0$, and $i(\xi_1 + \xi_3) = 0$, so that $x_1' = (1, i, -1)$; and hence $x_1 = (1/\sqrt{3})(1, i, -1)$ is a characteristic vector of unit length, corresponding to the characteristic root 0. Next we determine $x_2' = (\eta_1, \eta_2, \eta_3)$ such that $x_2'(A - \sqrt{3}iI) = 0$; $(-\sqrt{3}i)\eta_1 + i\eta_2 - \eta_3 = 0$, $i\eta_1 - \sqrt{3}i\eta_2 + i\eta_3 = 0$, and $\eta_1 + i\eta_2 - \sqrt{3}i\eta_3 = 0$. Solving these equations gives $x_2' = (1 + \sqrt{3}i, \sqrt{3} + i, 2)$, so that $x_2 = (1/\sqrt{12})(1 + \sqrt{3}i, \sqrt{3} + i, 2)$ is a characteristic vector corresponding to the characteristic root $\sqrt{3}i$. In like manner we find that $x_3 = (1/\sqrt{12})(-1 + \sqrt{3}i, \sqrt{3} - i, -2)$ is a characteristic vector of unit length corresponding to the characteristic root $-\sqrt{3}i$. If we take

$$U^* = \begin{bmatrix} x_1 \\ x_2 \\ x_3 \end{bmatrix}$$

so that

$$U = (1/\sqrt{12}) \begin{bmatrix} 2 & 1 - \sqrt{3}i & -1 - \sqrt{3}i \\ -2i & \sqrt{3} - i & \sqrt{3} + i \\ -2 & 2 & -2 \end{bmatrix},$$

then $UU^* = I_3$ and

$$U^*A = \begin{bmatrix} x_1 \\ x_2 \\ x_3 \end{bmatrix} A = \begin{bmatrix} 0 \\ \sqrt{3}ix_2 \\ -\sqrt{3}ix_3 \end{bmatrix} = \begin{bmatrix} 0 & 0 & 0 \\ 0 & \sqrt{3}i & 0 \\ 0 & 0 & -\sqrt{3}i \end{bmatrix} \begin{bmatrix} x_1 \\ x_2 \\ x_3 \end{bmatrix},$$

and $U^*AU = \text{diag}(0, \sqrt{3}i, -\sqrt{3}i)$, as desired.

Theorem 2

A matrix A in K is unitarily similar to a diagonal matrix in K if and only if $AA^* = A^*A$.

PROOF   If $D = U^*AU$, with D diagonal and U unitary, then $DD^* = D^*D$ gives $U^*AUU^*A^*U = U^*A^*UU^*AU$ and $AA^* = A^*A$. Conversely, assume that $AA^* = A^*A$. Write $A = H + S$ with $H = (A + A^*)/2 = H^*$ and $S = (A - A^*)/2 = -S^*$. Then $SH = HS$, and Lemma 7 provides a unitary U in K_n such that U^*HU and U^*SU are triangular. Then $B = U^*AU = U^*(H + S)U$ is also triangular and satisfies $B^*B = BB^*$. By Lemma 8, B is diagonal and the proof is complete.

A matrix A in K_n is called *normal* in case $AA^* = A^*A$. Thus A is normal if and only if U^*AU is diagonal for some unitary U in K_n. We have encountered three types of normal matrices: hermitian ($A^* = A$); skew ($A^* = -A$); and unitary ($AA^* = I_n$). We may distinguish among these types by means of the characteristic roots.

Corollary to Theorem 2

A normal matrix A in K_n is (i) hermitian if and only if all the characteristic roots of A are real; (ii) skew if and only if all the characteristic roots of A are pure imaginaries; and, (iii) unitary if and only if all the characteristic roots of A have absolute value 1.

Let H in K_n be hermitian so that all the characteristic roots c_i, where $i = 1, \cdots, n$, of H are real. We may choose our notation so that $c_1 \geq c_2 \geq \cdots \geq c_n$. Then it is easy to see that

(1) $$c_1 |x|^2 \geq xHx^* \geq c_n |x|^2.$$

For, let $UHU^* = \operatorname{diag}(c_1, \cdots, c_n)$ with U unitary in K_n; then $xHx^* = xU^*UHU^*(xU^*)^* = c_1 |y_1|^2 + \cdots + c_n |y_n|^2$, if we set $xU^* = [y_1, \cdots, y_n]$. Since $|x|^2 = |xU^*|^2 = |y_1|^2 + \cdots + |y_n|^2$, the relations (1) follow. They show, in fact, that c_1 is the maximum of xHx^* for $|x| = 1$ and that c_n is the minimum of xHx^* for $|x| = 1$. We call H *positive definite* or *positive semidefinite*, and write $H > 0$ or $H \geq 0$ for the case $c_n > 0$ or $c_n \geq 0$, respectively. Hence $H > 0$ or $H \geq 0$ if and only if $xHx^* > 0$ or $xHx^* \geq 0$ for every nonzero x in $V_n(K)$.

If A is in K_n, then AA^* is hermitian and $xAA^*x^* = |xA|^2$. Hence $xA = 0$ if and only if $xAA^* = 0$, and it follows that A and AA^* have the same rank. We always have $AA^* \geq 0$, and we have $AA^* > 0$ if and only if A is nonsingular.

It is possible to introduce the square root of a positive semidefinite hermitian matrix.

Lemma 9

Let H in K_n satisfy $H^* = H \geq 0$. Then there is a unique matrix P in K_n such that $P^* = P \geq 0$ and $P^2 = H$.

PROOF   Let $d_1, \cdots, d_k$ be the distinct characteristic roots of H and let $c_j = \sqrt{d_j}$, where $j = 1, \cdots, k$. Let $I = E_1 + \cdots + E_k$ be the resolution of the identity for H, and set $P = c_1 E_1 + \cdots + c_k E_k$. Since each E_i is a real polynomial in H, it is clear that $P^* = P \geq 0$ and $P^2 = H$. If also $Q^* = Q \geq 0$ and $Q^2 = H$, then $QH = HQ$ yields $E_iQ = QE_i$ and, consequently, $PQ = QP$. There is then a unitary W in K_n such that $P_1 = WPW^*$ and $Q_1 = WQW^*$ are both triangular and hence both diagonal. But $P_1^2 =$

$Q_1{}^2$, with $P_1, Q_1 \geq 0$, then gives $P_1 = Q_1$ and $P = Q$. As for real numbers, we shall denote P by $\sqrt{H}$.

Illustrative
Example

Let

$$H = \begin{bmatrix} 4 & i \\ -i & 4 \end{bmatrix}$$

in K_2. Find a matrix P in K_2 such that $P^* = P \geq 0$ and $P^2 = H$.
We find

$$\det (xI - H) = \det \begin{bmatrix} x - 4 & -i \\ i & x - 4 \end{bmatrix}$$
$$= x^2 - 8x + 15 = (x - 3)(x - 5).$$

We have $1/(x - 3)(x - 5) = (-1/2)/(x - 3) + (1/2)/(x - 5)$, and hence

$$E_1 = (-1/2)(H - 5I) = (-1/2) \begin{bmatrix} -1 & i \\ -i & -1 \end{bmatrix},$$

$$E_2 = (1/2)(H - 3I) = (1/2) \begin{bmatrix} 1 & i \\ -i & 1 \end{bmatrix}.$$

Thus

$$P = \sqrt{3}E_1 + \sqrt{5}E_2 = (1/2) \begin{bmatrix} \sqrt{3} + \sqrt{5} & i(-\sqrt{3} + \sqrt{5}) \\ i(\sqrt{3} - \sqrt{5}) & \sqrt{3} + \sqrt{5} \end{bmatrix}$$

is the required hermitian square root of H.

We may use the square root to obtain a polar decomposition for A in K_n which generalizes the usual polar form for a complex number.

Theorem 3

Let A be in K_n. Then $A = \sqrt{AA^*}U$ for some unitary U in K_n. If A is nonsingular, then U is uniquely determined by A.

PROOF   Set $P = \sqrt{AA^*}$. If A is nonsingular, so is P. With $U = P^{-1}A$ we have $UU^* = P^{-1}AA^*P^{-1} = P^{-1}P^2P^{-1} = I$; consequently U is unitary and is uniquely determined by A.

If A is singular, then A and P have the same rank r. Choose an orthonormal basis $x_1 = y_1A, \cdots, x_r = y_rA$ for the row space of A. Then $x_1' = y_1P, \cdots, x_r' = y_rP$ is an orthonormal basis for the row space of P, since

$$(y_iP \,|\, y_jP) = (y_i \,|\, y_jP^2)$$
$$= (y_i \,|\, y_jAA^*) = (y_iA \,|\, y_jA) \qquad (i, j = 1, \cdots, r).$$

Extend the bases $x_1, \cdots, x_r$ and $x_1', \cdots, x_r'$ to orthonormal bases for $V_n(K)$. Let U be the matrix such that $x_i = x_i'U$, where $i = 1, \cdots, n$. Then U is unitary, being the product of two unitary matrices, and $x_i' = x_iU^*$. Then $(xA \,|\, x_i) = (xA \,|\, y_iA) = (xP \,|\, y_iP) = (xP \,|\, x_i') = (xP \,|\, x_iU^*) = (xPU \,|\, x_i)$, where $i = 1, \cdots, r$. But $(xA \,|\, x_j) = (xPU \,|\, x_j) = (xP \,|\, x_j') = 0$ for $j > r$, since $x_j \perp xA$ and $x_j' \perp xP$. Hence $xA = xPU$ for every x in $V_n(K)$, and $A = PU$ as claimed.

Illustrative
Example

Find the polar decomposition for

$$A = \begin{bmatrix} 1 & i \\ -1 & -i \end{bmatrix}.$$

Here

$$AA^* = \begin{bmatrix} 1 & i \\ -1 & -i \end{bmatrix}\begin{bmatrix} 1 & -1 \\ -i & i \end{bmatrix} = \begin{bmatrix} 2 & -2 \\ -2 & 2 \end{bmatrix},$$

and

$$\det(xI - AA^*) = \det\begin{bmatrix} x - 2 & 2 \\ 2 & x - 2 \end{bmatrix} = x^2 - 4x.$$

We have

$$1/(x^2 - 4x) = (-1/4)/x + (1/4)/(x - 4),$$

so that

$$E_1 = (-1/4)(AA^* - 4I) \qquad \text{and} \qquad E_2 = (1/4)AA^*.$$

Thus

$$P = \sqrt{AA^*} = (1/2)AA^* = \begin{bmatrix} 1 & -1 \\ -1 & 1 \end{bmatrix}.$$

Now, $x_1 = (1/\sqrt{2})(1, i) = (1/\sqrt{2})(1, 0)A$ is an orthonormal basis for the row space of A and $x_1' = (1/\sqrt{2})(1, -1) = (1/\sqrt{2})(1, 0)P$ is an orthonormal basis for the row space of P. Further, $x_1 = (1/\sqrt{2})(1, i)$ and $x_2 = (1/\sqrt{2})(i, 1)$ is an orthonormal basis for $V_2(K)$, and so is $x_1' = (1/\sqrt{2})(1, -1)$ and $x_2' = (1/\sqrt{2})(1, 1)$. From

$$\begin{bmatrix} x_1 \\ x_2 \end{bmatrix} = \begin{bmatrix} x_1' \\ x_2' \end{bmatrix} U$$

we get

$$U = [(x_1')^*, (x_2')^*]\begin{bmatrix} x_1 \\ x_2 \end{bmatrix} = (1/2)\begin{bmatrix} 1 & 1 \\ -1 & 1 \end{bmatrix}\begin{bmatrix} 1 & i \\ i & 1 \end{bmatrix}$$

$$= (1/2)\begin{bmatrix} 1+i & i+1 \\ -1+i & 1-i \end{bmatrix}.$$

We may verify that

$$PU = (1/2)\begin{bmatrix} 1 & -1 \\ -1 & 1 \end{bmatrix}\begin{bmatrix} 1+i & i+1 \\ -1+i & 1-i \end{bmatrix} = \begin{bmatrix} 1 & i \\ -1 & -i \end{bmatrix} = A.$$

The nonuniqueness of U in this case is clear from our construction.

We can make this factorization even closer to the usual $z = |z|e^{i\theta}$ by means of the following. The characteristic roots $u_1, \cdots, u_n$ of a unitary matrix U have absolute value 1, and hence $u_p = \exp(i\theta_p)$ for real numbers θ_p, where $p = 1, \cdots, n$. Let W be a unitary matrix such that $WUW^* = \text{diag}(u_1, \cdots, u_n)$. Define $H = W^* \text{diag}(\theta_1, \cdots, \theta_n)W$. Then $e^{iH} = W^* \text{diag}(u_1, \cdots, u_n)W = U$. Thus every A in K_n has the form $A = Pe^{iH}$ where P and H are hermitian and $P \geq 0$.

We shall conclude this chapter with some formulas for the characteristic roots of a hermitian matrix H in K_n; these are due to Weyl and have come to be referred to as the *maximum-minimum principle*. Choose notation so that, if

$$\det(xI - A) = (x - c_1)\cdots(x - c_n),$$

we have $c_1 \geq c_2 \geq \cdots \geq c_n$. (Observe that in the list $c_1, \cdots, c_n$ each distinct characteristic root appears according to its multiplicity as a root of $\det(xI - A) = 0$.) For a subspace S of $V_n(K)$, let $m(S)$ denote the minimum value of xHx^* for x in S and $|x| = 1$. Then c_i is the maximum value of $m(S)$ for those S for which $\dim S = i$. Choose an orthonormal basis $x_1, \cdots, x_n$ such that $x_jH = c_jx_j$, where $j = 1, \cdots, n$. Let S be a subspace with $\dim S = i$, and define T as the subspace spanned by $x_i, \cdots, x_n$, so that $\dim T = n - i + 1$. Then $\dim S + \dim T = n + 1 = \dim(S + T) + \dim(S \cap T)$. It follows that $S \cap T \neq 0$. Choose y in $S \cap T$ with $|y| = 1$. Then

$$y = \sum_{j=i}^{n} a_jx_j \quad \text{and} \quad \sum_{j=i}^{n} |a_j|^2 = 1,$$

$$yHy^* = \sum_{j=i}^{n} |a_j|^2 c_j \leq c_i.$$

We have proved that, if $\dim S = i$, then $m(S) \leq c_i$. But for $S = \langle x_1, \cdots, x_i \rangle$ we have $m(S) = c_i$ since, if

$$z = \sum_{k=1}^{i} b_kx_k \quad \text{and} \quad |z|^2 = \sum_{k=1}^{i} |b_k|^2 = 1,$$

then

$$zHz^* = \sum_{k=1}^{i} |b_k|^2 c_k \geq c_i \quad \text{and} \quad x_iHx_i^* = c_i.$$

Theorem 4

Let $c_1 \geq c_2 \geq \cdots \geq c_n$ be the characteristic roots of $H = H^*$ in K_n. Then c_i is the maximum for subspaces S of dimension i of the minimum of xHx^* for x in S and $|x| = 1$.

EXERCISES FOR CHAPTER 11

1. In $V_2(K)$, let $L((1, 0)) = (0, i)$ and $L((0, 1)) = (i, 0)$. Find L^*.

2. Let $A \in K_n$ be normal, so that $AA^* = A^*A$. Prove directly that the roots of the minimum polynomial $m(x)$ of A are distinct.

3. Let $A \in K_n$ be normal and $yA = cy$. Prove that $yA^* = \bar{c}y$. [*Hint:* Put $w = yA^* - \bar{c}y$ and show that $ww^* = 0$.]

4. Let $A \in K_n$ be normal. Show that distinct characteristic subspaces of A are orthogonal.

5. Use Exercises 3, 4, and 2 to obtain another proof of Theorem 2.

6. Supply the proof of Theorem 1.

7. Prove Lemma 4 for $A = A^*$.

8. Prove Lemma 5 for $A = A^*$.

9. Prove Lemma 6 for $A = A^*$.

10. Find conditions on $A \in K_2$ in order that $A^*A = AA^*$.

11. Find a unitary matrix U such that U^*AU is diagonal if

$$A = \begin{bmatrix} i + 1 & 1 \\ 1 & 1 + i \end{bmatrix}.$$

12. Find a unitary matrix U such that U^*AU is diagonal if

$$A = \begin{bmatrix} 1 & 0 & i \\ 0 & 1 & 0 \\ -i & 0 & 1 \end{bmatrix}.$$

13. If H is hermitian, prove that $U = (I - iH)(I + iH)^{-1}$ is unitary.

14. Let $AA^* = A^*A$ and let $B = I + A$ be nonsingular. Prove that $B^{-1}B^*$ is unitary.

15. Prove that the set of all unitary matrices in K_n is a group under matric multiplication.

16. Let $A \in F_n$, where F is a field and $A^2 = A$. Prove that Trace A = rank A. (Recall that Trace $A = a_{11} + \cdots + a_{nn}$.)

17. Show that, if $A \in K_n$, then AA^* and A^*A have the same characteristic roots.

18. Find the polar form for the matrix

$$A = \begin{bmatrix} 1 & i \\ 0 & 2 \end{bmatrix}.$$

19. Verify the maximum-minimum principle of Weyl for

$$A = \begin{bmatrix} 0 & 1 & 1 \\ 1 & 0 & 1 \\ 1 & 1 & 0 \end{bmatrix}.$$

20. Prove the quadrilateral inequality

$$|x| + |y| + |z| + |x + y + z| \geq |x + y| + |x + z| + |y + z|$$

for x, y, and z in a unitary space.

21. In Theorem 3, show that A normal implies $PU = UP$. Is the converse true?

22. Let $A \in K_n$, $H_1 = (1/2)(A + A^*)$, and $H_2 = (1/2i)(A - A^*)$. Let c_1 and d_1 be respectively the greatest and the least characteristic roots of H_1, and c_2 and d_2 the greatest and least characteristic roots of H_2. Then for any characteristic root λ of A we have

$$d_1 \leq Re(\lambda) \leq c_1 \quad \text{and} \quad d_2 \leq Im(\lambda) \leq c_2.$$

23. Let $A \in K_n$. Let c and d be the greatest and least characteristic roots of A^*A. Show that $c \leq |\lambda|^2 \leq d$ for every characteristic root λ of A.

24. Prove that, if U is unitary, then there is a hermitian matrix H such that $U = e^{iH}$.

25. Let A and B be normal matrices of K_n with characteristic roots $\alpha_1, \cdots, \alpha_n$ and $\beta_1, \cdots, \beta_n$, respectively. Assume that there

are orderings of $\alpha_1, \cdots, \alpha_n$ and $\beta_1, \cdots, \beta_n$ such that the characteristic roots of $\lambda A + \mu B$ are $\lambda\alpha_1 + \mu\beta_1, \cdots, \lambda\alpha_n + \mu\beta_n$ for all $\lambda, \mu \in K$. Prove that $AB = BA$.

26. For $A, B \in K_n$, set $C = AB - BA$ and assume $CA = AC$. Prove that $C^n = 0$.

27. Let A be normal in K_n and let B in K_n satisfy $BA = AB$. Prove that $BA* = A*B$.

28. Let the minimum polynomial of A in K_n have distinct roots. Define $\Delta_A X = XA - AX$. Show that $\Delta_A^{(s)} X = 0$ implies that $\Delta_A X = 0$. Here $\Delta_A^{(s)} X = \Delta_A(\Delta_A^{(s-1)} X)$.

12

QUADRATIC FORMS
AND WITT'S
THEOREM

In many applications one seeks a second approximation at a critical value of a function, in order to assess the stability of the function in a neighborhood of the critical point. This leads to the examination of quadratic expressions, to which matric theory can contribute some insight. The purpose of this chapter is to introduce the basic concept of quadratic form and to give an indication of the elementary properties of such forms. We prove an elementary version of Witt's Theorem and apply it to obtain the classical theorem of Sylvester on real quadratic forms.

/1/ QUADRATIC FORMS

Let D be a division ring in which $2 \neq 0$ and let V be a D vector space of dimension n. A map q of V into D is called a D *quadratic form in V* in case, first,

$$q(\alpha x) = \alpha^2 q(x)$$

for all α in D and x in V and, second, the function

$$b(x, y) = (1/2)[q(x + y) - q(x) - q(y)]$$

is bilinear in the sense that

$$b(x + x', y) = b(x, y) + b(x', y),$$
$$b(x, y + y') = b(x, y) + b(x, y'),$$
$$b(\alpha x, y) = \alpha b(x, y) = b(x, \alpha y)$$

for all x, y, x', and y' in V and all α in D. Notice that when $q(x)$ is a D quadratic form in V, then $b(x, x) = q(x)$ for all x in V, since

$$b(x, x) = (1/2)[q(2x) - 2q(x)] = (1/2)[4q(x) - 2q(x)] = q(x).$$

Thus we may employ $b(x, y)$ or $q(x)$ in our discussion of D quadratic forms.

For the purpose of this brief introduction to quadratic forms it is convenient to assume that our division ring D is commutative and hence a field. We shall write $D = F$ henceforth to emphasize this assumption.

If $x_1, \cdots, x_n$ is an F basis for V, then we may write $x = \xi_1 x_1 + \cdots + \xi_n x_n$ where $[\xi_1, \cdots, \xi_n]$ are the coordinates of x relative to the basis $x_1, \cdots, x_n$ of V. Then

$$q(x) = b(x, x) = b\left(\sum_{i=1}^{n} \xi_i x_i, \sum_{j=1}^{n} \xi_j x_j\right) = \sum_{i, j=1}^{n} \xi_i \xi_j b(x_i, x_j).$$

We call $B = [b(x_i, x_j)]$, where $i, j = 1, \cdots, n$, the *matrix of the quadratic form* $q(x)$ *relative to the basis* $x_1, \cdots, x_n$ *of* V. The symmetry of $b(x, y)$ implies that $B = B^T$, and we call B a *symmetric matrix*. It is clear that, if we start with a symmetric matrix B of elements of F and a basis $x_1, \cdots, x_n$ of V, then we may, for $x = \xi_1 x_1 + \cdots + \xi_n x_n$ and for $\xi = [\xi_1, \cdots, \xi_n]$, define $q(x) = \xi B \xi^T$ and thereby obtain a quadratic form $q(x)$ in V for which the associated bilinear form is $b(x, y) = \xi B \eta^T$ if $y = \eta_1 x_1 + \cdots + \eta_n x_n$ and $\eta = [\eta_1, \cdots, \eta_n]$.

Illustrative
Example

Let $q((\xi_1, \xi_2, \xi_3)) = \xi_1 \xi_2 + \xi_1 \xi_3 + \xi_2 \xi_3$ for $\xi_1, \xi_2, \xi_3 \in R_e$. Then q is a quadratic form in $V_3(R_e)$. The bilinear form associated with q is

$$b(x, y) = (1/2)(\xi_1 \eta_2 + \eta_1 \xi_2 + \xi_1 \eta_3 + \eta_1 \xi_3 + \xi_2 \eta_3 + \eta_2 \xi_3)$$

where $x = (\xi_1, \xi_2, \xi_3)$ and $y = (\eta_1, \eta_2, \eta_3)$. If we choose the usual basis $x_1 = (1, 0, 0)$, $x_2 = (0, 1, 0)$, $x_3 = (0, 0, 1)$ for $V_3(R_e)$, then the matrix of q is

$$B = (1/2) \begin{bmatrix} 0 & 1 & 1 \\ 1 & 0 & 1 \\ 1 & 1 & 0 \end{bmatrix}.$$

How does the matrix B of the quadratic form $q(x)$ in V depend on the basis $x_1, \cdots, x_n$ in V? Let $x_1', \cdots, x_n'$ be a second basis for V and write

$$x_i = \sum_{j=1}^{n} p_{ij} x_j' \quad (i = 1, \ldots, n).$$

where $P = [p_{ij}]$, for $i, j = 1, \cdots, n$, is the matrix of the transformation of coordinates $\xi' = [\xi_1', \cdots, \xi_n']$ to $\xi = [\xi_1, \cdots, \xi_n]$. Thus we have $\xi' = \xi P$ or $\xi = \xi'Q$ with $Q = P^{-1}$. Hence

$$q(x) = \xi B \xi^{\mathrm{T}} = \xi' Q B Q^{\mathrm{T}} (\xi')^{\mathrm{T}}.$$

Consequently, we see that our change of basis replaces B by QBQ^{T} with Q nonsingular in F_n. When $D = F$ is a field, we shall call matrices B and C in F_n *congruent in F* if we have $C = QBQ^{\mathrm{T}}$ with Q nonsingular in F.

Illustrative
Example

Relative to the basis $x_1 = (1, 0, 0)$, $x_2 = (0, 1, 0)$, $x_3 = (0, 0, 1)$ for $V_3(R_a)$, let

$$B = \begin{bmatrix} 0 & 1 & 1 \\ 1 & 0 & 1 \\ 1 & 1 & 1 \end{bmatrix}$$

define a quadratic form

$$q(x) = 2\xi_1\xi_2 + 2\xi_1\xi_3 + 2\xi_2\xi_3 + \xi_3{}^2$$

where $x = (\xi_1, \xi_2, \xi_3)$. What is the matrix of $q(x)$ relative to the new basis $x_1' = (1, 1, 0)$, $x_2' = (1, 1, 1)$, $x_3' = (1, 0, 1)$? Now $x = \xi_1'x_1' + \xi_2'x_2' + \xi_3'x_3'$ gives $(\xi_1, \xi_2, \xi_3) = (\xi_1' + \xi_2' + \xi_3', \xi_1' + \xi_2', \xi_2' + \xi_3') = (\xi_1', \xi_2', \xi_3')Q$ with

$$Q = \begin{bmatrix} 1 & 1 & 0 \\ 1 & 1 & 1 \\ 1 & 0 & 1 \end{bmatrix}.$$

Hence $\xi B \xi^{\mathrm{T}} = \xi' Q B Q^{\mathrm{T}} (\xi')^{\mathrm{T}}$ and the required matrix is

$$QBQ^{\mathrm{T}} = \begin{bmatrix} 2 & 4 & 3 \\ 4 & 7 & 5 \\ 3 & 5 & 3 \end{bmatrix}.$$

One sees at once that if A and B are congruent in F, then A and B have the same rank. This necessary condition is far from sufficient, however. For example, let $F = R_e$, $q(x) = x^2$, $q_2(x) = -x^2$; then $B = 1$, $B_2 = -1$; these are not congruent in R_e, since $1 = -a^2$ is impossible for $a \in R_e$.

/ 2 / REDUCTION OF THE MATRIX

OF A QUADRATIC FORM

TO DIAGONAL FORM

In this section we assume that $D = F$ is a field. Let the quadratic form $q(x)$ in V have the (symmetric) matrix B relative to the basis $x_1, \cdots, x_n$ of V. We shall show how to find a new basis $x_1', \cdots, x_n'$ of V relative to which the matrix B' of $q(x)$ is diagonal. To do this we first observe that the effect of an elementary operation $\xi' = \xi E$ is to replace B by EBE^T. Since every nonsingular P in F_n is a product of a finite number of elementary matrices, we seek to diagonalize B by means of a finite number of elementary operations of the following types.

Type I: interchange two rows and the corresponding two columns of B.

Type II: add α (in F) times the ith row of B to the jth row of B and add α times the ith column of B to the jth column of B, where $i \neq j$.

Type III: multiply the ith row and the ith column of B by $\alpha \neq 0$ in F.

The diagonalization process is as follows. We may assume that $B \neq 0$. If all $b_{ii} = 0$, choose $b_{ij} = b_{ji} \neq 0$ and add the ith row to the jth row and the ith column to the jth column to obtain $2b_{ij} \neq 0$ in the (j, j) position. By an interchange of rows (and corresponding columns) we may assume that $b_{11} \neq 0$. Adding suitable multiples of the first row to the remaining rows (and adding the *same* multiples of the first column to the remaining columns) produces a matrix of the form

$$\begin{bmatrix} a & 0 \\ 0 & B_1 \end{bmatrix}$$

in which $B_1^T = B_1$. We then repeat the whole process on B_1.

Illustrative
Example

Let F be the real field and

$$B = \begin{bmatrix} 0 & 2 \\ 2 & 0 \end{bmatrix}.$$

Then

$$E_1 B E_1^{\mathrm{T}} = \begin{bmatrix} 4 & 2 \\ 2 & 0 \end{bmatrix},$$

$$E_2 E_1 B E_1^{\mathrm{T}} E_2^{\mathrm{T}} = \begin{bmatrix} 4 & 0 \\ 0 & -1 \end{bmatrix}.$$

Observe that the result of the diagonalization process is by no means unique.

/ 3 / WITT'S THEOREM

Our assumption that $D = F$ is a field is still in effect. It is clear that symmetric matrices A and B in F_n which are congruent in F ($PAP^{\mathrm{T}} = B$ with P nonsingular) must have the same rank. Also, if A is nonsingular and $B = PAP^{\mathrm{T}}$, then

$$\begin{bmatrix} A & 0 \\ 0 & 0 \end{bmatrix} \quad \text{and} \quad \begin{bmatrix} B & 0 \\ 0 & 0 \end{bmatrix}$$

are congruent in F, since

$$\begin{bmatrix} P & 0 \\ 0 & I \end{bmatrix} \begin{bmatrix} A & 0 \\ 0 & 0 \end{bmatrix} \begin{bmatrix} P^{\mathrm{T}} & 0 \\ 0 & I \end{bmatrix} = \begin{bmatrix} B & 0 \\ 0 & 0 \end{bmatrix}.$$

Conversely, if

$$\begin{bmatrix} A & 0 \\ 0 & 0 \end{bmatrix} \quad \text{and} \quad \begin{bmatrix} B & 0 \\ 0 & 0 \end{bmatrix}$$

are congruent and A is nonsingular, then A and B are congruent in F. For

$$\begin{bmatrix} P & Q \\ R & S \end{bmatrix} \begin{bmatrix} A & 0 \\ 0 & 0 \end{bmatrix} \begin{bmatrix} P^{\mathrm{T}} & R^{\mathrm{T}} \\ Q^{\mathrm{T}} & S^{\mathrm{T}} \end{bmatrix} = \begin{bmatrix} B & 0 \\ 0 & 0 \end{bmatrix}$$

implies that $PAP^{\mathrm{T}} = B$ and, since B is nonsingular, so is P.
This result is a special case of Witt's Theorem.

Witt's Theorem

If $a \in F$ and the matrices

$$\begin{bmatrix} a & 0 \\ 0 & A \end{bmatrix} \quad \text{and} \quad \begin{bmatrix} a & 0 \\ 0 & B \end{bmatrix}$$

are congruent in F, then A and B are congruent in F.

PROOF   We must first reduce our problem to the case in which
A (and hence B) is nonsingular. Now A and B have the same rank
r, and there are nonsingular matrices U and V such that

$$UBU^{\mathrm{T}} = \begin{bmatrix} B_1 & 0 \\ 0 & 0 \end{bmatrix} \quad \text{and} \quad VAV^{\mathrm{T}} = \begin{bmatrix} A_1 & 0 \\ 0 & 0 \end{bmatrix},$$

where A_1 and B_1 are nonsingular r-by-r matrices. It follows that

$$\begin{bmatrix} a & 0 \\ 0 & B \end{bmatrix} \quad \text{and} \quad \begin{bmatrix} a & 0 & 0 \\ 0 & B_1 & 0 \\ 0 & 0 & 0 \end{bmatrix}$$

are congruent in F and so are

$$\begin{bmatrix} a & 0 \\ 0 & A \end{bmatrix} \quad \text{and} \quad \begin{bmatrix} a & 0 & 0 \\ 0 & A_1 & 0 \\ 0 & 0 & 0 \end{bmatrix}.$$

By the special case of Witt's theorem already proved, we infer
that

$$\begin{bmatrix} a & 0 \\ 0 & A_1 \end{bmatrix} \quad \text{and} \quad \begin{bmatrix} a & 0 \\ 0 & B_1 \end{bmatrix}$$

are congruent in F. From now on in our proof we may assume that
A and B are nonsingular matrices and that $a \neq 0$.

Now we are prepared to complete the proof of Witt's theorem. By assumption, there is a nonsingular matrix

$$\begin{bmatrix} p & Q \\ R & S \end{bmatrix}$$

such that

$$\begin{bmatrix} a & 0 \\ 0 & B \end{bmatrix} = \begin{bmatrix} p & Q \\ R & S \end{bmatrix} \begin{bmatrix} a & 0 \\ 0 & A \end{bmatrix} \begin{bmatrix} p & R^T \\ Q^T & S^T \end{bmatrix}.$$

This yields the following equations:

$$a = p^2 a + QAQ^T,$$
$$0 = paR^T + QAS^T,$$
$$B = aRR^T + SAS^T.$$

Our strategy in the proof will be to take $P = S - uRQ$ and try to select u in F so that $B = PAP^T$. After a bit of computation we find that

$$PAP^T = B + a(u^2 - (up - 1)^2)RR^T.$$

It will suffice, then, to choose u so that $u^2 = (up - 1)^2$. If $p = 1$, then $u = 1/2$ in F will do. If $p \neq 1$, then we solve $u = up - 1$ for $u = (p - 1)^{-1}$ in F, which is satisfactory. By such a choice of u we obtain $B = PAP^T$. The nonsingularity of P follows at once from this equation, since B is nonsingular so that P must have maximum possible rank.

As an application of Witt's theorem, we prove another theorem.

Sylvester's Theorem

Let A be a real symmetric matrix $(A \in (R_e)_n, \ A^T = A)$ of rank r. Then A is congruent in the real field to a matrix

(1)
$$\begin{bmatrix} I_p & 0 & 0 \\ 0 & -I_q & 0 \\ 0 & 0 & 0 \end{bmatrix}$$

in which $p + q = r$. The number p is uniquely determined by A and is called the *index* of A.

PROOF   Since the square root of a positive real number is a real number, the achievement of the canonical form (1) from a diagonal matrix congruent to A is immediate. To show that p is uniquely determined by A (and hence that (1) *is* a canonical form), suppose the contrary; that is, suppose that

$$\begin{bmatrix} I_p & 0 & 0 \\ 0 & -I_q & 0 \\ 0 & 0 & 0 \end{bmatrix} \quad \text{and} \quad \begin{bmatrix} I_h & 0 & 0 \\ 0 & -I_k & 0 \\ 0 & 0 & 0 \end{bmatrix}$$

are congruent in R_e and that $p > h$ (so that also $q < k$, because $p + q = h + k = r$). Use of Witt's Theorem a few times yields that I_t and $-I_t$ are congruent in R_e, where $t = p - h = k - q$. But then we get

$$I_t = -SS^T$$

and, in particular, $1 = -\sum_{i=1}^{t} s_{1i}^2$, which is impossible in the real field.

Illustrative
Example

Find the index of

$$A = \begin{bmatrix} 0 & 1 & 1 \\ 1 & 0 & 1 \\ 1 & 1 & 0 \end{bmatrix}$$

in $V_3(R_e)$. The diagonalization process shows that A is congruent to diag $(1, -1, -1)$ in R_e. Hence the index of A is 1.

The study of the congruence of quadratic forms leads us into advanced topics in number theory and in geometry. A canonical form for congruence in the rational field is known, but it is far beyond the scope of this text. The geometry associated with a given quadratic form is also very interesting. The beautiful book, *Geometric Algebra*, by Emil Artin, discusses this aspect of quadratic forms.

EXERCISES FOR CHAPTER 12

1. Let

$$A = \begin{bmatrix} 0 & 1 & 0 \\ 1 & 0 & -1 \\ 0 & -1 & 0 \end{bmatrix}$$

be in $(R_a)_3$. Find a diagonal matrix in $(R_a)_3$ congruent to A.

2. Repeat Exercise 1, replacing R_a by R_e.

3. Let

$$A = \begin{bmatrix} 1 & 1 & 1 \\ 1 & 1 & 1 \\ 1 & 1 & 1 \end{bmatrix}.$$

Find a diagonal matrix congruent to A in R_a and in R_e.

4.† Let

$$A = \begin{bmatrix} 2 & 1 & 1 \\ 1 & 2 & 1 \\ 1 & 1 & 2 \end{bmatrix}$$

in $(R_a)_3$. Show that A is congruent to I in R_a.

5.† Let $n = m^2 + m + 1$ and $A = mI_n + U$ be in $(R_a)_n$, where U is a matrix of 1's. Show that A is congruent to $\mathrm{diag}(1, mI_{n-1})$ in R_a.

† This is *not* an easy exercise.

6. Let A be as in Exercise 4. Let x_1, x_2, x_3 be the usual basis for $V_3(R_a)$, and let A be the matrix of q relative to x_1, x_2, x_3. Find the matrix of q relative to $x_1' = (1, 1, 1)$, $x_2' = (1, 1, 0)$, $x_3' = (1, 0, 0)$.

7. Find the index, in $(R_e)_2$, of

$$\begin{bmatrix} 1 & 1 \\ 1 & 1 \end{bmatrix}.$$

8. Find the index, in $(R_e)_3$, of

$$\begin{bmatrix} 1 & 2 & 3 \\ 2 & 1 & 3 \\ 3 & 3 & 1 \end{bmatrix}.$$

9.† Assume Lagrange's Theorem: every positive integer is the sum of four integral squares. Prove that nI_4 is congruent I_4.

10.† Let $n = m^2 + m + 1$ and let $m \equiv 2 \pmod 4$. Show that $A = mI_n + U$ as in Exercise 5 is congruent to I_n in R_a only if mI_2 is congruent to I_2 in R_a.

11. Show that the following are congruent in R_e

$$\begin{bmatrix} 1 & 0 & 0 \\ 0 & 1 & 0 \\ 0 & 0 & -4 \end{bmatrix} \quad \text{and} \quad \begin{bmatrix} 9 & 3 & -3 \\ 3 & 2 & -4 \\ -3 & -4 & 2 \end{bmatrix}.$$

12. Let A be a real skew matrix: $A^T = -A$. Show that A is congruent to diag $(S, \cdots, S, 0, \cdots, 0)$, where

$$S = \begin{bmatrix} 0 & 1 \\ -1 & 0 \end{bmatrix}.$$

13. Find a nonsingular matrix $P \in (R_e)_4$ such that $P^T A P = $ diag (S, S) if

$$A = \begin{bmatrix} 0 & 2 & 0 & 4 \\ -2 & 0 & -1 & -2 \\ 0 & 1 & 0 & -3 \\ -4 & 2 & 3 & 0 \end{bmatrix}.$$

14. Show that, if $A^T = A$ and $A \in K_n$, then A is congruent in K to diag $(I_r, 0)$ where r is the rank of A.

15. Let A, $B \in K_n$ be hermitian: $A^* = A$ and $B^* = B$. Call A and B *conjunctive* in K if $B = P^*AP$ with P nonsingular in K_n. Parallel the discussion of the text to prove that every nonzero hermitian $A \in K_n$ is conjunctive to one and only one of the matrices diag $(I_p, -I_q, 0)$. Here p is the index of A and $p + q$ is the rank of A.

16. *Cochran's Theorem:* Let B_s be normal matrices of K_n of rank r_s, where $s = 0, \cdots, k$, such that $B_0 + \cdots + B_k = I$ and $n = r_0 + \cdots + r_k$; then there is a unitary matrix U such that U^*B_sU is a diagonal matrix of zeros and ones, where $s = 0, \cdots, k$. [*Hints:* Use induction on k and Exercise 23 of Chapter 6.]

INTRODUCTORY

SET THEORY

The purpose of this appendix is to review the fundamental facts about sets and maps, as they form the common basis of most of mathematics. Since terminology and notation vary somewhat in this subject, a secondary purpose of the appendix is to settle these matters as far as this text is concerned.

/1/ OPERATIONS

WITH SETS

By a set a mathematician means an assemblage of individuals in a single entity. If P is a property of individuals, then the following,

$$A = \{x; x \text{ has the property } P\},$$

is a set, namely the set of all individuals having the property P. If S is a set, then "$x \in S$" denotes that the individual x is a member of the set S, "$A \subset S$" means that every $x \in A$ is a member of S but that $A \neq S$. When $A \subseteq S$ (that is, when $A \subset S$ or $A = S$), we call A a *subset* of S and we write

$$2^S = \{A; A \subseteq S\}$$

for the set of all subsets of S. The empty subset of S will be denoted by ϕ_S. If $A \subseteq S$, then the *complement of A in S* is

$$A' = \{x \in S; x \notin A\},$$

and, more generally, if $A, B \subseteq S$, then

$$A \setminus B = \{x \in A; x \notin B\}$$

is the *complement of B in A*. Another common notation for the complement of B in A is $A \sim B$. Both notations are modified forms of $A - B$, which has to be avoided in most applications. The *union* of two subsets $A, B \subseteq S$ is

$$A \cup B = \{x \in S; x \in A \text{ or } x \in B\}.$$

The *intersection* of two subsets $A, B \subseteq S$ is

$$A \cap B = \{x \in S; x \in A \text{ and } x \in B\}.$$

The *sum* of two subsets $A, B \subseteq S$ is

$$A + B = \{x \in S; x \in A \text{ or } x \in B \text{ but } x \notin A \cap B\}$$
$$= (A \cap B') \cup (A' \cap B).$$

These operations have a lot of more or less obvious properties:

(1) $A \cap A = A = A \cup A, \quad A + A = \phi_S.$

(2) $A \cap (B + C) = (A \cap B) + (A \cap C).$

(3) $A \cap (B \cup C) = (A \cap B) \cup (A \cap C).$

(4) $A \cup (B \cap C) = (A \cup B) \cap (A \cup C).$

(5) $(A \cup B)' = A' \cap B'.$

(6) $A'' = A, \quad (A \cap B)' = A' \cup B'.$

(7) $A \cup B = B \cup A, \quad A \cap B = B \cap A,$
$A + B = B + A.$

(8) $(A \cup B) \cup C = A \cup (B \cup C),$
$(A \cap B) \cap C = A \cap (B \cap C),$
$(A + B) + C = A + (B + C).$

The notions of union and intersection extend at once to families (that is, sets) of subsets of S. If $\mathscr{F} \subseteq 2^S$, then

$$\cup \mathscr{F} = \{x \in S; x \in F \text{ for some } F \in \mathscr{F}\}.$$

Thus if $\mathscr{F}$ is a family of subsets of S, then the union of $\mathscr{F}$ ($\cup \mathscr{F}$) consists of the set of all $x \in S$ which belong to at least one member F of the family $\mathscr{F}$. Also

$$\cap \mathscr{F} = \{x \in S; x \in F \text{ for every } F \in \mathscr{F}\}.$$

Thus the intersection of a family $\mathscr{F}$ of subsets of S ($\cap \mathscr{F}$) is the set of all $x \in S$ which belong to *every* member F of $\mathscr{F}$. It is a consequence of our definitions that

$$\cup \phi_{2^S} = \phi_S \quad \text{and} \quad \cap \phi_{2^S} = S.$$

The second of these equations usually has a startling effect on the reader. However, $\mathscr{F} = \phi_{2^S}$ means that $\mathscr{F}$ has no members at all, and hence the requirement that an element $x \in S$ belongs to every member F of $\mathscr{F}$ is met by *every* element $x \in S$.

/ 2 / CARTESIAN PRODUCTS OF SETS —

RELATIONS, FUNCTIONS, AND MAPS

Given two sets S and T, we may form the set of ordered pairs

$$S \times T = \{(a, b); a \in S, b \in T\}$$

which is called the *cartesian product of S and T*.

The notion of "ordered pair" (a, b) of individuals is basic in mathematics. We feel no need for a formal definition of this notion, but we emphasize that $(a, b) = (c, d)$ if and only if $a = c$ and $b = d$. Observe that we adhere rigidly to the use of equality as identity.

Subsets of $S \times T$ are called *relations* (between elements of S and elements of T). Thus, if $R \subseteq S \times T$, then we write sRt iff† $(s, t) \in R$. The basic relation of mathematics is, of course, equality which is that subset $=$ of $S \times S$ defined by

$$\{(s, s); s \in S\}.$$

Certain other subsets of $S \times S$ show some of the important properties of equality. These relations arise through a decomposition of S into nonoverlapping subsets. A family $\mathscr{D} \subseteq 2^S$ is a *decomposition* of S in case $\cup \mathscr{D} = S$ and, if $D_1, D_2 \in \mathscr{D}$, then $D_1 = D_2$ or $D_1 \cap D_2 = \phi_S$. Given a decomposition $\mathscr{D}$ of S, we may introduce a relation $E_{\mathscr{D}} \subseteq S \times S$ by declaring that $(a, b) \in E_{\mathscr{D}}$ (that is, $aE_{\mathscr{D}}b$) whenever for some $D \in \mathscr{D}$ we have $a, b \in D$. Thus $aE_{\mathscr{D}}b$ iff a and b belong to the same member D of the decomposition $\mathscr{D}$. We immediately verify that $E_{\mathscr{D}}$ has the following properties:

(1) Reflexive law: if $a \in S$, then $aE_{\mathscr{D}}a$.
(2) Symmetric law: if $a, b \in S$ and $aE_{\mathscr{D}}b$, then $bE_{\mathscr{D}}a$.
(3) Transitive law: if $a, b, c \in S$, and $aE_{\mathscr{D}}b$ and $bE_{\mathscr{D}}c$, then $aE_{\mathscr{D}}c$.

† The "word" *iff* is a contraction of *if and only if*. Since this phrase occurs so often in mathematics many writers nowadays employ the contracted form.

A relation $E \subseteq S \times S$ which satisfies (1), (2), and (3) is called an *equivalence relation* in S. We may start, if we like, with an equivalence relation E in S and construct a decomposition of S by means of the equivalence classes

$$a^E = \{b \in S; aEb\}.$$

We may easily prove that

$$\mathscr{D} = \{a^E; a \in S\}$$

is a decomposition of S for which $E = E_{\mathscr{D}}$. That $\cup \mathscr{D} = S$ follows from the fact that $a \in a^E$, which is a consequence of (1). Suppose that $a^E \neq b^E$; if $x \in a^E \cap b^E$, then aEx and bEx. By (2) and (3), we obtain that aEb. But then $y \in a^E$ yields $y \in b^E$, since aEy and aEb gives bEy by (2) and (3). Similarly, $y \in b^E$ yields $y \in a^E$, so that $a^E = b^E$, contrary to $a^E \neq b^E$.

One notes that it is immaterial logically whether one uses decompositions of S or equivalence relations in S; in fact, much use is made of *both* concepts in mathematics.

A function is a special kind of relation. We call $f \subseteq S \times T$ a *function* if $(s, t), (s, t') \in f$ implies that $t = t'$. The *domain* of a function $f \subseteq S \times T$ is dom $f = \{s \in S; (s, t) \in f$ for some $t \in T\}$. The *range* of $f \subseteq S \times T$ is $f(S) = \{t \in T; (s, t) \in f$ for some $s \in S\}$. If $f \subseteq S \times T$ is a function and $s \in$ dom f, then $(s, t) \in f$ for one and only one $t \in T$. We write $(s, t) \in f$ iff sft iff $t = f(s)$ iff $t = sf$.

A *map* $f \subseteq S \times T$ is a function f whose domain is S. To indicate that we are dealing with a map of S *into* T we write $f: S \to T$. If the range of f is T, we say that f maps S *onto* T. A map f of S into T is *faithful* if $f(a) = f(b)$ implies that $a = b$. Note that two maps $f: S \to T$ and $g: S \to T$ are equal if and only if $f(s) = g(s)$ for every s in S.

/ 3 / COMPOSITION OF RELATIONS

AND MAPS, INVERSES

When one has two relations $R \subseteq S \times T$ and $M \subseteq T \times U$, one may compose them by defining

$$RM = M \circ R = \{(s, u); \text{ we have } sRt \text{ and } tMu \text{ for some } t \in T\}.$$

This is an associative composition; that is, if also $N \subseteq U \times V$, then $(RM)N = R(MN)$. If R and M are maps of S into T and T into U, respectively, then RM is a map of S into U. It is natural to use a diagram to indicate this:

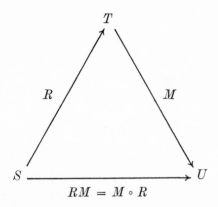

$$RM = M \circ R$$

Observe that the composed map RM is defined by

$$s(RM) = (sR)M \qquad \text{or} \qquad (M \circ R)(s) = M(R(s)).$$

If $R \subseteq S \times T$ is a relation, then one defines

$$R^{-1} = \{(t, s); (s, t) \in R\}$$

as the inverse of R. Even when R is a map of S into T, R^{-1} need not always be a function. In fact, if R is a map of S into T, then R^{-1} is a function if and only if R is a faithful map, and it maps T into S if and only if R is a faithful map of S onto T.

The set

$$S^S = \{f; f: S \to S\}$$

of all maps of S into S is closed under the associative composition of maps. The special map e_S defined by $e_S(s) = s$ for all $s \in S$ is called the identity map of S (onto S). We have $e_S f = f e_S = f$ for all $f \in S^S$. The faithful maps f of S onto S have the property that f^{-1} is also a faithful map of S onto S. One sees at once that $ff^{-1} = e_S = f^{-1}f$ for such a map f. Faithful maps of S onto S are called permutations of S and their totality is denoted by

$$S! = \{f; f \text{ is a faithful map of } S \text{ onto } S\}.$$

It is easy to prove that $S!$ is closed under composition of maps and that $S!$ forms a group, the group of permutations of S. (See Exercise 15 of this Appendix.)

Let $f: S \to T$ be a map of S into T. If $A \subseteq S$, then we define

$$Af = \{xf; x \in A\},$$

or, equivalently,

$$f(A) = \{f(x); x \in A\}.$$

One readily verifies that

$$(A \cup B)f = (Af) \cup (Bf)$$

for $A, B \subseteq S$. In fact, if $\mathscr{F} \subseteq 2^S$, then

$$(\cup \mathscr{F})f = \cup \{Ff; F \in \mathscr{F}\}.$$

Thus we see that maps preserve unions. For intersections, the result is different. See Exercise 11 of this Appendix.

/4/ THE CANTOR-BERNSTEIN

THEOREM

It is customary to say that the cardinal number of a set S is the same as the cardinal number of a set T, $\#(S) = \#(T)$, in case there is a faithful map of S onto T. An interesting fact is that if $f: S \to T$ and $g: T \to S$ are faithful maps, then $\#S = \#T$. This is called the Cantor-Bernstein Theorem. We give a proof due to Banach.

Banach's Lemma

Let $f: S \to T$ and $g: T \to S$ be faithful maps. Then there is a subset A of S such that $(Af)'g = A'$.

PROOF   Define $h = fg$ to obtain a faithful map of S into S, and with $W = (Tg)'$ put

$$A = W \cup Wh \cup Wh^2 \cup \cdots,$$

where $h^2 = h \circ h$, etc. Then $A = W \cup Ah$. Then $t \notin Af$ iff $tg \notin$ $Afg = Ah$ iff $tg \notin W \cup Ah = A$. Thus $tg \in A'$ iff $t \in (Af)'$ and, since $A' \subseteq W' = Tg$, we have $(Af)'g = A'$, as desired.

To prove the Cantor–Bernstein Theorem from Banach's Lemma, define $s\varphi = sf$ for $s \in A$ and $s\varphi = sg^{-1}$ for $s \in A'$. Then $S\varphi = (A \cup A')\varphi = Af \cup (Af)' = T$, and φ is faithful.

$/ 5 /$ THE AXIOM OF INFINITY AND THE PEANO POSTULATES FOR THE POSITIVE INTEGERS

Dedekind called a set S *infinite* when a faithful map f of S into S exists such that $Sf \subset S$. He assumed (as we do) that there are infinite sets. Let, then, S be an infinite set and choose a particular element $s_0 \in S$ such that $s_0 \notin Sf$. Then the set

$$P = \cap \{A \subseteq S; s_0 \in A \quad \text{and} \quad Af \subseteq A\}$$

has the following properties:

(1) $s_0 \in P$.
(2) f is a faithful map of P into P and $Pf \subset P$.
(3) If $Q \subseteq P$ and Q satisfies the following two requirements
    (i)   some x in P and not in Pf is in Q,
    (ii) $Qf \subseteq Q$,
   then $Q = P$.

PROOF   Clearly, $s_0 \in P$. If $s \in P$ and $A \subseteq S$ satisfies $s_0 \in A$ and $Af \subseteq A$, then $sf \in A$ because $s \in A$. This proves that if $s \in P$, then $sf \in A$ for every A for which $s_0 \in A$ and $Af \subseteq A$, consequently $sf \in P$. Thus $Pf \subset P$. Suppose $s_0 \neq x \in P \setminus Pf$. Let $A = P \setminus \{x\}$; then $s_0 \in A$ and $Af \subseteq A$ because $x \notin Pf$. But then $A \supseteq P$, while $x \in P$ and $x \notin A$, a contradiction. Hence, in (3), the x of the first requirement must be s_0, and so $s_0 \in Q$ and $Qf \subseteq Q$, so that $Q \supseteq P \supseteq Q$ and $P = Q$.

The postulates (1), (2), and (3) were expressed by Peano in the following way.

(1) P is a nonempty set.

(2)   There is a faithful map σ of P into P such that $P\sigma \subset P$.

(3)   If $Q \subseteq P$ and Q satisfies the following two requirements

      (i)   some x in P and not in $P\sigma$ is in Q,

      (ii) $Q\sigma \subseteq Q$,

then $Q = P$.

These axioms may be used to define the system of positive integers from which one may proceed to construct in succession the systems of integers, rational numbers, real numbers, complex numbers, real quaternions, and Cayley octaves, which form the basis of classical mathematical analysis.

Let us assume that we have constructed the ring of integers Z on the basis of Peano's Axioms. Some of this construction is the subject of the exercises at the close of this appendix. The remainder of this section will be devoted to the task of making the phrase "is defined," used on page 7 of the text, more precise.

Principle of Induction for the Integers

Let S be a nonempty subset of Z such that $m \in S$ iff $m + 1 \in S$; then $S = Z$.

PROOF   Let $s \in S$ and let Q be the subset of P such that $k \in Q$ when $s + k \in S$. Then $1 \in Q$ and, if $k \in Q$, then $(s + k) + 1 = s + (k + 1) \in S$, which shows that $k + 1 \in Q$; hence $Q = P$. Let Q_1 be the subset of P such that $j \in Q_1$ when $s - j \in S$. Since $(s - 1) + 1 = s \in S$, we see that $1 \in Q_1$. If $j \in Q_1$, then $s - (j + 1) = (s - j) - 1$, and $((s - j) - 1) + 1 = s - j \in S$ shows that $j + 1 \in Q_1$; hence $Q_1 = P$. We now see that $\{s + m; m \in Z\} \subseteq S$. Given $n \in Z$, we may write $n = s + (n - s)$; hence $Z \subseteq S \subseteq Z$ and $S = Z$.

Principle of Inductive Definition for P

Let S be a set, let $\alpha : S \to S$, and let $s_1 \in S$; then there is a unique map $f : P \to S$ such that (i) $f(1) = s_1$ and (ii) $f(k + 1) = \alpha(f(k))$ for all $k \in P$.

PROOF   Let Q be the subset of P of those positive integers m such that there is a unique map f_m of $\{x \in P; x \leq m\}$ into S satisfying $f_m(1) = s_1$ and $f_m(k + 1) = \alpha(f_m(k))$ for $1 \leq k < m$. By setting $f_1(1) = s_1$, we see that $1 \in Q$. If $m \in Q$, we define $f_{m+1}(x) = f_m(x)$ for $x \leq m$ and $f_{m+1}(m + 1) = \alpha(f_m(m))$. We easily check that $f_{m+1}(1) = s_1$ and that $f_{m+1}(k + 1) = \alpha(f_{m+1}(k))$ for $1 \leq k < m + 1$. The uniqueness of f_{m+1} follows from the uniqueness of f_m and the requirement that $f_{m+1}(m + 1) = \alpha(f_{m+1}(m)) = \alpha(f_m(m))$. We have proved that $m \in Q$ implies that $(m + 1) \in Q$, and we conclude that $Q = P$. We may now define $f(m) = f_m(m)$ for all $m \in P$. Then $f(1) = f_1(1) = s_1$ and $f(k + 1) = f_{k+1}(k + 1) = \alpha(f_{k+1}(k)) = \alpha(f_k(k)) = \alpha(f(k))$. To see that f is unique, we let g also satisfy (i) and (ii), and define Q_1 as the set of $k \in P$ for which $f(k) = g(k)$. Then, using (i) and (ii) we see that $1 \in Q_1$ and, if $k \in Q_1$, then $k + 1 \in Q_1$. Hence $Q_1 = P$ and $f = g$.

Principle of Inductive Definition for Z

Let S be a set, $s_0 \in S$, and let $\alpha : S \to S$ be a permutation of S; then there is a unique map $h : Z \to S$ such that (i) $h(0) = s_0$ and (ii) $h(k + 1) = \alpha(h(k))$ for all $k \in Z$.

PROOF   A unique map $h_1 : P \to S$ exists such that $h_1(1) = \alpha(s_0)$ and $h_1(k + 1) = \alpha(h_1(k))$ for all $k \in P$. A unique map $h_2 : P \to S$ exists such that $h_2(1) = \alpha^{-1}(s_0)$ and $h_2(k + 1) = \alpha^{-1}(h_2(k))$ for all $k \in P$. Define $h(0) = s_0$ and $h(k) = h_1(k)$ for $k \in P$, and define $h(k) = h_2(-k)$ for $-k \in P$. It is then easy to prove that (i) and (ii) hold. The uniqueness of h is obtained by applying induction in Z.

Illustrative
Examples

Let $a \in R$, where R is a ring. Let $\alpha(x) = xa$ for $x \in R$. Then the principle of inductive definition in P yields a unique map $f : P \to R$ such that $f(1) = a$ and $f(k + 1) = (f(k))a$ for all $k \in P$. Writing $f(k) = a^k$ yields a precise definition of the positive integral powers of a.

Let $a \in R$, where R is a ring. Let $\alpha(x) = x + a$ for $x \in R$. Clearly, α is a permutation of R. Then the principle of inductive definition in Z yields a unique map $h : Z \to R$ such that $h(0) = 0$ and $h(k + 1) = h(k) + a$ for all $k \in Z$. Writing $h(k) = ka$ yields a precise definition of the integral multiples of a.

/ 6 / THE "AXIOM" OF CHOICE, ZERMELO'S THEOREM, TRANSFINITE INDUCTION, AND ZORN'S LEMMA

Let S be a set and $\mathscr{F} \subseteq 2^S$ a family of nonempty subsets of S. The "axiom" of choice asserts that there is a map $\gamma : \mathscr{F} \to S$ such that $F\gamma \in F$ for every $F \in \mathscr{F}$. That is to say, we may choose an element $F\gamma$ from each of the members F of the family $\mathscr{F}$. There has been a good deal of discussion of the propriety of this "axiom" in mathematics. It is now abundantly clear that one must accept it, or reject the main body of mathematics.† The basic consequence of the axiom is our next theorem.

Zermelo's Theorem

If S is a set, then there is a relation $R \subseteq S \times S$ such that R *well-orders* S; that is:

(1) aRa for all $a \in S$.
(2) aRb and bRa implies $a = b$.
(3) aRb and bRc implies aRc.
(4) Given $a, b \in S$, then aRb or bRa.
(5) If $A \subseteq S$ and $A \neq \phi_S$, then A has a least element relative to R; that is, we have some $a_0 \in A$ such that $a_0 Ra$ for every $a \in A$.

We apply the axiom of choice to the family $\mathscr{F}$ of all non-empty subsets A of S. We shall use the notation "$p \Rightarrow q$" for "statement p implies statement q."

† Some very recent spectacular results by Paul Cohen of Stanford University indicate that there may be additional complicated "axioms" which have not as yet been generally accepted but which are equally vital for mathematics. The present state of the foundations of mathematics seems to be almost as exciting as the present state of the foundations of theoretical physics.

Let $A\gamma \in A$ for every $A \neq \phi_S$. Call a family $\mathscr{T} \subseteq 2^S$ *tight* when (i) $\mathscr{S} \subseteq \mathscr{T} \Rightarrow \cap\, \mathscr{S} \in \mathscr{T}$ and (ii) $\phi_S \subset A \in \mathscr{T} \Rightarrow A^- = A \setminus \{A\gamma\} \in \mathscr{T}$. The notation A^- in statement (ii) is used merely for convenience in this section. Note that 2^S is a tight family. Observe that (i) with $\mathscr{S} = \phi_{2^S}$ shows that $S \in \mathscr{T}$ for every tight family $\mathscr{T}$. Define

$$\mathscr{P} = \cap\, \{\mathscr{T} \subseteq 2^S;\ \mathscr{T} \text{ is tight}\}.$$

Then $\mathscr{P}$ is a tight family. For, if $\mathscr{S} \subseteq \mathscr{P}$, then $\mathscr{S} \subseteq \mathscr{T}$ for every tight family $\mathscr{T}$, and statement (i) gives $\cap\, \mathscr{S} \in \mathscr{T}$ for every tight family $\mathscr{T}$ and it follows that $\cap\, \mathscr{S} \in \mathscr{P}$. Again, if $\phi_S \subset A \in \mathscr{P}$, then $\phi_S \subset A \in \mathscr{T}$ for every tight family $\mathscr{T}$, and hence, by (ii), $A^- \in \mathscr{T}$ for every tight family $\mathscr{T}$ and it follows that $A^- \in \mathscr{P}$. Note that $\mathscr{P}$ is the least of all the tight families.

Lemma 1

Let $\phi_S \subset P \in \mathscr{P}$ be comparable to every member of $\mathscr{P}$; that is, if $Q \in \mathscr{P}$, then $P \subseteq Q$ or $Q \subseteq P$. Then

$$\mathscr{T}_P = \{A \in \mathscr{P};\ A \supseteq P \text{ or } A \subseteq P^-\}$$

is a tight family and hence $\mathscr{T}_P = \mathscr{P}$.

PROOF If $\mathscr{S} \subseteq \mathscr{T}_P$ and $B \supseteq P$ for every $B \in \mathscr{S}$, then $\cap\, \mathscr{S} \supseteq P$, while if $B \subseteq P^-$ for some $B \in \mathscr{S}$, then $\cap\, \mathscr{S} \subseteq P^-$; hence $\cap\, \mathscr{S} \in \mathscr{T}_P$. Now let $\phi_S \subset A \in \mathscr{T}_P$. Then $A \supseteq P$ or $A \subseteq P^-$. But $A^- \subset A$ yields $A^- \in \mathscr{T}_P$ if $A \subseteq P^-$. We must now show that $A^- \in \mathscr{T}_P$ when $A \supseteq P$. If $A^- \supseteq P$, then $A^- \in \mathscr{T}_P$. If $A^- \not\supseteq P$, then $P \supset A^-$ because A^- is in $\mathscr{P}$ and every member of $\mathscr{P}$ is comparable to P. But $A \supseteq P \supset A^-$ are two relations that force $A = P$ and $A^- = P^- \in \mathscr{T}_P$.

Lemma 2

The family

$$\mathscr{T} = \{B \in \mathscr{P};\ \text{if } A \in \mathscr{P}, \text{ then } B \supseteq A \text{ or } A \supseteq B\}$$

is a tight family and hence $\mathscr{T} = \mathscr{P}$.

PROOF   Let $\mathscr{S} \subseteq \mathscr{T}$. Consider A in $\mathscr{P}$. Then for B in $\mathscr{S}$ we have $B \supseteq A$ or $A \supseteq B$. If $B \supseteq A$ for every B in $\mathscr{S}$, then $\cap \, \mathscr{S} \supseteq A$, while if $A \supseteq B$ for some B in $\mathscr{S}$, then $A \supseteq \cap \, \mathscr{S}$. Since $(\cap \, \mathscr{S}) \in \mathscr{P}$, it follows that $(\cap \, \mathscr{S}) \in \mathscr{T}$. Let $\phi_S \subset B \in \mathscr{T}$ and let $A \in \mathscr{P}$. Because B is comparable to every member of $\mathscr{P}$, by Lemma 1, $A \supseteq B \supset B^-$ or $A \subseteq B^-$. Thus $B^- \in \mathscr{T}$, and $\mathscr{T}$ is a tight family.

Corollary

Every two members of $\mathscr{P}$ are comparable, that is, if A, $B \in \mathscr{P}$, then $A \supseteq B$ or $B \supseteq A$.

Lemma 3

If $\phi_S \subset M \subseteq S$, then there is a unique $M^* \in \mathscr{P}$ such that $M^* \supseteq M$ and $M^*\gamma \in M$.

PROOF   Define $M^* = \cap \, \{A \in \mathscr{P}; A \supseteq M\}$. Then $M^* \in \mathscr{P}$ and $M^* \supseteq M$. Suppose that $M^*\gamma \notin M$; then $(M^*)^- \supseteq M$, $(M^*)^- \in \mathscr{P}$, so that $(M^*)^- \supseteq M^*$, a contradiction. Hence $M^*\gamma \in M$. If $N \in \mathscr{P}$, $N \supseteq M$, and $N\gamma \in M$, then $N \supseteq M^*$. Suppose $N \supset M^*$; then by Lemma 1 with $P = N$ and $A = M^*$, $N^- \supseteq M^* \supseteq M$, contrary to $N\gamma \in M$. Hence $N = M^*$, proving the lemma.

Corollary 1

For $x \in S$, $\{x\}^*\gamma = x$, and, in particular, $\{M^*\gamma\}^*\gamma = M^*\gamma$.

PROOF   Since $\{x\}^*\gamma \in \{x\}$, it follows that $\{x\}^*\gamma = x$.

Corollary 2

For $x, y \in S$, we have that $\{x\}^* = \{y\}^*$ implies that $x = y$.

PROOF   By Corollary 1, $x = \{x\}^*\gamma = \{y\}^*\gamma = y$.

Lemma 4

If $\phi_S \subset M \subseteq S$, then $M^* = \{M^*\gamma\}^*$.

PROOF   Let $x = M^*\gamma$. Then $M^* \in \mathscr{P}$, $M^* \supseteq \{x\}$, and $M^*\gamma = x \in \{x\}$. Thus $M^* = \{x\}^*$ by the uniqueness assertion of Lemma 3.

The mapping $x \to \{x\}^*$ is a faithful map of S into $\mathscr{P}$. We define xRy as meaning $\{x\}^* \supseteq \{y\}^*$. The properties (1), (2), and (3) are immediate, and (4) follows from Lemma 2. As for (5), take $a_0 = A^*\gamma$; then for $a \in A$ we have $\{a_0\}^* \supseteq \{a\}^*$ or $\{a_0\}^* \subseteq (\{a\}^*)^-$ by Lemma 1. But, by Lemma 4, $\{a_0\}^* = A^* \supseteq A$ and $\{a_0\}^* \subseteq (\{a\}^*)^-$ gives $a \in (\{a\}^*)^-$, contrary to $\{a\}^*\gamma = a$. Thus for $a \in A$ we have $\{a_0\}^* \supseteq \{a\}^*$ which is $a_0 R a$ and we have proved that a_0 is the least element in A relative to R. The proof of Zermelo's Theorem is complete.

One useful consequence of Zermelo's Theorem is that it permits one to use induction in all infinite sets. If the relation R well-orders the set S and $y \in S$, let us call $x \in S$ a *predecessor* of y when $x \neq y$ and xRy. We may now formulate the following principle.

Principle of Transfinite Induction

Let S be a set and let $R \subseteq S \times S$ well-order S. If $P \subseteq S$ satisfies the requirement $y \in P$ whenever all the predecessors of y are in P, then $P = S$. For, if $P \neq S$, we may choose the least element y (relative to R) in $S \setminus P$. But then xRy and $x \neq y$ forces $x \in P$, in violation of our requirement.

This principle is used mainly to define mappings by transfinite induction. Again let $R \subseteq S \times S$ well-order S. Assume that $f \subseteq S \times T$ is a function with the property that $y \in \text{dom } f$ whenever all the predecessors of y are in $\text{dom } f$. Then $\text{dom } f = S$, and f maps S into T.

For our final theorem of the chapter we need some terminology. If S is a set and $\mathscr{C} \subseteq 2^S$, then (i) $\mathscr{C}$ is a *chain* if every two elements of $\mathscr{C}$ are comparable ($A, B \in \mathscr{C}$ implies $A \subseteq B$ or $A \supseteq B$), (ii) U is an upper bound for $\mathscr{C}$ if $A \subseteq U$ for every A in $\mathscr{C}$, and

(iii) M is a *maximal element of* $\mathscr{F} \subseteq 2^S$ if $M \in \mathscr{F}$ and if $A_1 \supseteq M$ for $A_1 \in \mathscr{F}$ implies that $A_1 = M$.

We conclude this Appendix with Zorn's Lemma and a proof of it.

Zorn's Lemma

Let S be a set and $\mathscr{F} \subseteq 2^S$ be nonempty. If every chain $\mathscr{C} \subseteq \mathscr{F}$ has an upper bound in $\mathscr{F}$, then $\mathscr{F}$ has a maximal element.

PROOF   Well-order $\mathscr{F}$ by a relation R. Let A_0 be the least element (relative to R) in $\mathscr{F}$. We wish to define a map $\Gamma : \mathscr{F} \to \mathscr{F}$ such that (i) $A_0\Gamma = A_0$, (ii) $A\Gamma = A$ if $A \supseteq B\Gamma$ for all predecessors B of A in $\mathscr{F}$, and (iii) $A\Gamma = A_0$ if $A \not\supseteq B\Gamma$ for some predecessor B of A in $\mathscr{F}$. To achieve this, we first prove that for every A in $\mathscr{F}$ there is a unique map h_A of $\{B \in \mathscr{F} ; BRA\}$ into $\mathscr{F}$ such that (iv) $A_0 h_A = A_0$, (v) $A_1 h_A = A_1$ if $A_1 \supseteq Bh_A$ for all predecessors B of A_1 in $\mathscr{F}$, and (vi) $A_1 h_A = A_0$ if $A_1 \not\supseteq Bh_A$ for some predecessor B of A_1 in $\mathscr{F}$.

Let $\mathscr{G}$ be the subset of $\mathscr{F}$ for which $A \in \mathscr{G}$ if and only if such a unique h_A exists. Suppose that $\mathscr{G} \neq \mathscr{F}$ and select the least element C (relative to R) in $\mathscr{F}$ and not in $\mathscr{G}$. If B is a predecessor of C in $\mathscr{F}$, set $Bh = Bh_B$ and put $Ch = C$ if $C \supseteq Bh$ for all predecessors B of C in $\mathscr{F}$ and put $Ch = A_0$ otherwise. Clearly h satisfies (iv), (v), and (vi). For we see that $A_0 \in \mathscr{G}$ and $A_0 h = A_0$. Let A_1 in $\mathscr{F}$ satisfy $A_1 RC$ and $A_1 \supseteq Bh$ for all predecessors B of A_1 in $\mathscr{F}$. Then for $A_1 \neq C$ we have $A_1 h = A_1 h_{A_1} = A_1$ while if $A_1 = C$ we have $Ch = C$ by the definition of h. Similarly we see that $A_1 h = A_0$ if $A_1 \not\supseteq Bh$ for some predecessor B of A_1 in $\mathscr{F}$. The uniqueness of h is immediately obtained from the uniqueness of h_B for $B \in \mathscr{G}$ and the requirements (iv), (v), and (vi). But this proves that $C \in \mathscr{G}$, a contradiction. Thus $\mathscr{G} = \mathscr{F}$ and we may define $A\Gamma = Ah_A$ for all $A \in \mathscr{F}$. We have defined a map Γ of $\mathscr{F}$ into $\mathscr{F}$ for which $\mathscr{F}\Gamma = \mathscr{C}$ is a chain. Choose $M \in \mathscr{F}$ an upper bound for $\mathscr{C}$. If $A_1 \in \mathscr{F}$ and $A_1 \supseteq M$, then $A_1\Gamma = A_1 \in \mathscr{C}$, so that $M \supseteq A_1$ and $A_1 = M$.

Zorn's Lemma is a very useful tool for proving existence theorems in algebra and analysis.

EXERCISES FOR THE APPENDIX

1. The diagrams of Venn are useful in dealing with the algebra of subsets of a set.

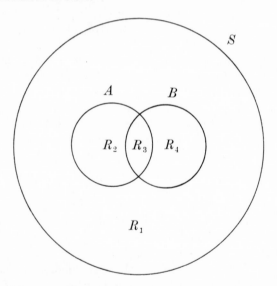

The set S is thought of as everything inside the large circle, while the subsets A and B are thought of as everything inside the small circles, labeled A and B. One may number the regions R_1, R_2, R_3, R_4 and observe that $A = R_2 \cup R_3$, $B = R_3 \cup R_4$, $A' = R_1 \cup R_4$, $A \cup B = R_2 \cup R_3 \cup R_4$,

$A \cap B = R_3$, $A \dotplus B = R_2 \cup R_4$. Use such diagrams to verify the list of rules for set operations.

2. Let S be a finite set and, for $A \subseteq S$, let $N(A)$ denote the number of elements in A. Show that $N(A \cup B) = N(A) + N(B) - N(A \cap B)$.

3. Show that $N(A \cup B \cup C) = N(A) + N(B) + N(C) - N(A \cap B) - N(B \cap C) - N(C \cap A) + N(A \cap B \cap C)$ for $A, B, C \subseteq S$.

4. Generalize Exercise 3 to n subsets $A_1, \cdots, A_n$ of S.

5. Of 100 people, exactly 7 have no shoes and exactly 40 have no hats. At least how many have both shoes and hats?

6. In 2^S, show that $A \dotplus A = \phi_S$.

7. A *Boolean expression* is a formula built from subsets $A_1, \cdots, A_k$ of a set S by use of the operations $'$, $\cup$, $\cap$. For example, $A_1 \cup A_2' \cup A_3$ is a Boolean expression. Show that every Boolean expression may be written with the symbols S, $A_1, \cdots, A_k$, $\dotplus$, and $\cap$ alone. Is the resulting form unique?

8. The expressions $E_1 = A_1 \cup A_2 \cup A_3$, $E_2 = A_1 A_2 \cup A_2 A_3 \cup A_3 A_1$, and $E_3 = A_1 A_2 A_3$ are symmetric in A_1, A_2, and A_3. Write E_1, E_2, and E_3 in terms of A_1, A_2, and A_3, using $\dotplus$ and $\cap$ alone.

9. Let R_e denote the set of real numbers. Determine whether the following relations, where $f \subseteq R_e \times R_e$, are functions.

   (a) $f = \{(x, y); x^2 + y^2 = 1\}$.
   (b) $f = \{(x, y); x^2 + y^2 = 0\}$.
   (c) $f = \{(x, y); x^2 + y^2 = -1\}$.
   (d) $f = \{(x, y); y = \sin x\}$.
   (e) $f = \{(x, y); x = \sin y\}$.
   (g) $f = \{(x, y); y = e^x\}$.
   (h) $f = \{(x, y); x = e^y\}$.
   (i) $f = \{(x, y); y^2 = (x - 4)(9 - x^2)\}$.

10. In Exercise 9, find dom f if f is a function. For which functions f is f^{-1} also a function?

11. Let $f: S \to T$ and define, for $A \subseteq S$,

$$f(A) = \{f(x); x \in A\}.$$

Show that $f(A \cup B) = f(A) \cup f(B)$ for all $A, B \subseteq S$, while $f(A \cap B) = f(A) \cap f(B)$ for all $A, B \subseteq S$ if and only if f is faithful. We say that maps preserve unions, but only faithful maps preserve intersections.

12. Let f map S into T. Then for $B \subseteq T$, we define

$$f^{-1}(B) = \{x \in S; f(x) \in B\}.$$

Verify that $f^{-1}(B_1 \cap B_2) = f^{-1}(B_1) \cap f^{-1}(B_2)$ and that, if $\mathscr{B} \subseteq 2^T$, then

$$f^{-1}(\cap \mathscr{B}) = \cap \{f^{-1}(B); B \in \mathscr{B}\},$$
$$f^{-1}(\cup \mathscr{B}) = \cup \{f^{-1}(B); B \in \mathscr{B}\}.$$

13. Let $f: S \to T$ be faithful. Derive a formula for $f^{-1}(B')$, where $B \subseteq T$.

14. Given a map $f: S \to S$, show there is a map $g: S \to S$ such that $gf = e_S$ ($fg = e_S$) if and only if f is onto (faithful). Did you use the axiom of choice?

15. A set G together with a map of $G \times G$ into G denoted by $(a, b) \to ab$ is called a *group* if (i) $(ab)c = a(bc)$ for all a, b, c in G, (ii) for some e in G we have $ea = a = ae$ for every a in G, and (iii) for each a in G we have $aa^{-1} = e = a^{-1}a$ for some a^{-1} in G. Verify in detail that $S!$ is a group in which $e = e_S$. Show that, for a group G, the map R_a defined by $xR_a = xa$ for x in G is in $G!$. Show that $a \to R_a$ defines a faithful map of G into $G!$ and that $R_{ab} = R_a R_b$.

16. Factor the relation "x is an uncle of y."

17. Let Z denote the set of integers 0, ± 1, ± 2, $\cdots$. Let m be a positive integer and define $a \equiv_m b$ to mean that $a - b$ is divisible by m. Show that $\equiv_m$ (read "congruence modulo m") is an equivalence relation in Z. What is the corresponding decomposition of Z?

18. Show that if $a \equiv_m b$, then $a + c \equiv_m b + c$ and $ac \equiv_m bc$ for every integer c. Is it true that $ac \equiv_m bc$ implies that $a \equiv_m b$? If not, can you supply a sufficient condition on c?

19. Let R_e denote the set of all real numbers. Define $a \sim b$ as meaning that $a - b$ is rational. Show that $a \sim b$ is an equivalence relation in R_e.

20. Let $C'(R_e)$ denote the set of all real-valued functions defined and differentiable for every real number. Define $f E g$ as $f'(x) = g'(x)$ for all real numbers x. Show that E is an equivalence relation in $C'(R_e)$. Show that each equivalence class contains one and only one member f such that $f(0) = 0$.

21. Let P, together with the map σ of P into P, satisfy Peano's Axioms. Prove that the subset $P \setminus \sigma(P)$ has only one element;

call this element 1. Show that for each n in P there is a unique map α_n of P into P such that

(1) $\alpha_n(1) = \sigma(n)$ and $\alpha_n(\sigma(m)) = \sigma(\alpha_n(m))$

for every m in P. [*Hints:* Let Q be the subset of P for which such a map exists; then 1 is in Q, since we may take $\alpha_1 = \sigma$. Show that, if n is in Q, the definition $\alpha_{\sigma(n)}(m) = \alpha_n(\sigma(m))$ of $\alpha_{\sigma(n)}$ works. To prove the uniqueness of α_n, let β_n also satisfy (1) and let Q be the subset of P such that $\alpha_n(q) = \beta_n(q)$ for q in Q. Then 1 is in Q and, if m is in Q, so is $\sigma(m)$.] We may now, for m and n in P, define $m + n = \alpha_n(m)$. Thus begins the development of the usual properties of the positive integers from Peano's Axioms.

22. Prove that addition in the positive integers is commutative, associative, and cancelative: $m + n = n + m, (m + n) + p = m + (n + p)$, and $m + n = m + p$ implies that $n = p$ for positive integers m, n, p.

23. Show that there is no map f of S onto 2^S.

24. A diagram of sets and maps

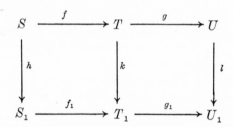

is called *commutative* if, whenever a set A of the diagram is mapped into a set B of the diagram by two sequences of (one or more) maps of the diagram, the composites of the two sequences of maps are equal. List sufficient conditions for the given diagram to be commutative.

25. (O. Frink.†) One may describe a Boolean algebra abstractly as a set B with a binary composition ab and a unary operation a', such that, for a fixed $0 \in B$, (i) $ab = ba$, (ii) $(ab)c = a(bc)$, (iii) $aa = a$, and (iv) $ab = a$ if and only if $ab' = 0$. Using

† Professor Frink is a contemporary American mathematician who first obtained the results stated in Exercise 25.

(i) to (iv), prove that $a'a = 0$ and $a0 = 0$. Call $P \subseteq B$ a *point* if P is maximal in the family of subsets of B which are closed under multiplication and do not contain 0. For $a \in B$, define R_a as the set of all points P containing a. Prove that, if P is a point and $ab \in P$, then $a \in P$. Use Zorn's Lemma to prove that, if $a \in B$ and $a \neq 0$, then there is a point $P \in R_a$. Prove that $a \to R_a$ defines a map of B into 2^B which is faithful and satisfies $R_{ab} = R_a \cap R_b$ and $R_{a'} = (R_a)'$.

BIBLIOGRAPHY

ALBERT, A. A., *Introduction to Algebraic Theories*, Univ. Chicago Press, Chicago, 1941.

ARTIN, E., *Geometric Algebra*, Interscience, New York, 1957.

BERBERIAN, S. K., *Introduction to Hilbert Space*, Oxford Univ. Press, New York, 1961.

BIRKHOFF, G., and MACLANE, S., *Survey of Modern Algebra*, rev. ed., Macmillan, New York, 1953.

JACOBSON, N., *Lectures in Abstract Algebra*, Volume I (*Basic Concepts*) and Volume II (*Linear Algebra*), Van Nostrand, New York, 1951 and 1953.

JOHNSON, R. E., and KIOKEMEISTER, F., *Calculus with Analytic Geometry*, 3rd ed., Allyn and Bacon, Boston, 1964.

KELLEY, J. L., *General Topology*, Van Nostrand, New York, 1955.

KERSCHNER, R., and WILCOX, L. R., *The Anatomy of Mathematics*, Ronald Press, New York, 1950.

McCOY, N. H., *Rings and Ideals*, Mathematical Assoc. America, Baltimore, 1948.

———, *Introduction to Modern Algebra*, Allyn and Bacon, Boston, 1960.

MACDUFFEE, C. C., *Vectors and Matrices*, Mathematical Assoc. America, Menasha, Wisconsin, 1943.

MIRSKY, L., *An Introduction to Linear Algebra*, Oxford Univ. Press, Oxford, 1955.

PERLIS, S., *Theory of Matrices*, Addison-Wesley, Cambridge, Mass., 1952.

SCHREIER, O., and SPERNER, E., *Modern Algebra and Matrix Theory* (English trans.), Chelsea Pub. Co., New York, 1952.

INDEX OF SYMBOLS

INDEX